DESIGNING COMPETITIVE ELECTRICITY MARKETS

INTERNATIONAL SERIES IN
OPERATIONS RESEARCH & MANAGEMENT SCIENCE

Frederick S. Hillier, Series Editor
Department of Engineering-Economic Systems and
  Operations Research
Stanford University
Stanford, California

Saigal, Romesh
  LINEAR PROGRAMMING: A Modern Integrated Analysis

Nagurney, Anna/ Zhang, Ding
  PROJECTED DYNAMICAL SYSTEMS AND VARIATIONAL INEQUALITIES WITH
APPLICATIONS

Padberg, Manfred/ Rijal, Minendra P.
  LOCATION, SCHEDULING, DESIGN AND INTEGER
PROGRAMMING

Vanderbei, Robert J.
  LINEAR PROGRAMMING: Foundations and Extensions

Jaiswal, N.K.
  MILITARY OPERATIONS RESEARCH: Quantitative Decision Making

Gal, Tomas / Greenberg, Harvey J.
  ADVANCES IN SENSITIVITY ANALYSIS AND PARAMETRIC PROGRAMMING

Prabhu, N.U.
 FOUNDATIONS OF QUEUEING THEORY

Fang, S.-C./Rajasekera, J.R./ Tsao, H.-S.J.
  ENTROPY OPTIMIZATION AND MATHEMATICAL PROGRAMMING

Yu, Gang
 OPERATIONS RESEARCH IN THE AIRLINE INDUSTRY

Ho, Teck-Hua / Tang, Christopher S.
 PRODUCT VARIETY MANAGEMENT

El-Taha, Muhammad / Stidham, Jr., Shaler
 SAMPLE-PATH ANALYSIS OF QUEUEING SYSTEMS

Miettinen, Kaisa M.
 NONLINEAR MULTIOBJECTIVE OPTIMIZATION

DESIGNING COMPETITIVE ELECTRICITY MARKETS

by

Hung-po Chao
and
Hillard G. Huntington

Kluwer Academic Publishers
Boston/Dordrecht/London

Distributors for North, Central and South America:
Kluwer Academic Publishers
101 Philip Drive
Assinippi Park
Norwell, Massachusetts 02061 USA
Telephone (781) 871-6600
Fax (781) 871-6528
E-Mail <kluwer@wkap.com>

Distributors for all other countries:
Kluwer Academic Publishers Group
Distribution Centre
Post Office Box 322
3300 AH Dordrecht, THE NETHERLANDS
Telephone 31 78 6392 392
Fax 31 78 6546 474
E-Mail <orderdept@wkap.nl>

 Electronic Services <http://www.wkap.nl>

Library of Congress Cataloging-in-Publication Data

Designing competitive electricity markets / by Hung-po Chao and
    Hillard G. Huntington.
            p.   cm. -- (International series in operations research &
    management science ; 13)
    Papers presented at the first Workshop on Markets for Electricity,
    Economics, and Technology held at Stanford University on March 7-8,
    1997.
    Includes bibliographical references and index.
    ISBN 0-7923-8282-X (hardbound). -- ISBN 0-7923-8283-8 (pbk.)
    1. Electric utilities--Management--Congresses. I. Chao, Hung-po,
    1950-   II. Huntington, Hillard G.   III. Workshop on Markets for
    Electricity, Economics, and Technology (1st : 1997 : Stanford
    University)   IV. Series.
    HD9685.A2D374   1998
    333.793'2'0688--dc21   98-36769
                                                                            CIP

Copyright © 1998 by Kluwer Academic Publishers.

Printed on acid-free paper.

Printed in the United States of America

CONTENTS

Foreword

This volume contains papers that were discussed at the first workshop on Markets for Electricity: Economics and Technology (MEET) held at Stanford University on March 7-8, 1997. The workshop's focus was how to design competitive electricity markets in an industry undergoing rapid changes in both economics and technology. We are very appreciative of the generous funding support provided by Dr. Gail McCarthy, Director of Strategic Science and Technology at Electric Power Research Institute.

We would like to acknowledge all the workshop participants, including Paul Joskow, Martin Baughman, William Hogan, Robert Wilson, Granger Morgan, Paul Kleindorfer, Shmuel Oren, Edward Kahn, Stephen Rassenti, Stephen Stoft, Stephen Peck, Victor Niemeyer, Jeremy Bloom, Martin Weinberger and Al Pak, for their significant contributions in discussing these issues at that workshop.

CONTRIBUTING AUTHORS

Martin L. Baughman is Professor of Electrical and Computer Engineering, University of Texas at Austin.

Hung-po Chao is Area Manager of Policy and Risk Analysis, Electric Power Research Institute, Palo Alto, California, and Consulting Professor with Department of Engineering-Economic Systems and Operations Research, Stanford University.

William W. Hogan is Lucius N. Littauer Professor of Public Policy and Administration, John F. Kennedy School of Government, Harvard University, Cambridge, Massachusetts and Senior Advisor, Putnam, Hayes & Bartlett, Inc., Cambridge, Massachusetts.

Hillard G. Huntington is Executive Director, Energy Modeling Forum, Stanford University, Stanford, California.

Paul L. Joskow is Elizabeth and James Killian Professor of Economics, Massachusetts Institute of Technology, Cambridge, Massachusetts.

Edward P. Kahn is Vice President, National Economic Research Associates, San Francisco, Califonria.

Paul R. Kleindorfer is Professor of Decision Sciences, Economics, and Public Policy and Management, and Co-Director, Risk Management and Decision Processes Center, University of Pennsylvania, Philadelphia, Pennsylvania.

M. Granger Morgan is Head, Department of Engineering and Public Policy, and Lord Chair Professor in Engineering, Carnegie Mellon University, Pittsburgh, Pennsylvania.

Shmuel S. Oren is Professor of Industrial Engineering and Operations Research, University of California at Berkeley.

Stephen C. Peck is Vice President, Environment Division, Electric Power Research Institute, Palo Alto, California.

Stephen J. Rassenti is Assistant Director, Economic Science Laboratory, University of Arizona, Tucson, Arizona.

Vernon L. Smith is Regents' Professor of Economics, University of Arizona, Tucson, Arizona.

Robert B. Wilson is Atholl McBean Professor of Economics, Graduate School of Business, Stanford University, Stanford, California.

1 INTRODUCTION: ECONOMIC AND TECHNOLOGICAL PRINCIPLES IN DESIGNING POWER MARKETS

Hung-po Chao and Hillard G. Huntington

Background

As a consequence of complex interactions of political, socioeconomic and technological forces, the electric power industry, both in the United States and abroad, is undergoing a fundamental transformation in institutional structure. Public ownership or regulated private monopoly is being replaced by market designs that emphasize greater decentralization and competition. As electric restructuring spreads rapidly across countries and states, however, a growing concern shared by some leading industry experts is that in many instances, policy makers are pushing their proposals into practice more quickly than policy analysts can provide answers to difficult questions of market design. In this process, different structures for organizing this industry are evolving without a firm basic understanding of their implications for long term market performance. There is a risk that the process may be inadvertently locked into an inferior market design which will be costly to change.

This volume represents an initial effort to develop the guiding principles for evaluating alternative proposals for reorganizing the U.S. electric power industry.

A workshop, convened by the Electric Power Research Institute and held at Stanford University in March 1997, provides the initial spark for preparation of the edited papers included in this volume. The authors are prominent economists, operation researchers, and engineers who have been instrumental in the development of the conceptual framework for electric power restructuring. Several participants bring an international perspective, having conducted analysis of different countries' experiences. In this volume, rather than espousing a particular market design for the industry's future, each author focuses on an important issue or a set of issues and tries to frame the questions for designing electricity markets. The collection seeks to understand the economic and technological basis for comparing different proposals. In this volume, framing the questions for understanding the industry's development ten years from now takes precedence over providing immediate answers for the current political debates on industry competition.

While these papers address diverse aspects of institutional change, a common theme on robust market designs can be discerned. The institutional change in the electric power industry, which is driven by the introduction of competition, involves complex interactions between economics and technology. Obviously, the organization of electricity markets has been dictated by some fundamental technological characteristics of electricity demand and supply, such as nonstorability. While some authors emphasize the importance of existing conditions for shaping decisions about institutional design, others stress the effect of any particular institutional change on future economic and technical choices. Existing economic and technical conditions can affect the extent of allowable decentralization and the scope of required coordination, which will shape the types of institutions appropriate for restructuring the market. At the same time, the adopted institutions will influence future economic choices and technological options, on which the success of institutional change will ultimately depend.

The covered issues are extensive: the role of the system operator, the problems of ensuring longer-term investment in expanding the transmission system and in industry research and development, the problems in pricing that are created by arbitrarily segmenting related markets, the relationship between efficiency in the near and long term, ownership rights and incentives, and designing experiments to better understand the operation of different auction mechanisms. Benefiting from a two-day workshop and internal reviews of each other's papers, the authors exploit the commonalities among contributions more fully than otherwise.

The intended audience for this volume includes policy makers, policy-oriented academics, and corporate leaders with an interest in designing workable and more efficient electricity markets. The arguments in each chapter are based upon sound economic principles but do not require expertise in mathematical modeling or technical economic analysis. Professionals with background and training in economics, engineering, operations research, and public policy should be interested in this volume. University teachers wishing to supplement a graduate or undergraduate course in the economics of industrial organization or industry behavior may be interested in this volume to provide students with a broader appreciation of restructuring issues within an important economic sector.

Organization of the Book

The initial chapter by Paul Joskow addresses fundamental market structure issues for the industry as a whole. Can you achieve long-run economic efficiency without short-run operational efficiency?

Joskow observes that the traditional vertically integrated market in the US was designed to incorporate important investment and operations complementarities between generation and transmission. Combining these functions within one entity potentially improved decisions where close coordination of generation and transmission was important but it also extended the potential for monopoly inherent in transmission to the generation function. This structure allowed the industry to provide short-run transmission operations reasonably efficiently, but led to longer-run inefficiencies in investment resulting from regulation of a monopolistic industry. The fundamental issue in market design is to balance the potential gains in longer-run efficiencies with the transaction costs associated with new rules and institutions for implementing decentralized operations and investment decisions.

Ready access to transmission is essential for promoting competition among regionally dispersed generating units and loads. In the next chapter, Bill Hogan considers the case for applying zonal rather than nodal pricing for electricity transmission.

Theory tells us that a separate price for each location on the system (nodal pricing) will incorporate the costs associated with transmission losses and congestion and lead to a better economic outcome than systems imposing more uniform prices. However, designers may choose zonal pricing, imposing a single price for an area much larger than a node, in order to avoid clear winners and losers. While zonal pricing appears to be a ready simplification involving fewer prices than nodal pricing, it could actually be more complicated and controversial along a dense electricity transmission system. Nodal pricing maintains the flexibility to adopt to changing market conditions, while zonal pricing ties participants to rigid rules that may induce perverse effects.

In the next two chapters, Paul Kleindorfer and Shmuel Oren discuss important conceptual problems in defining the transmission function. How should ownership rights be defined? Which functions should a system operator assume in a system seeking to maximize coordination and centralization and how do these functions change in a system allowing more decentralized decisions and participation?

Kleindorfer probes the problems of defining and regulating ownership rights for facilitating the newer decentralized systems. He notes that unbundling now for transparency necessitates rebundling later for effective power services. Ownership and decision rights rather than pricing will determine how efficient the market will become. These factors influence the transaction costs involved in contracting, spot markets, and other mechanisms for rebundling the product. They also affect the form which regulatory oversight of transmission should take.

He discusses two alternatives for organizing the system operator. In one, a single entity operates the daily system and owns and operates the transmission assets. The key regulatory issue here would be to provide incentives for the asset-holding entity to avoid such inefficient strategies as "asset-padding" or overinvestment. In the second, the two functions are separated into different entities. The central problem here concerns the proper incentives to encourage an asset-thin operator with no "wires" ownership to properly contract for asset use and to keep system-wide transmission costs (including the transaction costs of contracting) minimal. This latter case also includes the case in which the system operator acts primarily as a traffic cop for enforcing trade and usage rules for transmission assets.

Oren considers the scope of the transmission function and how different functions would be performed in a design emphasizing centralized coordination and in one stressing decentralization. He emphasizes that all market designs must define the role of the system operator for organizing the critical transmission function. One approach emphasizes a minimal role, where the operator would intervene only as a last resort when markets fail to respond. The primary benefits of allowing maximal decentralized decision making are longer-term technology innovation, the emergence of new products and services, and prudent investment. Another approach emphasizes a substantially larger role in centralizing the key transmission functions, particularly in a constrained environment. The operator seeks to emulate the short-term efficiency properties of the market. The success of this approach depends partly upon whether suppliers provide truthful cost and constraints bids.

Chapters 6 and 7 examine the details of design implementation in an interesting interaction between theory and empirical observation. Observing how actual systems are being designed and how they operate, Robert Wilson analyzes theoretically several pricing problems that can potentially create significant economic inefficiencies. Stephen Rassenti and Vernon Smith describe studies that seek to observe market behavior from carefully constructed experiments for simulating market behavior. Although empirical in focus, basic economic theory determines which experiments are conducted.

Wilson observes that restructuring in states like California has resulted in a sequence of separated forward markets for energy, transmission, and ancillary services. Sequencing promotes transactional clarity but imposes efficiency losses relative to having simultaneous markets where the products are joint. Under these constraints, the fundamental pricing problem is how to ensure the overall efficiency of this sequence of separate markets. He discusses three pricing problems in sequenced markets, offering some possible solutions:

- What is the proper formulation of the system operator's objective in selecting and using ancillary services when energy and capacity markets are separated?

- Can energy prices be unbundled in a transparent way from transmission capacity charges in systems using nodal prices and a sequence of markets for energy and capacity?
- Can the producer's concern about how costs vary with the duration of the plant's operation be integrated into a market design that allows consumers' valuation to fluctuate with the time of use?

Rassenti and Smith note that artificial political constraints can often have unintended and seriously distorting effects on auctions. Market rules need to be flexible to allow adaptation to new and unforeseen events. The requirement in many market designs that bids must be hourly throughout the day or that capacity must be separated from energy bids are examples of an overly specified market design that will induce participants to find alternatives.

Empirical observation informed by theoretical considerations is essential for improving market design. Experiments confirm that markets seem to operate more efficiently when suppliers decide how much capacity to remove (to prevent a price decrease) than when they bid a price for providing a given capacity level. Markets behave differently when demanders bid what they want to pay for different amounts. Generally, producers can push prices higher than when demand is determined exogenously.

Initial conditions, such as ownership rights, frequently constrain the power system's evolution. Since ownership issues are largely local by nature, there may be limited opportunity to draw lessons that span international boundaries when such constraints predominate. Ed Kahn argues in Chapter 8 that economic and commercial innovation will resolve technical constraints more readily than constraints arising from ownership issues. He illustrates the differences between technical and ownership constraints with a number of examples. Congestion arising from regional differences in production costs represents a technical constraint; congestion caused by "pancaking", where each region layers another transmission charge on top of others as electrons pass through its system, demonstrates a problem with ownership rights and high transaction costs. Ownership constraints also feature prominently in the problems of coordinating water supplies in integrated hydroelectric systems or where supply entitlements (e.g., take-or-pay fuel contracts or minimum stable generation levels) induce plants to bid a zero price so as to be always dispatched.

While much of the controversy surrounding market design issues focuses on the short run, the big payoffs or losses may be in the long run. Who will be making the required investment in new transmission facilities, for whom, and how are these expansions to be financed? Moreover, what are the prospects for sustained research and development in a fragmented industry of relatively small players? The next chapters by Martin Baughman and Granger Morgan explore these important issues.

Restructuring has transformed the transmission role from merely moving electrons to encompass a range of trading functions as well, argues Baughman in Chapter 9. A fundamental issue of market design is developing institutional structures and incentives to assure appropriate transmission investments are made in the future. The design must resolve when the investment is made, where it is located, and which entity pays for the expansion and assumes the risk. Most restructuring proposals have focused on how to facilitate short-run transactions and operations, without addressing the critical long-run concern about the adequacy of future investments.

Taking an even longer horizon in Chapter 10, Morgan is not optimistic about the prospects for funding the needed research and development in an electricity world dominated by decentralized decisions. He notes that while new technologies did not drive the rush towards decentralized markets, research and development will shape the relative success of future decentralized markets to allocate power efficiently. Market design must be sufficiently flexible to allow the opportunity to reap the potential gains from emerging commercialization and technological opportunities. It is unlikely that many decentralized participants will invest to expand the technological opportunities, due to the public nature of R&D benefits spilling over to other participants. The current political climate is not conducive to joint public R&D strategies, but this situation could change.

In Chapter 11 Robert Wilson integrates a number of key factors in designing competitive wholesale electricity markets. This process begins with the structural conditions to create enough competitors and avoid monopoly power in generation and local monopolies due to transmission constraints. Once these conditions are in place, the process shifts to the relationship between markets for energy, transmission, and ancillary services. Finally, there is the development of detailed procedural rules and governance issues, some of which must be designed to mitigate market power and collusion.

Wilson makes it clear that he favors designs that combine two extreme options to gain the advantages of each from operating together. He clarifies some key issues such as the advantages and disadvantages of bilateral markets and of pools, the demands for energy and for transmission and how these two markets are related, and the critical distinction between energy markets that are static in the sense that the initial market clearing is also the final one and those that are iterative with repeated bidding determining the final prices. While iterative markets require procedural rules to reinforce serious bidding, they allow bidders to cover their fixed costs without resort to *ad hoc* measures.

Chao and Peck note that the design of electricity market is complicated by some intrinsic technological characteristics associated with the electric power transmission system. In Chapter 12, they describe a market design that incorporates externalities created by loop flows. A key element that enables a more decentralized market design is the introduction of link-based tradable transmission capacity rights that match physical power flows. In this system, simultaneous market trading of energy and transmission capacity rights achieves efficient outcome. Naturally, this raises a critical question about how to ensure adequate levels of reliability in decentralized markets. In this design, the system operator offers electricity consumers and generators a menu of priority insurance options, which provide partial or full financial protection against interruptions, and establish scheduling priority according to the self-selected insurance options. An advantage of this design is that the system operator will be motivated to maintain system reliability in a socially optimal manner. Overall, this chapter underscores the important role of incentive in market design.

Issues of Market Design

The authors lay out a series of issues that need to be resolved for introducing new market designs successfully. Several key themes emerge.

The primary motivation behind industry restructuring is to promote long-run efficiency gains through competition that stimulates technical innovation and efficient investment.

All contributors recognize the paramount importance of long-run efficiency. To achieve these long-run gains through greater competition, short-run operations must be revamped in conjunction with the changing structure of markets and institutions. While the organization of short-run operations may influence the evolving market structure in the long term, however, no one thinks that improved short-run operations, per se, constitute the primary objective on their own.

Restructuring requires unbundling of electrical services and creation of new institutions. This process will involve additional transaction costs which should be considered in market design.

While the inefficiencies in the industry's current organization are well known and easily recognizable, new market designs will bring new rules on trading and contracting arrangements as well as new institutions governing ownership and decision rights. How these rules and institutions are implemented and evolve over time will crucially affect transaction costs of participants in these new markets and hence the overall efficiency of new market designs. These additional transactions costs may be easily absorbed when competition produces significant gains in economic efficiency and when the new rules provide clear incentives for economic behavior. If the rules are not implemented smoothly, transactional costs could mount and limit the gains from restructuring.

There exist some differences on the relative importance of reliable short-run price signals in promoting long-term economic efficiency.

Joskow emphasizes that short-run signaling is critical for sending the proper long-run incentives for deciding where and when to invest in additional transmission, generation, and loads. For example, short-run market prices could send the wrong signals if they fail to incorporate congestion costs or when they fail to incorporate fully important interdependencies between decisions. Wilson cautions that until a coherent scheme for daily operations is in place it may be fruitless to design long-term incentives which might not be compatible with the structure of the short-term markets.   Indeed, if the institutions for achieving efficient short-run resource allocation are not in place, there is little hope of achieving longer-run efficiency gains.

On the other hand, Oren does not think that short-term price signals have to be precise in order to prompt efficient investment. More important, in his opinion, is the existence of a market structure that facilitates the technological development and product redefinition that is critical for achieving long-run gains in economic efficiency.   Kleindorfer argues that short-run pricing may not be as important as promoting simple and transparent transmission pricing and establishing the proper institutions governing ownership and decision rights for transmission. He states, "transparency, simplicity, and system integrity must be the initial guiding principles of transmission provision and regulation ... and lastly efficiency in short-term pricing."

At the core of this disagreement are some definable analytical issues that include:

- How prevalent is congestion?
- Can decentralized markets overcome intertemporal complementarities between generation supplied at different times due to start-up and ramping costs and constraints?
- Are there important complementarities between energy and ancillary services caused by their being joint products?
- How significant are real-time operating constraints such as transmission constraints and unplanned outages?
- Are network externalities a significant problem or only a minor nuisance?
- How pervasive are short run market power problems, where firms can manipulate price due to their strategic location?

One should evaluate market design holistically, striving for compatibility across regions and for consistency across market segments.

Policy makers should avoid designing systems or parts of systems in isolation from each other, running the risk of being incompatible with other states that may be a potential partner in electricity trade. Within a single regional electricity market, policy makers should not impose artificial, unnecessary constraints that often can be quite debilitating to thriving nascent markets.

Initial conditions influence how market will evolve.

The physical characteristics of electricity, such as nonstorability or "loop flow", impose some important constraints on market design. In addition, extant ownership and decision rights may preclude certain evolution paths for restructuring. Designs that do not account for these initial conditions may be particularly doomed.

Policy makers have probably underappreciated the importance of customer choice and product diversity in achieving long-run efficiency gains.

Many existing market designs emphasize supply-side bidding with little participation from electricity consumers or suppliers or distributors representing them. However, knowing how much consumers value electricity at different locations and times or reliability or other ancillary services may be the key to resolving many potential market design problems. In addition, as Joskow cautions, customer choice may be the only defense against "turkey stuffing" by regulators, the tendency to slip in selected social objectives into the pricing of distribution services. While restructuring involves the replacement of regulation by market forces in many levels of the industry, regulators will remain important players in such functions as distribution.

There may be some long-run decisions that require public intervention because they involve important externalities or public goods.

While all contributors agree on the merits for opening generation investment decisions to the market, some are reluctant to open transmission investment to the same decentralized forces. Unlike generation, Joskow reminds us, transmission raises the problems of network externalities and large sunk costs or economies of scale where private market prices may not adequately recover the investment.

Morgan discusses the significant problems of ensuring a steady flow of research and development expenditures in a fragmented industry of smaller entities. Such an industry may not have the capacity or desire to invest in a number of new technologies that could reshape the industry but whose societal value lies in the spillover benefits provided to those not investing.

Informed public policy requires impartial evaluation and frequent monitoring of market performance under different rules and institutions.

The adoption of a particular market design for a specific region is a political process that necessarily involves tradeoffs between transparency, political interests, and economic efficiency considerations. As a result, often it is not known at the outset how well a particular design will perform. Public policy makers can learn about the relative merits and disadvantages of alternative designs from monitoring the behavior of participants in a specific institutional environment. Such evaluation could involve one or more of the following approaches: empirical observations and international comparison of how actual regional electricity markets operate, experiments revealing how real people behave in different laboratory environments, and computer simulations of market outcomes based upon assumed behavior. All approaches are likely to be useful, depending upon the policy issues under consideration. Moreover, the U.S. should draw useful lessons internationally from the experience of other countries with operating markets, such as Chile, Argentina, United Kingdom, Norway-Sweden-Finland, Australia, New Zealand, etc

2 RESTRUCTURING, COMPETITION AND REGULATORY REFORM IN THE U.S. ELECTRICITY SECTOR[1]

Paul L. Joskow

Economical and reliable supplies of electricity make possible many of the services that we associate with modern life. From electric lights and microwave ovens, to television, telephones, and computers, electricity is a critical input supporting a wide range of consumption, transportation and production activities. The electricity sector is also a major manufacturing sector, accounting for about $210 billion of annual sales, about $40 billion in annual investment and 35 percent of U.S. primary energy use.

For nearly a century, the electricity sector in all countries has been thought of as a "natural" monopoly industry, where efficient production of electricity required reliance on public or private monopoly suppliers subject to government regulation of prices, entry, investment, service quality and other aspects of firm behavior. But dramatic changes are now taking place in the structure of electric power sectors around the world. The changes are designed to foster competition in the generating segment of the industry and to reform the regulation of the transmission and distribution functions, which continue to be viewed as natural monopolies. In the United States, reforms are being introduced most quickly in California and the Northeast, but many other states are moving quickly to introduce competition and reform regulation. Pilot programs that unbundle retail prices into separate generation, transmission, distribution and transition cost charges and that allow retail consumers to choose among a large number of competing generation service suppliers are already underway in New Hampshire, Massachusetts and Illinois. California, Rhode Island, Massachusetts, New Hampshire and perhaps other states are expected to give retail consumers the opportunity to choose among competing electricity suppliers as early as 1998.

Structural and regulatory reform of the electricity sectors in the U.S. and other countries is following the basic model previously applied to network industries such as telephones and natural gas. Potentially competitive segments (the generation of electricity) are being separated structurally or functionally from natural monopoly segments (the physical transmission and distribution of electricity). Prices for, entry to and exit from the competitive segments are being deregulated, and customers are given the opportunity to choose among competing suppliers. Services provided by the natural monopoly segments are being unbundled from the supply of competitive services, nondiscriminatory access to "essential" network facilities mandated and prices for use of these facilities determined by new regulation mechanisms that are designed to control costs better than traditional rate-of-return regulation procedures.

While the basic model for structural and regulatory reform in electricity is fairly straightforward, the details of the institutional reforms that are necessary to improve on the performance of the present U.S. system are complex. Moreover, much of the pressure for reform in the United States reflects rent-seeking behavior by various interest groups pursuing private agendas that may not always be consistent with efficiency goals. At the same time, there are good public interest reasons to believe that structural and regulatory reforms that foster competition can lead to real cost savings in the long run *if* appropriate supporting institutional arrangements are put in place. Because of the critical role that economical and reliable supplies of electricity play in our economy, there is a profound public interest in ensuring that these reforms improve rather than degrade the performance of the electricity sector over the long run.

This paper discusses the electricity sector reforms that are taking place in the United States. The first half of the paper discusses the physical attributes of electric power networks: the industrial and regulatory structure that emerged during the last century to govern resource allocation in the sector, the performance attributes of the sector and the sources of the pressures for reform. The second half of the paper discusses a number of issues that must be confronted to create efficient competitive markets for generation services and to reform the regulation of the residual monopoly segments to support the evolution of the competitive segments that must rely on them.

The Organization of the Electric Power Sector in the United States

The basic structure of the U.S. electricity sector and its regulation is discussed in detail elsewhere (Joskow and Schmalensee, 1983, 1986; Joskow, 1989, 1996). I provide only a very brief description here as background for the discussion of the reforms presently underway. Electricity is supplied to consumers in the United States by investor-owned or publicly owned (municipal, state, and federal) utilities that have de facto exclusive franchises to sell electricity to retail customers in specific geographic areas. The discussion here focuses on the investor-owned segment of the industry, which accounts for over 75 percent of U.S. retail electricity sales and is the major focus of the reforms taking place in the United States.

Today, retail consumers must buy their electricity from the regulated monopoly supplier that has the legal right to distribute electricity at their locations. These franchised monopolies have a legal obligation to supply and to plan for the needs of all retail customers within their franchise areas and to make electricity available at prices approved by state regulatory commissions. Most utilities have historically met their obligations to supply by owning and operating all of the facilities required to supply a complete "bundled" electricity product to retail customers. That is, the typical utility is vertically integrated into four primary electricity supply functions: generation, transmission, distribution and retailing.

The *generation* of electricity involves the creation of electric energy using falling water, internal combustion engines, steam turbines powered with steam produced with fossil fuels, nuclear fuel and various renewable fuels, wind driven turbines and photovoltaic technologies. The *distribution* of electricity to residences and businesses at relatively low voltages relies on wires and transformers along and under streets and other rights of way. The distribution function typically involves both the provision of the services of the distribution "wires" to consumers as well as a set of *retailing* functions, including making arrangements for supplies of power from generators, metering, billing and various demand management services. These retailing functions have typically been viewed as an integral component of the distribution function. The *transmission* of electricity involves the use of wires, transformers and substation facilities to affect the high voltage "transportation" of electricity between generating sites and distribution centers, which includes the interconnection and integration of dispersed generating facilities into a stable synchronized AC (alternating current) network, the scheduling and dispatching of generating facilities that are connected to the transmission network to balance the demand and supplies of electricity in real time, and the management of equipment failures, network constraints and relations with other interconnected electricity networks.

Several key attributes of the supply and demand for electricity have important implications for whether and how competition can be introduced. The demand for electricity varies widely from hour to hour during an individual day and from day to day over the year, and electricity cannot be stored or inventoried economically by consumers or distributors. As a result, the generation and consumption of electrical energy must be balanced continuously to maintain the frequency, voltage and stability of an electric power network and to avoid sudden losses of power.

Although generation and transmission are typically discussed as separate segments of the vertical supply chain, there are important operating and investment complementarities between them that explain the evolution of an industry structure based on vertical integration of generation and transmission (Joskow and Schmalensee, 1983; Joskow, 1996). The transmission system is not simply a transportation network that moves power from individual generating stations to demand centers, but a complex "coordination" system that integrates a large number of generating facilities dispersed over wide geographic areas to provide a reliable flow of electricity to dispersed demand nodes while adhering to tight physical requirements to maintain network frequency, voltage and stability.

Electric power networks are not switched networks like railroad or telephone networks, where a supplier makes a physical delivery of a product at point *A*, and it is then physically transported to a specific customer at point *B*. A free flowing AC network is an integrated physical machine that follows the laws of physics (Kirchoff's laws). When a generator turns on and off, it affects system conditions throughout the interconnected network. A failure of a major piece of equipment in one part of the network can affect the stability of the entire system. Efficient and effective remedial responses to equipment failures can involve coordinated reactions of multiple generators located far from the site of the failure. Finally, there is generally no meaningful direct physical relation between the electric power produced by a specific generator connected to the network and a specific customer taking energy from the network. This creates significant challenges for accurately measuring and settling consumer and generator financial obligations in a competitive electricity market.

The primary economic rationale for vertical integration between generation and transmission is that it internalizes with an organization the operating and investment complementarities between these supply functions, with their associated potential public goods and externality problems. Vertical integration also responds to challenges that decentralized market mechanisms face; for example, coordinating the efficient operation of generation and transmission capacity in real time in response to continuously changing demand and supply conditions, the need to balance the supply of generation and electricity consumption continuously at every point on the network, and the accurate measurement and billing of consumers and suppliers for injections to and withdrawals from the network. However, vertical integration between the network functions that have natural monopoly characteristics and the generation function effectively turns the supply of generating service into a monopoly as well, even if, as is the case in the United States there are numerous generating plants connected to the network and limited economies of scale associated with generation per se in isolation from the coordination functions performed by the network (Joskow and Schmalensee, 1983). In turn, this leads to the extension of government regulation and any inefficiencies it entails, to the prices, costs, and investment decisions related to the generation segment, which is potentially competitive.

It is sometimes argued that one reason that creating a separate competitive generation sector now makes sense is that the generation of electricity is no longer a natural monopoly as a consequence of technological change. This view is incorrect. Generation per se has not really been a strong natural monopoly requiring very large generating companies spanning a large fraction of regional wholesale power markets for many years (Joskow and Schmalensee, 1983). Just look at the United States, where hundreds of utilities own and operate generating plants, with little evidence that huge generating companies are necessary to exploit available economies of scale. Cheap natural gas and the new aero-derivative combined-cycle generating technology (CCGT) have certainly significantly reduced the minimum efficient scale of new generating facilities and reduced planning and construction lead times and facilitated siting as well. These developments have increased the feasibility of creating competitive generation markets quickly, but have not fundamentally transformed a sector with natural monopoly characteristics to one where these characteristics are completely absent. Rather, it is the attributes of the transmission network and its ability to aggregate and facilitate the efficient operation of generating facilities dispersed over wide geographic areas, over time frames from seconds to decades, that has played the most important role in defining the vertical and horizontal structure of this industry.

While the investor-owned utilities in the United States are typically vertically integrated into generation, transmission and distribution, there are over 100 of them serving specific geographic areas. They vary widely in size. In addition, thousands of relatively small unintegrated public and cooperative distribution entities exist that buy power from unaffiliated generating and transmission entities. The decentralized industry structure that has emerged in the United States is not ideally matched to the physical attributes of the electric power networks that have evolved over time. From a physical perspective, the U.S. sector (combined with portions of Canada and northern Mexico) is composed of three large synchronized AC networks, the Eastern Interconnection, the Western Interconnection and the Texas Interconnection. These three networks are not each under the physical control of a single network operator. Instead, there are over 140 separate "control areas" superimposed on the three networks where individual vertically integrated utilities or groups of utilities operating through power pooling arrangements are responsible for generator dispatch, network operations and maintaining reliability on specific portions of the networks.

To harmonize and rationalize the dispersed ownership and control of facilities that are physically interconnected and whose operations have impacts on facilities in remote control areas, the U.S. industry has developed a complex set of operating protocols--bilateral and multilateral agreements designed to maintain reliability, to facilitate coordinated operations, to facilitate trades of power between control areas and to minimize free-riding problems. These operating protocols, developed by a hierarchy of cooperative "technical" organizations, are essential for the reliable and efficient operation of synchronized networks when there are many hands on the wheel.

The decentralized structure of the U.S. electricity sector has also led to the development of competitive wholesale markets through which utilities buy and sell electricity among one another to reduce the costs of supplying their franchise customers. Wholesale power transactions and supporting transmission or "wheeling" arrangements are regulated by the Federal Energy Regulatory Commission (FERC). Wholesale trade expanded rapidly in the 1970s, initially in response to large differences in the short-run marginal cost of hydroelectric coal, oil and natural gas generating units, as well as variations in demand and capacity availability among utilities in the same region.

The Public Utility Regulatory Policy Act of 1978 (PURPA), which required utilities to buy power from cogenerators and small power producers using renewable fuels (Joskow, 1989, 1996), significantly spurred long-term contracts between vertically integrated utilities and certain types of independent generating companies. The Energy Policy Act of 1992 and state programs requiring utilities to meet additional generation needs through competitive bidding further expanded opportunities for independent power producers to sell electricity to utilities for resale.   The independent producers account for only about 8 percent of U.S. generating capacity, but essentially all of that has been created since 1980, and in the last few years, independent producers have accounted for more than 50 percent of annual generating capacity additions.

Industry Performance and Pressures For Reform

To understand why electricity sector reform is taking place now, it is natural to look first at the performance of the industry as a stimulus for reform. However, the electric power sector in the United States has performed fairly well. In particular, it supplies electricity with high levels of reliability; investment in new capacity has been readily financed to keep up with (or often exceed) demand growth; system losses (both physical and those due to theft of service) are low; and electricity is available virtually universally. This contrasts sharply with the performance of the electricity sectors in many other countries. The average price of electricity in the United States today is about 6.9 cents/kWh.   The average price charged to residential customers is about 8.4 cents/kWh, and the price to industrial customers is about 4.7 cents/kWh. The difference between the residential and industrial prices largely reflects differences in load factor and the voltage level at which electricity is supplied. These prices are at the low end of the range of prices for OECD countries and have been falling in real terms for the last decade.

Despite these generally favorable performance attributes, there are a variety of apparent inefficiencies that are targets of opportunity for structural and regulatory reforms.

In the short run, the current system does a good job efficiently dispatching generating plants, making cost-reducing energy trades between generating utilities, maintaining network reliability, and dealing with congestion and emergencies. Restructuring for competition and regulatory reform is unlikely to lead to significant short-run cost savings.

However, medium-run efficiency gains may be associated with improving the operating performance of the existing stock of generating facilities and increasing the productivity of labor operating these facilities. The operating performance of both fossil and nuclear units varies widely even after controlling for age, size and fuel attributes, and some utilities have performance that lags behind industry norms

(Joskow and Schmalensee, 1987). In addition, regulatory cost recovery rules may encourage utilities to continue to operate generating plants even though it would be economical to close them. Other countries that have restructured their electricity sectors have experience significant improvements in labor productivity. For example, the number of workers that have been shed by the electricity sector in England and Wales since the 1990 privatization and restructuring is quite impressive (Newbery and Pollitt, 1996). The potential gains from improvements in labor productivity and wage concessions must be kept in perspective, however. In the United States, wages and benefits account for only about 12 percent of the total cost of supplying electricity, and labor productivity is higher in the U.S. electricity sector than in the countries that have already gone through a restructuring process. Overall, my sense is that the opportunities for costs savings in the United States in the medium run are significant, but not enormous.

The most important opportunities for cost savings are associated with long-run investments in generating capacity. The cost of building reasonably comparable generating facilities varies significantly. These variations have been revealed most starkly in the context of nuclear generating facilities (Lester and McCabe, 1993), but appear as well in large fossil-fuel generating plants (Joskow and Rose, 1985). Significant variations also exist in the speed with which utilities have adopted new generating technologies (Rose and Joskow, 1990). Indeed, it is evident that PURPA's requirement that utilities contract with certain independent power suppliers, combined with competitive generation procurement programs in the late 1980s, helped to stimulate the technological innovation in combined-cycle generating technology (CCGT) using natural gas as a fuel. Finally, traditional regulatory pricing principles, based on the prudent investment standard and recovery of investment costs, implicitly allocates most of the market risks associated with investments in generating capacity to consumers rather than producers. Once regulators approve the construction costs of a generating plant or the terms of an energy supply contract, these costs (amortized in the case of capital investments) continue to be included in regulated prices over the life of the investment or contract, independent of whether the market values of these commitments rise or fall over time as energy prices, technology, and supply and demand conditions change. Accordingly, regulated prices reflect current market values of electricity only by accident.

While potential performance improvements in these and other dimensions represent plausible "public interest" motivations for structural and regulatory reform in the United States, they are not the primary stimulus to reform today. As White (1997) has explored in detail, the primary stimulus for reform of the U.S. electricity sector is the gap that exists in some parts of the United States between the implicit price of generation services embedded in regulated bundled electricity prices and the "unbundled" price of generation services that would be available in the wholesale market if consumers could buy it directly, paying the local utility only for transmission and distribution costs.

Table 1

Average Electricity Prices for Selected States, 1995

(cents/kWh)

State	All Sectors	Residential	Industrial
Massachusetts	10.3	11.4	8.6
Connecticut	10.5	12.0	8.1
New York	10.8	14.0	5.6
Virginia	6.3	7.9	4.0
Florida	7.1	7.8	5.2
Indiana	5.3	6.8	3.9
Wisconsin	5.4	7.2	3.8
Illinois	7.7	10.4	5.3
Texas	6.1	7.7	4.0
Arizona	6.2	9.1	5.3
Oregon	4.7	5.5	3.5
California	9.9	11.6	7.5
U.S. Average	6.9	8.4	4.7

Source: U.S. Energy Information Administration, *Electric Power Annual 1995*, Volume 1, p. 39.

As noted earlier, the average price of electricity at retail is about 6.9 cents/kWh. Of that price, about 3.8 cents/kWh is associated with the costs of generating electricity and the rest with transmission, distribution, and unallocated general and administrative expenses. However, the averages reflect wide regional differences in regulated electricity prices, as shown in Table 1. In the Northeast and California, the average price of electricity is around 10 cents/kWh, while in Indiana it is about 5.5 cents/kWh, and in Oregon less than 4.5 cents/kWh. Some of this variation in prices can be explained by regional differences in fuel costs, the mix of customers, average utilization rates and load factors, and differences in population density and construction costs. However, a large fraction of the variation in prices reflects differences in the sunk costs of generation investments and past long-term purchase power contracts.

As already noted, regulated retail prices reflect the amortization of the sunk costs associated with past regulator-approved investments in generating plants (for example, nuclear power plants) and prices paid for energy under long-term purchase contracts mandated by PURPA signed many years ago, when expectations about fossil fuel prices and demand growth were very different from what eventually transpired. Thus, in much of the Northeast and California, the average cost of generation services reflected in regulated retail prices is in the 6-7 cent/kWh range, reflecting historical investments in nuclear power plants and high-priced

PURPA contracts that regulators required utilities to sign. In Indiana and Oregon, the average cost of generation services reflected in retail prices is 2-3 cents/kWh, reflecting low-cost coal-fired and hydroelectric generation resources, limited commitments to nuclear power and state regulatory policies that did not require utilities to sign expensive long-term PURPA power supply contracts.

More importantly for understanding the source of the interest group pressures for reform, the short-run unregulated price of electricity in the wholesale market is about 2.5 cents/kWh, and the long-run marginal cost in the 3-4.0 cent/kWh range, reflecting a combination of excess generating capacity, the abundant supply of cheap natural gas and the combined-cycle generating technology that can transform natural gas into electricity very efficiently. Thus, in areas like the Northeast and California, there is a "price gap" of 3-4 cents/kWh between the price of generation service included in regulated retail rates and current and projected wholesale market prices in these areas, while in other parts of the country the gap is negligible or even negative. If generation services were instantly priced at current and projected market values in those areas where the price gap is positive, the net present value of the losses to utilities would be on the order of $100 billion.

Electricity sector reform efforts at the state level have been concentrated in the states where the gap is largest (White, 1997; Joskow, 1997). They have been led by large industrial customers interested in lower electricity prices and by the independent power providers and new electricity marketers who can profit if reforms allow them to sell directly to end-use customers at prevailing wholesale market prices and if these customers are relieved of their responsibility to pay for generating plant investments and long-term contractual commitments their utility made in conjunction with its historical public supply obligations. Not surprisingly, with $100 billion at stake, this in turn has led to a heated debate about the allocation of obligations for the existing sunk cost commitments between utilities, customers and independent power producers who signed high-price, long-term contracts--the so-called "stranded cost" problem (Sidak and Spulber, 1996). FERC and most state commissions that have dealt with the issues have allowed utilities to recover these stranded costs in the form of nonbypassable access charges in return for utility support and assistance in implementing competitive reforms quickly and, in a few cases, in return for "voluntary" generation divestiture.

Major Issues in Restructuring the U.S. Electricity Sector

Let me now turn to some of the major institutional issues that arise as the United States endeavors to implement regulatory and structural reforms aimed at creating a more competitive market for the generation of electricity, shrinking the domain of price and entry regulation and reforming the regulation of residual monopoly services. *The key technical challenge is to expand decentralized competition in the supply of generation services in a way that preserves the operating and investment efficiencies that are associated with vertical and horizontal integration, while mitigating the significant costs that the institution of regulated monopoly has created.*

What is the Right Model?

Two basic models for promoting competition in the electricity sector have been under discussion in the United States for the past several years. The first is the "portfolio manager model," in which the local distribution utility retains its traditional obligation to supply customers within its de facto exclusive franchise areas with bundled retail electricity service. However, in this model, the distributor relies on competitive procurement mechanisms to buy electricity from the lowest cost suppliers in competitive wholesale markets rather than building new generating facilities to serve growing electricity demand in its franchise area. The price for the electricity received by retail consumers continues to be regulated since the consumers must buy their electricity from the local monopoly distributor. But the regulation of the generation cost component of the retail price would presumably be based on market price indicia rather, as in the traditional method, than trying to track the underlying accounting costs and performance of generating plants owned by the distributor. This portfolio manager, or "wholesale competition model," was the framework envisioned by both the Public Utility Regulatory Policy Act of 1978 (PURPA) and the Energy Policy Act of 1992. It promotes both the continued growth of the independent power sector and associated competitive wholesale markets and retains the traditional retail monopoly over retail sales of electricity.

The key technical challenge is to expand decentralized competition in the supply of generation services in a way that preserves the operating and investment efficiencies that are associated with vertical and horizontal integration, while mitigating the significant costs that the institution of regulated monopoly has created.

The second model is the "customer choice," or "retail wheeling" model. In this model, retail customers can access the wholesale market directly by purchasing unbundled distribution and transmission services from their local utility. Individual consumers take on the obligation to arrange for their own generation service supplies with independent competing electricity suppliers. The electricity suppliers can either be companies with physical generating assets or marketers that provide a bundled product of generation service procurement and risk management services (and no doubt will be calling us while we are having dinner). In this model, generators can sell energy in a competitive spot market, as well as arrange for longer term financial contracts with electricity supply intermediaries or directly with retail consumers. The role of local distributors is to provide "wires services" to retail customers for "access" to the power market. A network operator of some kind is responsible for operating (or owning and operating) the transmission network so that reliability is maintained and competition to supply energy from competing generators can proceed efficiently. The prices for these distribution and transmission services would still be subject to (better) regulation since they continue to be monopoly services.

Variations on the customer choice model have been adopted in England and Wales, Chile, Argentina, New Zealand, Norway and elsewhere, although the retail customers' freedom to choose has typically either been phased in over time or limited to large customers. The restructuring initiative that began in California in 1994 has stimulated much more interest in the customer choice model in the United States. This model is now guiding the restructuring for competition and regulatory reform initiatives in New England, New York, Pennsylvania, Illinois and other states and is the focus of legislation that has recently been introduced in the U.S. Congress.

The portfolio manager model involves the smallest changes in organizational arrangements and retains the largest continuing role for regulation. In this model, regulators will almost inevitably retain responsibility for supervising how utilities purchase generating capacity--especially if utilities continue to own and to operate their existing generating facilities. While competitive procurement mechanisms for generation supplied by third parties could minimize regulatory supervision, there remains room for considerable regulatory intervention into decisions about the kinds of generating sources utilities will contract with and the prices that should be paid. This creates considerable opportunities for regulatory mischief driven by the kinds of interest group pressures that are partially responsible for the inefficiencies in the present system.

The customer choice model represents a much more dramatic change in utility and regulatory responsibilities and in organizational and financial arrangements. The major potential benefit of the customer choice model over the portfolio manager model is that by allowing end-use customers to manage their own electricity supply, this approach substantially reduces the ability of regulators to control the generation market, including service prices, entry to and exit from the generation segment and the forms of the contractual arrangements that support new generation investments. In theory, the customer choice model reduces the domain of regulation to the distribution and transmission segments and relies on market forces to govern the performance of the generation segment, the segment where performance has historically been the poorest and regulation-induced inefficiencies the largest.

Transmission Network Governance and Pricing Structures

All of the models for creating new competitive market structures in electricity being discussed in the United States recognize that there must be a single network operator responsible for controlling the physical operation of a control area, coordinating generator schedules, balancing demand for and supply of generation services flowing over the network in real time and coordinating with neighboring control areas. Also, the general agreement seems to be that it would be desirable to consolidate the 140 control areas that now exist into a smaller number of regional control areas. However, there is much less agreement about precisely what the network operator's function should be, what information it needs to perform its tasks well, the ownership structure of the network operator and how it should be regulated.

Transmission pricing is a particularly challenging problem because of the existence of transmission constraints from time to time, complementarities between generation and transmission and potential network externalities arising from the interrelationships between generators and demand at different locations on the network (Hunt and Shuttleworth, 1996). We must get transmission pricing right to decentralize competitive generation supply decisions efficiently over time and space on an AC network. Two "pure" approaches are being pursued for organizing the trading of energy on the network, the associated prices for transmission service and the management of network congestion and reliability standards.

The "tradable physical rights" framework involves defining physical transmission rights to inject energy at one or more points on the network for "receipt" at one or more other points on the network. In practice, it could work in this way. Engineering power flow models are used to determine the "available transmission capacity" (ATC) of a particular transmission system based on a variety of assumptions about system conditions and reliability. ATC is essentially the capacity a specific transmission interface has to accommodate generator schedules for 24 hours a day, 365 days a year, with high probability. The rights to use the ATC over a "contract path" from a set of injection points to one or more receipt points on the network are then sold to generators, distributors, retail marketers or directly to consumers, who can either use the rights themselves to buy and sell electricity on the network or trade them to third parties for their use. If the demand to use an interface rises beyond the ATC to handle all of the preferred schedules, the price for the fixed quantity of rights to use that transmission interface will rise to balance supply and demand.

The primary problem with this approach is that there is no unambiguous way to define a full set of contingent delivery and receipt property rights from one point on the network to another. The capacity to transfer power across one interface depends on demand, generation and power schedules elsewhere in the system, and thus it can vary widely with supply and demand conditions on the network. To avoid significant conflicts between rights for simultaneous use of different interfaces on the network, ATC must be defined conservatively to reflect a set of "stressed" system conditions. As a result, during many hours, more transmission capacity will be available for use than has been allocated to users. There will also be conflicts of rights under certain system conditions, when the capability of the network to accommodate schedules is less than the quantity of usage rights that have been allocated to use it. In addition, for this approach to work well, a set of transmission rights markets must evolve to operate in tandem with forward and real time energy markets. The tradable physical rights approaches that are being proposed recognize these problems, but argue that the approach can be employed without significant efficiency losses since there is a relatively small number of transmission interfaces where congestion is a significant issue and that market mechanisms, monitoring and enforcement institutions can be created to assure that transmission rights markets and energy markets clear efficiently (Walton and Tabors, 1996; Tabors, 1996; Chao and Peck, 1996).

The second broad organizational framework, the "nodal pricing" approach, follows directly from the work of my late colleague Fred Schweppe (1988) and has been extended significantly by William Hogan (1992, 1993; Harvey, Hogan and Pope, 1996). Basically, the network operator runs a set of day-ahead and hour-ahead auction markets for energy (as well as the ancillary network support services required in any approach) and uses the bids submitted to it to derive a "least cost" merit order schedule of generators selected to supply energy and an associated set of market clearing prices. On the supply side, the network operator accepts supply bids from generators offering supplies in the day-ahead and hour-ahead markets, or congestion reservation prices for generators or intermediaries seeking to schedule generators on the network but who do not want to participate directly in the auction markets run by the network operator.

On the demand side, customers articulate their willingness to pay for electricity, which includes their willingness to contract or expand their use at different times as price varies. The network operator then feeds the bids into an optimization program that takes into account network operating constraints to determine prices and quantities for electricity to balance supply and demand continuously at each node. (A "node" is a point on the network where electricity is either supplied to the network or withdrawn from the network at a point of connection with a distribution system or large industrial consumer.) The transmission price for power physically flowing from one node to another is then the difference between the prices at each of the nodes. Ideally, these prices take all network interdependencies into account.

There has been a lot of controversy about which of these models is the best one to pursue, as well as how they might be combined effectively. Some of the controversy reflects reasonable differences of opinion about how best to create an efficient competitive electricity market that properly reflects all of the physical complexities of electric power networks. Some of the controversy also reflects rent-seeking behavior by market participants who envision financial opportunities that emerge by creating network operating and resource allocation institutions that have high transactions costs and are inefficient (Stoft, 1997).

Supporters of the tradable physical rights approach emphasize that it maximizes the freedom individual suppliers have to structure transactions and minimizes the role of the network operator, which they argue is a potential monopoly "central planner" that could abuse its authority. The network operator does not participate directly in the bulk of the electricity market transactions, does not determine market clearing prices in day-ahead and hour-ahead markets for energy and plays only a secondary role in managing network congestion economically. Its job is "limited" to maintaining the physical integrity of the network, enforcing transmission rights, managing conflicts between the exercise of rights to schedule generation and the actual capacity of the network to accommodate schedules, buying and selling a variety of network support and reliability services that are not self-supplied by energy traders using the network, measuring and settling imbalances between those that have contracted to supply energy to serve consumers and their actual measured consumption.

The nodal pricing approach envisions a more active and central role for the network operator in the energy markets than does the tradable rights approach. In particular, the network operator runs day-ahead and hour-ahead markets for energy and ancillary network support services and uses the information obtained from these auctions to establish a least cost merit order generator dispatch schedule that matches demand and supply, to manage network constraints economically, and to define market clearing prices at each supply and demand node on the network consistent with network operating constraints. Basically, the network operator does what control area operators do today, except it relies on bids from competing generators as inputs into its least cost generator dispatch optimization programs. Proponents of the nodal pricing approach argue that the tradable rights approach does not solve the fundamental network externality problems that arise when congestion becomes important, will lead to inefficient allocations of scarce transmission capacity and further inefficiencies in the commitment and dispatch of generators, and will increase transactions costs for smaller consumers and generators seeking to participate in the market.

A related set of issues has arisen with regard to investments that increase capacity of the network to transfer energy from supply nodes to consumption nodes. Who should be responsible for identifying economical opportunities to expand transmission capacity, and who should pay for it? One approach would rely primarily on private parties to propose and pay for upgrades to the transmission network. The alternative vests responsibility for identifying needed transmission upgrades in the network operator and would share the costs of these facilities among those who use the system.

Transmission investment decisions do not immediately strike me as being ideally suited to relying entirely on the invisible hand. Transmission investments are lumpy, characterized by economies of scale and can have physical impacts throughout the network. The combination of imperfectly defined network property rights, economies of scale and long-lived sunk costs for transmission investments, and imperfect competition in the supply of generating services can lead to either underinvestment or overinvestment in transmission at particular points on the network if we rely entirely on market forces (Nasser, 1997). However, there is no reason why the primary initiative for transmission upgrades should not be left to private parties, especially if a reasonably good allocation of capacity rights, whether physical or financial, is created. The network operator could then determine whether proposed upgrades have adverse uncompensated effects on some users of the network, or whether there are inadequate private market incentives for investment because of scale economies or free-riding problems. In those cases the network operator could identify investment projects that the transmission owners would be obligated to build and the associate costs could be recovered from all network users. This appears to be the direction in which public policy is now moving.

Vertical Control Issues

Most of the transmission-owning utilities in the United States have ownership interests in generators that utilize these transmission facilities. In both models of restructuring the electricity industry, these firms would own and operate both competitive assets (generation) and regulated monopoly assets (transmission). As a result, a transmission network operator may have the incentive and ability to favor its own generators and disfavor competitors' generators when it makes decision about the operation of and investments in the transmission network. Three types of "fixes" are being proposed to deal with these potential "self-dealing" problems.

One approach involves complete structural separation of generation, transmission and distribution by creating separate transmission or grid companies through vertical divestiture of generating plants. This is the structure in England and Wales, Norway and Argentina. In the United States, this step might be accompanied by horizontal integration of the pieces of the transmission network presently under separate ownership, creating a smaller number of regional "grids," each with a single control area operator. This vertical separation of ownership of generation from transmission assets was relatively easy to accomplish in other countries where restructuring took place as part of the privatization of state-owned assets. It is much harder to accomplish in the United States, since we are dealing primarily with private firms. Nevertheless, a few utilities are in the process of selling some or all of the generating capacity to resolve stranded cost recovery issues or to deal with market power problems (discussed below). More are likely to follow in the next few years.

A second approach would require functional separation of generation, transmission and distribution within existing vertically integrated firms--essentially, separating the regulated and competitive portions of the firms into separate divisions with separate cost accounting and limitations on communications between employees across divisions--combined with open access obligations and access pricing rules for use of the transmission and distribution networks approved and enforced by regulators. This approach requires the incumbent vertically integrated firms to unbundle the services they supply, separate costs attributable to different segments, post visible prices for these services and apply them to their own competitive transactions as well as to transactions involving third parties using their network. FERC's Open Access Rule (Order 888 issued in 1996) embodies this approach. The problem with this tact is that it may be difficult for regulators to enforce network access obligations, to unbundle properly the prices for competitive and monopoly services, and to specify appropriate access prices.

A third approach is a halfway house between the first two, which embodies the open access and unbundling requirements of the second approach while responding to residual self-dealing concerns without waiting for generation divestiture to be accomplished. Vertically integrated utilities in a region would turn the operation of their transmission systems over to an independent system operator (ISO); effectively, they would lease their system to the ISO. The ISO would be a nonprofit organization with an independent board of directors representing a wide range of interest groups. Then, the ISO would be responsible for all network functions over a geographic expanse that more closely matches the physical characteristics of a synchronized alternating-current system. This approach is emerging as the primary transition mechanism for dealing with vertical control problems in the United States.

The reliance on ISOs raises all types of governance issues that would benefit from further analysis. Can the ownership of the transmission assets be completely separated from the use of these assets without distorting operating and investment decision? Should the ISO be public or private? Should it be a separate company or a "cooperative" controlled by suppliers and customers? How is the ISO's board of directors selected, who does it represent, and what are the voting rules? How is the ISO's management selected, what objectives is it given, and how are incentives provided to the management? What role does the ISO play in new investments in transmission facilities? How should the ISO be regulated? Policies governing the creation of ISOs are moving forward rapidly before these questions have been answered satisfactorily, and this quick movement will probably lead to performance problems in the future.

Horizontal Market Power in the Supply of Generation Services

All of the restructuring proposals hope to encourage a competitive generation sector that is largely free from price and entry regulation. Accordingly, issues associated with diagnosing and mitigating horizontal market power at the generation level are attracting a lot of attention.

Concerns about horizontal market power have be heightened among U.S. policymakers in part because of the experience gained from the restructuring in England and Wales since 1990, where various studies have shown that there is a significant horizontal market power problem at the generation level (Green and Newbery, 1992; Newbery, 1995; Wolfram, 1996a,b; Wolak and Patrick, 1996; von der Fehr and Harbord, 1993). The market power problems in England and Wales are generally attributed to the decision of the Thatcher government to divide the old state-owned generating assets into only three private companies. Moreover, some generators have strategic locations on the grid and, from time to time, "must run for reliability." Naturally, when the generators know that they will be called to run by the network operator to maintain network reliability (almost) regardless of what they bid, they submit high bids. Certain generating stations at strategic locations on the grid in England and Wales charged prices six times higher than those of other generators before the regulator imposed a price ceiling on them (Office of Electricity Regulation, 1992).

Since the United States enters the restructuring process with a large number of companies with generating assets and with active wholesale markets for electricity, the challenge of creating a competitive generation sector should be less daunting. Moreover, the new CCGT technology is allowing generating plants to be built economically at relatively small scale and with much shorter planning and construction lead times, so entry from independent producers should play an important role in disciplining pricing behavior by incumbents.

Nevertheless, diagnosing horizontal market power associated with unregulated supplies of generation services must confront a number of significant analytical challenges (Borenstein et. al., 1995; Werden, 1996). It has long been recognized that an important factor in assessing horizontal market power at the generation level is the cost and availability of transmission capacity (Joskow and Schmalensee, 1983, ch. 12). The extent of congestion at points on a transmission network varies widely as supply and demand conditions change, both during a day and during a year, so that the relevant geographic markets change as well over time. Since electricity cannot be stored, considerable care must be taken in identifying what capacity is competitive under different supply and demand conditions. If demand is very inelastic, market power could be a potential problem even with a relatively large number of suppliers, under certain demand and supply conditions (Borenstein and Bushnell, 1997).

Creating a reasonably competitive generation market is certainly an important policy goal. However, creating a perfectly competitive generation market is not a realistic goal. The spatial attributes of generation markets and changing network conditions virtually assure that generation markets will never be perfectly competitive under all system conditions. But the test for deregulation of prices and entry into generation should not be whether competition is perfect--in the sense that prices must precisely equal marginal cost. If we applied such a test we would not have deregulated airlines, railroads, long distance telephone companies and many other industries. Clearly, policymakers will have to make some judgment about when there is enough competition so that any remaining costs of imperfect markets are less than the costs of continuing regulation.

Most of the reform proposals being discussed in the United States anticipate that basic transmission and distribution services will continue to be provided by a monopoly that will be subject to government regulation.

If or when significant horizontal market power problems are identified, two primary mechanisms are available for mitigation. One is to continue to subject incumbent generators to some type of price regulation. This may be a necessary solution to certain types of "local" market power problems where specific generators or groups of generators "must run for reliability." The second alternative is to require horizontal divestiture of generating facilities as a way of creating additional independent competitive suppliers. This solution is now being pursued in England and Wales and in California.

Regulating Residual Monopoly Services

Most of the reform proposals being discussed in the United States anticipate that basic transmission and distribution services will continue to be provided by a monopoly that will be subject to government regulation. There is general agreement that whatever residual monopoly services are left will be subject to "incentive regulation" (Joskow and Schmalensee, 1986; Laffont and Tirole, 1993), or what has now come to be called in the regulatory arena "performance-based regulation."

The general approach being pursued is some type of price cap mechanism, which typically sets a base price, assumes that the real price will decline at some rate over time because of productivity gains and allows for adjustments in base prices over time for prespecified external factors, including input price inflation. If the regulated entity can raise productivity and cut costs more quickly than expected, it can earn additional profits. This approach has been applied to AT&T and to a growing number of local telephone companies in the United States in the last decade, and it is applied widely to all privatized network industries in England and Wales. But while this type of regulation can provide powerful incentives for cost reduction, it can also provide incentives to lower costs by allowing the quality of the services provided by the regulated firm to deteriorate. Accordingly, performance-based regulation mechanisms are now including a growing list of customer service, reliability criteria and other performance criteria.

Almost no thought has been given to the regulatory mechanisms that will govern the behavior of the network operator and grid owners, especially in the context of the independent system operator (ISO) structures that are emerging as the favored governance structure for operating the transmission network and guiding investments to expand it. This is especially surprising in light of problems that have emerged in both England and Wales and Argentina in stimulating appropriate investments in transmission capacity that properly take into account the costs of network congestion. The difficult task for these regulations is to encourage low-cost operation while also providing incentives to make investments in transmission capacity that can cost-effectively reduce congestion on the network. As the details of the ISO proposals are defined more clearly, the appropriate regulatory mechanisms to apply to the management of the ISO and transmission owners will likely emerge as an important issue.

Concluding Thoughts

Electricity restructuring and regulatory reform is likely to involve both costs and benefits. On the benefit side, a competitive generation market can significantly reduce many of the medium- and long-term inefficiencies discussed above. However, I think that it will be very difficult to replicate the efficiencies of central economic dispatch and network operations that characterize the operation of well-managed vertically integrated transmission and generation companies. There are also likely to be additional inefficiencies associated with decentralized investments in generation and transmission capacity due to complementarities between generation and transmission that will be difficult to capture fully in market mechanisms.

Because the motivations for electricity sector reform in the United States are being driven largely by distributional considerations--in particular efforts to reallocate responsibilities for paying for sunk investment costs and contractual commitments--a danger exists that in the rush to implement reforms to satisfy the competing interest groups that longer run efficiency considerations will not be given adequate attention. If the restructuring of the electricity sector is done right, in a way that effectively addresses the challenges identified in this paper, the benefits can significantly outweigh the costs. But the jury is still out on whether policymakers have the will to implement the necessary reforms effectively.

Notes

[1] Reprinted from *Journal of Economic Perspectives,* 1997, 11(3): 119-138 by permission of the American Economic Association.

References

Borenstein, Severin, and James Bushnell, "An Empirical Analysis of the Potential for Market Power in California's Electricity Industry," University of California Energy Institute, March 1997.

Borenstein, Severin, James Bushnell, Edward Kahn, and Steven Stoft "Market Power in California Electricity Market," *Utilities Policy,* 1995, *5:*3-4, 219-36.

Chao, Hung Po, and Stephen Peck, "Market Mechanisms for Electric Power Transmission," *Journal of Regulatory Economics,* 1996, *10:*1, 61-80.

Green, Richard, "The English Electricity Industry in the 1990s." In Olsen, Ole Jess, ed., *Competition in the Electricity Supply Industry.* Copenhagen: DJOF Publishing Company, 1995, pp. 107-36.

Green, Richard, and David Newbery, "Competition in the British Electricity Spot Market, *Journal of Political Economy,* 1992, 100:5, 929-53.

Harvey, Scott, William Hogan, and Susan Pope, "Transmission Capacity Reservations Implemented Through a Spot Market With Transmission Congestion Contracts," *Electricity Journal,* 1996, *9:*9, 42-55.

Hogan, William, "Contract Networks for Electric Power Transmission," *Journal of Regulatory Economics,* 1992, *4:*3, 211-42.

Hogan, William, "Markets In Real Networks Require Reactive Prices," *Energy Journal,* 1993, *14:*3, 171-200.

Hunt, Sally, and Graham Shuttleworth, *Competition and Choice in Electricity.* West Sussex, Engl.: Wiley, 1996.

Joskow, Paul L., "Regulatory Failure, Regulatory Reform and Structural Change in the Electric Power Industry," *Brookings Papers on Economic Activity: Microeconomics,* 1989, 125-99.

Joskow, Paul L., "Introducing Competition in Network Industries: From Hierarchies to Markets in Electricity," *Industrial and Corporate Change,* 1996, *5:*2, 341-82.

Joskow, Paul L., "Comments on Power Struggles: Explaining Deregulatory Reforms in Electricity Markets," *Brookings Papers on Economic Activity: Microeconomics,* 1997, 251-64.

Joskow, Paul L., and Nancy Rose, "The Effects of Technological Change, Experience and Environmental Regulation on the Construction Costs of Coal-Burning Generating Units," *Rand Journal of Economics,* 1985, *16:*1, 1-27.

Joskow, Paul L., and Richard Schmalensee, *Markets for Power: An Analysis of Electric Utility Deregulation.* Cambrige: Massachusetts Institute of Technology Press, 1983.

Joskow, Paul L., and Richard Schmalensee, "Incentive Regulation for Electric Utilities," *Yale Journal on Regulation,* 1986, *4:*1, 1-49.

Joskow, Paul L., and Richard Schmalensee, "The Performance of Coal-Burning Electric Generating Units in the United States: 1960-1980," *Journal of Applied Econometrics,* 1987, 2:2, 85-109.

Laffont, J. J., and Jean Tirole, *A Theory of Incentives in Procurement and Regulation.* Cambridge: Massachusetts Institute of Technology Press, 1993.

Lester, Richard K., and Mark J. McCabe, "The Effect of Industrial Structure on Learning by Doing in Nuclear Power Plant Operations," *Rand Journal of Economics,* 1993, *24:*3, 418-38.

Nasser, Thomas-Olivier, "Imperfect Markets for Power: Competition and Residual Regulation in the Electricity Industry," unpublished Ph.D. dissertation, MIT Department of Economics, April 1997.

Newbery, David, "Power Markets and Market Power," *Energy Journal,* 1995, *16:*3, 39-66.

Newbery, David, and Michael G. Pollitt, "The Restructuring and Privatization of the CEGB: Was It Worth It?," mimeo, Department of Applied Economics, Cambridge University, 1996.

Office of Electricity Regulation, "Report on Constrained-on Plant," Birmingham, England, 1992.

Rose, Nancy L., and Paul L. Joskow, "The Diffusion of New Technology: Evidence From the Electric Utility Industry," *Rand Journal of Economics,* 1990, *21:*3, 354-73.

Schweppe, Fred, et al., *Spot Pricing of Electricity.* Boston: Kluwer Academic Publishers, 1988.

Sidak, J. Gregory, and Daniel F. Spulber, "Deregulatory Takings and Breach of the Regulatory Contract," *New York University Law Review,* October 1996, *71:*4, 851-999.

Stoft, Stephen, "What Should A Power Marketer Want?" *Electricity Journal,* forthcoming 1997.

Tabors, Richard, "A Market-Based Proposal for Transmission Pricing," *Electricity Journal,* 1996, *9:*9, 61-67.

von der Fehr, Nils-Henrik Morch, and David Harbord, "Spot Market Competition in the UK Electricity Industry," *Economic Journal,* May 1993, *103,* 531-46.

Walton, Steve, and Richard Tabors, "Zonal Transmission Pricing: Methodology and Preliminary Results for the WSCC," *Electricity Journal,* 1996, *9:*9, 34-41.

Werden, Gregory, "Identifying Market Power in Electric Generation," *Public Utilities Fortnightly*, 1996, *134*:4, 16-21.

White, Mathew, "Power Struggles: Explaining Deregulatory Reforms in Electricity Markets," *Brookings Papers on Economic Activity: Microeconomics,* 1997, 201-50.

Wolak, Frank, and Robert H. Patrick, "The Impact of Rules and Market Structure on the Price Determination Process in the England and Wales Electricity Market," mimeo, Stanford University Department of Economics, 1996.

Wolfram, Catherine, "Measuring Duopoly Power in the British Electricity Spot Market," mimeo, MIT Department of Economics, September 1996a.

Wolfram, Catherine, "Strategic Bidding in a Multi-Unit Auction: An Empirical Analysis of Bids to Supply Electricity in England and Wales," mimeo, Harvard Department of Economics, July 1996b.

3 NODES AND ZONES IN ELECTRICITY MARKETS: SEEKING SIMPLIFIED CONGESTION PRICING

William W. Hogan[1]

Introduction

Examples of pricing in networks illustrate the issues that accompany transmission congestion in a competitive electricity market.[2] In theory, pricing in a competitive electricity market with price-taking participants is at marginal cost. The competitive model is equivalent to a market with a central coordinator operating a pool. The many potential suppliers compete to meet demand, bidding energy supplies into the pool. The dispatcher chooses the welfare-maximizing combination of generation and demand to balance the system.[3] This optimal dispatch determines the market clearing prices. Consumers pay this price into the pool for energy taken from the spot market and generators in turn are paid this price for the energy supplied.

Inherently, energy pricing and transmission congestion pricing are intimately connected. A series of examples of pricing in the competitive electricity market model illustrates the determination of prices under economic dispatch in a network and relates transmission constraints to congestion rentals that lead to different prices

at different locations.   Use of the real nodes in the network appears to be a
requirement of locational pricing that captures the marginal costs of congestion in a
competitive market.   The asserted complexity of using the real nodes leads
frequently to proposals to aggregate the individual nodes into zones that would
appear to be simpler for commercial purposes.[4] The examples here explore this
issue to question the reality of the "simplification." In a market with choice, it is
important to get the prices right. To the extent that prices differ from true marginal
costs, there will be profit incentives to exploit the inconsistency. These incentives
then lead to rules to constrain the most perverse behavior. The rules then add a new
form of complexity and restrict the market. In the end, to the extent that zonal prices
differ from locational marginal costs, the zonal system would not be a
simplification, and locational pricing at the actual locations would be simpler and
allow for greater market flexibility.

Short-Run Transmission Pricing

An independent system operator (ISO) can implement a pricing regime to support
the competitive market. This pricing and access regime can accommodate both a
pool-based spot market and more traditional "physical" bilateral contracts. The key
is in how the ISO provides balancing services, adjusts for transmission constraints
and charges for transmission usage. The ISO would match buyers and sellers in the
short-term market.   The ISO would receive "schedules" that could include both
quantity and bidding information. For the participants in the pool, these schedule-
bids would be for loads or generation with maximum or minimum acceptable prices.
For the self-nominations of bilateral transactions, the schedule-bids would be for
transmission quantities with increment and decrement bids for both ends of the
transaction. These incremental and decremental bids would apply only for the short-
term dispatch and need not be the same as the confidential bilateral contract prices.
The responsibility of the ISO would be to integrate the schedules and the
associated bids for deviations from the schedules to find the economic combination
for all market participants. This range of schedule-bids would be more varied and
flexible, giving everyone more choices.

Basic Transmission Pricing Examples

A set of examples can illuminate the treatment of spot-market transactions and
bilateral transactions, under the ISO's responsibility to achieve an economic
dispatch. These examples are simple, but they capture the essential points in terms
of the alternatives available for bilateral transactions. The test of no conflict of
interest and non-discrimination is that, other things being equal, there should be no
incentive in the dispatch or pricing mechanism to favor either the spot market or the
bilateral transaction.

Figure 1

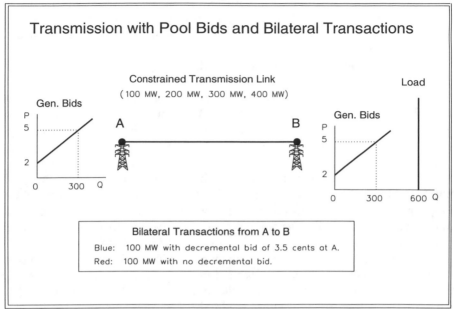

Figure 1

For simplicity, we ignore here any complications of market power or long-run issues, such as the creation of transmission congestion contracts, and focus solely on the short-run dispatch and pricing issues. A market with a single transmission line, as shown in the accompanying Figure 1, allows an illustration of the basic principles. What is less obvious, however, is that these same principles in no way depend on the special case of a single transmission line. Unlike many other approaches, such as ownership and physical control of the line, or the contract-path fiction, as expanded below in further examples for a grid, these pricing principles extend to a framework to support open access in a complicated network that includes the effects of loop flow.

The assumptions include:

- Two locations, A and B.
- Total load is for 600 MW at location B. For simplicity, the load is fixed, with no demand bidding.
- A transmission line between A and B with capacity that will be varied to construct alternative cases.
- Pool bid generation at both A and B. To simplify, each location has the same bid curve, starting at 2¢/kWh and increasing by 1¢/kWh for each 100 MW. Hence, a market price of 5 cents at A would yield 300 MW of pool-based generation at that location. Likewise for location B.
- Two bilateral transaction schedules, Blue and Red, each for 100 MW from A to B. Each bilateral transaction includes a separate contract price between the generator and the customer; the ISO does not know this contract price.

Blue provides a (completely discretionary) decremental bid at A of 3.5 cents. In other words, if the price at A falls to 3.5 cents, blue prefers to reduce generation and, in effect, purchase power from the pool. Blue may do this, for example, if the running cost of its plant is 3.5 cents, and it would be cheaper to buy than to generate.

Red provides no such decremental bid, and requests to be treated as a must run plant.

The ISO accepts the bids of those participating in the spot market at A and B and the bilateral schedules. The load is fixed at 600 MW. The bilateral transactions cover 200 MW, or the person responsible for the bilateral transaction must purchase power at B to meet any deficiency. The remaining 400 MW of load must be met from the spot market to include production at A or B, and use of the transmission line.

In determining the economic dispatch, the system operator treats the pool generation bids in the usual way. The Blue bilateral transaction is treated as a fixed obligation, with the 3.5 cent decrement bid as an alternative source of balancing adjustment at A. The Red bilateral transaction is treated as a fixed obligation, with no such balancing adjustment.

Assuming that the net of the fixed obligations with no balancing adjustments is feasible, which is the interesting case, we can vary the capacity on the link to see the results of the economic dispatch and the payments by the participants. The examples cover four cases, starting at 400 MW of transmission capacity, and reducing in increments of 100 MW. The details are in Table 1.

400 MW. In the case of 400 MW of transmission capacity, the economic dispatch solution is just balanced with no congestion. Everyone sees the same price of 4 cents. The payments for each party include:

- Pool Generation at A: Paid 4 cents for 200 MW.
- Pool Generation at B: Paid 4 cents for 200 MW.
- Pool Load at B: Pays 4 cents for 400 MW.
- Blue Bilateral: Pays zero cents for transmission of 100 MW.
- Red Bilateral: Pays zero cents for transmission of 100 MW.

Everybody is happy.

300 MW. In the case of 300 MW of transmission capacity, the economic dispatch solution encounters transmission congestion, and the prices differ by location. The price at A drops to 3.5 cents, and the price at B rises to 5 cents. The opportunity cost of transmission is 1.5 cents. The payments for each party include:

- Pool Generation at A: Paid 3.5 cents for 150 MW.
- Pool Generation at B: Paid 5 cents for 300 MW.
- Pool Load at B: Pays 5 cents for 400 MW.
- Blue Bilateral: Pays 1.5 cents for transmission of 50 MW. Blue makes up the remaining 50 MW obligation at B at a price of 5 cents.
- Red Bilateral: Pays 1.5 cents for transmission of 100 MW.

Everybody would prefer less congestion, but everyone is paying the opportunity cost of the transmission congestion. Note that at these prices, Blue is indifferent to bidding in its generation at 3.5 cents in the pool at A, or to continuing as a bilateral transaction. Further, note that the ISO reduced both pool and Blue transactions.

There is no artificial bias induced by the ISO's fulfilling the directives of the economic dispatch.

Table 1: Power Flows and Locational Prices					
	Alternative Cases				
Link Capacity A to B	MW	400	300	200	100
Total Load at B	MW	600	600	600	600
Price at A	cents/ kWh	4	3.5	3	2
Price at B	cents/ kWh	4	5	6	7
Transmission Price	cents/ kWh	0	1.5	3	5
Pool Generation at A	MW	200	150	100	0
Pool Generation at B	MW	200	300	400	500
Blue Bilateral Input at A	MW	100	50	0	0
Red Bilateral Input at A	MW	100	100	100	100

200 MW. In the case of 200 MW of transmission capacity, the economic dispatch solution encounters more transmission congestion, and the prices differ more by location. The price at A drops to 3 cents, and the price at B rises to 6 cents. The opportunity cost of transmission is 3 cents. The payments for each party include:
- Pool Generation at A: Paid 3 cents for 100 MW.
- Pool Generation at B: Paid 6 cents for 400 MW.
- Pool Load at B: Pays 6 cents for 400 MW.
- Blue Bilateral: Prefers not to generate and has no transmission. Blue makes up the 100 MW obligation at B at a price of 6 cents.
- Red Bilateral: Pays 3 cents for transmission of 100 MW.

Everybody would prefer less congestion, but everyone is paying the opportunity cost of the transmission congestion. Note that at these prices, Blue is better off than if it had actually generated. Of course, Blue would still be indifferent to bidding in its generation at 3.5 cents in the pool at A, or continuing as a bilateral transaction. Further, note that the ISO reduced both pool and Blue transactions.   There is no artificial bias induced by the ISO's fulfilling the directives of the economic dispatch. **100 MW**. In the case of 100 MW of transmission capacity, the economic dispatch solution encounters transmission congestion to the point of eliminating everything other than the must run plant, and the prices differ more by location. The price at A drops to 2 cents, and the price at B rises to 7 cents.   The opportunity cost of transmission is 5 cents. The payments for each party include:

- Pool Generation at A: No generation.
- Pool Generation at B: Paid 7 cents for 500 MW.
- Pool Load at B: Pays 7 cents for 400 MW.
- Blue Bilateral: Prefers not to generate and has no transmission.   Blue makes up the 100 MW obligation at B at a price of 7 cents.
- Red Bilateral: Pays 5 cents for transmission of 100 MW.

Everybody would prefer less congestion, but everyone is paying the opportunity cost of the transmission congestion. Note that at these prices, Blue is better off than if it had actually generated. Of course, Blue would still be indifferent to bidding in its generation at 3.5 cents in the pool at A, or continuing as a bilateral transaction. Further, note that the ISO reduced both pool and Blue transactions.   There is no artificial bias induced by the ISO fulfilling the directives of the economic dispatch.

The net spot-market payments that are made to and from the ISO are summarized in Table 2. Note that the cases of transmission congestion include net payments to the ISO. These net payments are equal to the value of the constrained transmission capacity.   These are the congestion payments that would be redistributed through a system of transmission congestion contracts, as illustrated below in further examples.

Implications

These examples for a single, isolated line are simple, but they capture the essential features.   These features generalize to a more complicated network under the economic dispatch model in the sense that participants can provide bids at their discretion. Some of the bids can be "must run." The locational prices are easily determined from the economic dispatch considering all the bids and schedules, not just those included in the power exchange. And although everyone would prefer a less congested system, all users would pay the short-run opportunity costs of their contribution to the congestion. Other things being equal, there would be no bias between spot market and bilateral transactions.

Note that if Blue and Red did not pay the opportunity cost of transmission, there would be a substantial bias in favor of the bilateral transactions. Furthermore, the locational prices are consistent with the efficient competitive outcome, as is best illustrated by Blue's willingness to adjust a bilateral transaction.

Table 2: Power Flows and Locational Prices					
	Alternative Cases				
Link Capacity A to B	MW	400	300	200	100
Price at A	cents/kWh	4	3.5	3	2
Price at B	cents/kWh	4	5	6	7
Transmission Price	cents/kWh	0	1.5	3	5
Payments to Independent System Operator					
Pool Load at B (400 MW)	cents (x1000)	1,600	2,000	2,400	2,800
Contract Load at B (200 MW)	cents (x1000)	0	0	0	0
Generation at A	cents (x1000)	(800)	(525)	(300)	0
Generation at B	cents (x1000)	(800)	(1,500)	(2,400)	(3,500)
Blue Transmission	cents (x1000)	0	75	0	0
Blue Imbalance at B	cents (x1000)	0	250	600	700
Red Transmission	cents (x1000)	0	150	300	500
Red Imbalance at B	cents (x1000)	0	0	0	0
Net to ISO	cents (x1000)	0	450	600	500

Contrary to a common argument -- that the ISO would have a bias in favor of spot market transactions -- the treatment of the Red bilateral transaction might lead to an accusation that there is a reverse bias in favor of the bilateral transaction. However, there are two important features of the pricing and access rules that run counter to this assertion.

First, the spot market participants could achieve the same result by bidding in generation at A at a zero reservation price, or lower. In fact, in performing the economic dispatch, the ISO treats the Red transaction as just this type of bid. Under these circumstances, the price at A could drop to zero, or lower, with a corresponding increase in the opportunity cost of transmission.

Furthermore, suppose that Red's true short-term generation cost is 3 cents, but it refused to make a decremental bid to the ISO. Then in the 100 MW case above, Red would have acted irrationally and would be worse off than if it offered such a decremental bid. It can also be shown that the cost thus imposed on Red is at least as large as the total cost imposed on everyone else in the market. Thus Red would pay for its own mistakes; the effect would be a net gain for the other generators and load (although there could be winners and losers, in aggregate everyone else would win).

Hence, the single line examples illustrate the use of locational prices for the various types of transactions that might take place in the short-term market. Locational pricing provides the opportunity costs price signals and the transmission price is the difference between the locational prices at source and sink. This equilibrium definition of the transmission price is obvious in the case of a single, radial connection between two points, and it applies equally well to a more general network that includes free-flowing loops and the strong network interactions that are characteristic of electric grids. However, most of the intuition about the determination of prices and the relationships of prices across locations do not extend to the real grid. In the presence of loop flow, the interactions are complicated and important. This reality needs to be understood to appreciate the arguments for and against zonal aggregation of spot prices.

Economic Dispatch On A Grid

The pricing results for a network can be quite different from those found for a single transmission line or a radial connection. The key difference is in the existence of loops that give rise to network interactions and create the phenomenon of "loop flow." Analogies built on the case of a single line can be misleading. The determination of market clearing prices at equilibrium, equal to the marginal costs that would arise from an economic dispatch, follows from the same principles. But the application and interpretation of these principles requires an extension of our intuition.

Consider the simple market model in Figure 2, which will serve as the starting point for a set of a succeeding examples for a grid that moves from the analogy of a single line to a grid with multiple loops. In this market there is one load center, a city in the East, supplied by generators located far away in the West, connected by transmission lines, and by local generators who are in the same region as the city customers. The plants in the West consist of an "Old Nuke" which can produce energy for a marginal cost of 2¢/kWh and a "New Gas" plant that has an operating cost of 4¢/kWh. These two plants each have a capacity of 100 MW, and are connected to the transmission grid which can take their power to the market in the East.

The competing suppliers in the East are a "New Coal" plant with operating costs of 3¢/kWh and an "Old Gas" plant that is expensive to use with a marginal cost of 7¢/kWh. Again these Eastern plants are assumed to have a capacity of 100 MW. The two plants in the West define the "Western Supply" curve, and the two plants in the East define the corresponding "Eastern Supply" curve. These supply curves could represent either engineering estimates of the operating costs or bids from the many owners of the plants who offer to generate power in the competitive market. For simplicity, we ignore transmission losses and assume that the same supply curves apply at all hours of the day.

Figure 2

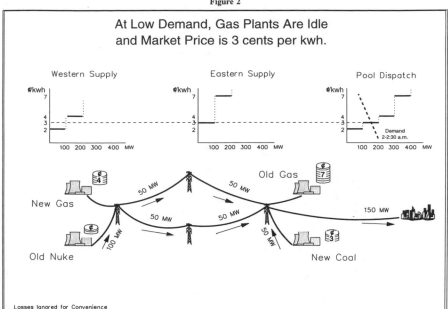

At Low Demand, Gas Plants Are Idle
and Market Price is 3 cents per kwh.

Under low demand conditions, as shown in Figure 2 for the early hours of the morning, the supply curves from the two regions define an aggregate market supply curve that the pool-based dispatchers can balance with the customer demands. The aggregate market supply curve stacks up the various generating plants from cheapest to most expensive. The pool-based dispatchers choose the optimal combination of plants to run to meet the demand at this hour. In Figure 2, the result is to provide 150 MW. The inexpensive Old Nuke plant generates its full 100 MW of capacity, and the New Coal plant provides another 50 MW. The New Coal plant is the marginal plant in this case, and sets the market price at 3¢/kWh for this hour. Hence the customers in the city pay 3¢/kWh for all 150 MW. The New Coal plant receives 3¢/kWh for its output, and this price just covers its running cost. The Old Nuke also receives 3¢/kWh for all its 100 MW of output. After deducting the 2¢/kWh running cost, this leaves a 1¢/kWh contribution towards capital costs and profits for Old Nuke owners.

In this low demand case, and ignoring losses, there is no additional opportunity cost for transmission. The 100 MW flows over the parallel paths of the transmission grid. But there is no constraint on transmission and, therefore, no opportunity cost. Hence the price of power is the same in the East and in the West. In the short run, there is no charge for use of the transmission system.

Figure 3

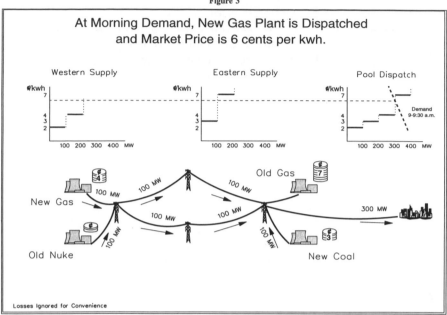

At Morning Demand, New Gas Plant is Dispatched
and Market Price is 6 cents per kwh.

If demand increases, say, at the start of the business day, the system operator must move higher up on the dispatch curve. For example, consider the conditions defined in Figure 3. This hour presents the same supply conditions, but a higher demand. Now the pool-based dispatchers must look to more expensive generation to meet the load. The Old Nuke continues to run at capacity, the New Coal plant moves up to its full capacity, and the New Gas plant in the West also comes on at full capacity. The New Gas plant in the West is the most expensive plant running, with a marginal cost of 4¢/kWh. However, this operating cost cannot define the market price because at this price demand would exceed the available supply, and the system operator must protect the system by maintaining a balance of supply and demand.

In this case, the result is to turn to those customers who have set a limit on how much they are willing to pay for electric energy at that hour. This short-run demand bidding defines the demand curve which allows the system operator to raise the price and reduce consumption until supply and demand are in balance. In Figure 3 this new balance occurs at the point where the market price of electricity is set at 6¢/kWh. Once again, the customers who actually use the electricity pay this 6¢/kWh for the full 300 MW of load at that hour. All the generators who sell power receive the same 6¢/kWh, which leads to operating margins of 2¢/kWh for New Gas, 3¢/kWh for New Coal, and 4¢/kWh for Old Nuke.

Once again, the pool-based dispatch in Figure 3 depends on excess capacity in the transmission system. The plants in the Western region are running at full capacity, and the full 200 MW of power moves along the parallel paths over the grid to join with New Coal to meet the demand in the East. There is a single market price of 6¢/kWh, and there is no charge for transmission other than for losses, which are ignored here for convenience in the example.

Transmission Constraints

With the plants running at full capacity, there might be a transmission constraint. To illustrate the impact of a possible transmission limit, suppose for sake of discussion that there is an "interface" constraint between West and East. According to this constraint, no more than 150 MW of power can flow over the interface.

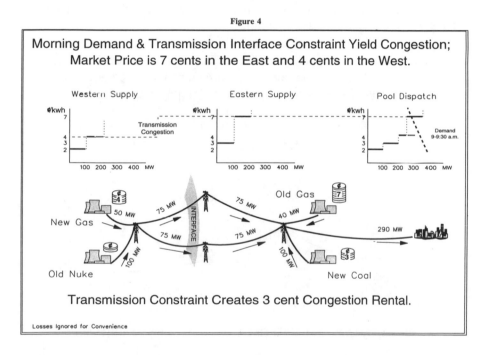

Figure 4

Morning Demand & Transmission Interface Constraint Yield Congestion; Market Price is 7 cents in the East and 4 cents in the West.

Transmission Constraint Creates 3 cent Congestion Rental.

Losses Ignored for Convenience

As shown in Figure 4, this transmission constraint has a significant impact on both the dispatch and market prices based on short-run marginal costs. In Figure 4 the level of demand from the city in the East is assumed to be the same as in the case of Figure 3. However, now the pool-based dispatcher faces a different aggregate market supply curve. In effect, only half of the New Gas output can be moved to the East. To meet the demand, it will be necessary simultaneously to turn off part of the New Gas output and substitute the more expensive Old Gas generation which is available in the East. This new dispatch increases the market price in the East to 7¢/kWh and necessarily induces a further reduction in demand, say, to a total of 290 MW. The New Coal and Old Gas plants receive this full price of 7¢/kWh for their 140 MW, which provides a 4¢/kWh operating margin or short-run profit for New Coal and allows Old Gas to cover its operating costs.

In the Western region, however, a different situation prevails. The transmission interface constraint has idled part of the output of the New Gas plant. Clearly the market price in the West can be no more than the operating cost of the plant. Likewise, since the plant is running at partial output, the market price can be no less than the operating cost of 4¢/kWh. This is the price paid to New Gas and Old Nuke, which covers New Gas operating costs and provides Old Nuke an operating margin of 2¢/kWh.

The 3¢/kWh difference between the market price in the East and the market price in the West is the opportunity cost of the transmission congestion. In effect, ignoring losses, the marginal cost of transmission between West and East is 3¢/kWh, and this is the price paid implicitly through the transactions with the system operator. Electricity worth 4¢/kWh in the Western region becomes worth 7¢/kWh when it reaches the Eastern region.

Figure 5

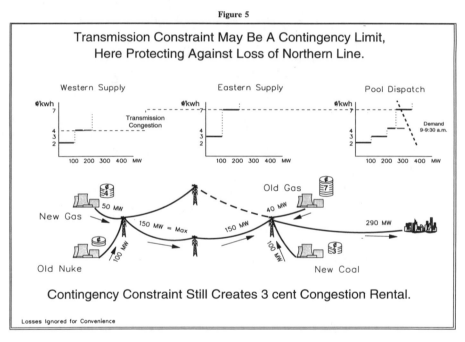

The transmission "interface" constraint is a convenient shorthand for a more complicated situation handled by the pool-based dispatchers. The interface limit depends on a number of conditions, and can change with changing loads. Typically it is not the case that there is a 75 MW limit on one or both of the parallel lines through which power is flowing in the grid. In normal operation, it may well be that the transmission lines could individually handle much more flow, say 150 MW each or twice the actual use. At most normal times, the lines may be far from any physical limit. However, the pool-based dispatchers must protect against contingencies--rare events that may disrupt operation of the grid. In the event of these contingencies, there will not be enough time to start up new generators or to completely reconfigure the dispatch of the system. The power flow through the grid will reconfigure immediately according to the underlying physical laws. Hence, generation and load in normal times must be configured, and priced, so that in the event of the contingency the system will remain secure.

For instance, suppose that the thermal capacity of the transmission lines is 150 MW, but the pool-based dispatchers must protect against the loss of a northern transmission line. In this circumstance, the actual power flows may follow Figure 4, with 75 MW on each line, but the pool-based dispatchers must dispatch in anticipation of the conditions in Figure 5. Here the northern line is out, and in this event the flow on the southern line would hit the assumed 150 MW thermal limit. This contingency event may never occur, but in anticipation of the event, and to protect the system, the system operator must dispatch according to Figure 5 even though the flows are as in Figure 4. In either case, the transmission constraint restricts the dispatch and changes the market prices. The price is 4¢/kWh in the West and 7¢/kWh in the East, with the 3¢/kWh differential being the congestion-induced opportunity cost of transmission. This "congestion rental" defines the competitive market price of transmission.

Buying and selling power at the competitive market prices, or charging for transmission at the equivalent price differential provides incentives for using the grid efficiently. If some user wanted to move power from East to West, the transmission price would be negative, and such "transmission" would in effect relieve the constraint. The transmission price is "distance- and location-sensitive," with distance measured in electrical rather than geographical units. And the competitive market prices arise naturally as a by-product of the optimal dispatch managed by the system operator.

The simplified networks in Figure 2 through Figure 5 illustrate the economics of least-cost dispatch and locational prices. However, these networks by design avoid the complications of loop flow that can be so important in determining prices and creating the difficulties with physical transmission rights. These examples differ from the single line case only in the explicit representation of the parallel flows on the lines, but as yet this has no effect on the prices. The extension of these examples and the basic pricing properties to more complicated networks includes the possibility of inputs and load around loops in the system. Here assume a transmission system as before but with the basic available generations and loads as shown in Figure 6. Our attention will focus on the prices at L-M and N-P, where the introduction of generators and load will reveal the impacts of the loops. The generators in Figure 6 define a basic supply configuration with quantities and prices, coupled with the associated loads, and all have the following characteristics:

- Generation available at four locations in the East (Y, Z) and West (A, B).
- Load in the East, consisting of the Yellow LDC at V and the Orange, Red and Blue LDCs at W.
- Load in the West, consisting of a Green LDC at C.
- Interface constraint of 150 MW between bus D and buses M and N.
- Thermal constraints of 90 MW between M and X and between N and X.
- The New Gas and Old Gas generating facilities each consist of two generating units whose marginal costs of production differ.

Figure 6

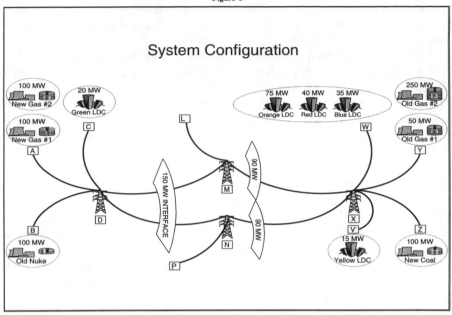

Figure 7

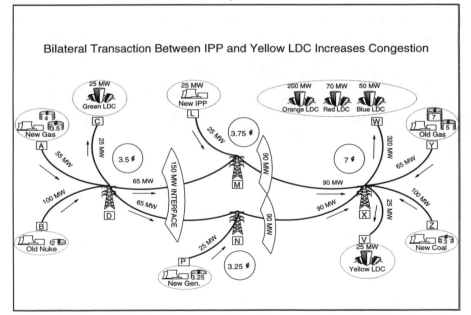

Loads in Figure 6 are illustrative and will vary systematically in each example. For convenience, losses are ignored in all examples.

The first example to introduce the effect of loop flow involves a new source of supply at a location on the loop. Here a low cost, large capacity generator becomes available in Figure 7 at bus "P." An IPP at bus "L" has bid in a must run plant at 25 MW, having arranged a corresponding sale to the Yellow distribution company at bus "V". Were it not for the IPP sale, more power could be taken from the inexpensive generators at bus "P" and at bus "A". However, because of the effects of loop flow, these plants are constrained in output, and there are different prices applicable at buses "D", "M", "N", and "X".

In a further example the constraints are modified to replace the interface limit with limits on the flows on individual lines. Here every line in the main loop is constrained by a thermal limit of 90 MW, replacing the interface limit. With these constraints in Figure 8, an added load of 150 MW at bus "L" alters the flows for the market equilibrium. In this case, the combined effect of the increased load and the constraints leads to a price of 8.25¢/kWh at bus "L". This illustrates that it is possible to have market clearing prices at some locations that are higher than the 7 cent marginal running cost of the old gas plant at bus "Y", the most expensive plant in the system. The interaction of the network constraints is such that with a reduction of load at bus "L" it would be possible to reduce output of the most expensive plant by even more, and make up the difference with cheaper sources of supply, causing the high price for load at "L."

Changing the network further adds new loops and even more examples of the effect on prices and dispatch caused by the network interactions. In this case, a new line has been added to the network in Figure 9, connecting bus "N" to bus "M". This line is assumed to have a thermal limit of 50 MW. The new line adds to the capability of the network in that the new pattern of generation lowers the overall cost of satisfying the same load. The total cost reduces from $20,962.50 in Figure 8 to $19,912.50 in Figure 9. Although the average cost of power generation fell, the marginal cost of power increased at bus "L", where the price is now 10.75¢/kWh. The new loop provides more options, but it also interacts with other constraints in the system. This set of interactions is the cause of the high price as it appears at bus "L".

As a final example that confirms the sometimes counterintuitive nature of least-cost dispatch and market equilibrium prices, add a new bus "O" between bus "M" and bus "N" in Figure 10, and lower the limit to 30 MW between bus "O" and bus "M". Bus "O" has a small load of 15 MW. The increased load of 15 MW at bus "O" actually lowers the total cost of the dispatch, as reflected in the negative price.

Each additional MW of load at bus "O" changes the flows to allow a dispatch that lowers the overall cost of meeting the total load. The optimal solution would be to pay customers at "O" to accept dump power, thereby relieving congestion elsewhere and providing benefits to the overall system.

This final example, therefore, illustrates and summarizes the types of interactions that can develop in a network with loop flow. Power can flow from high price nodes to low price nodes. The competitive market clearing price,

Figure 8

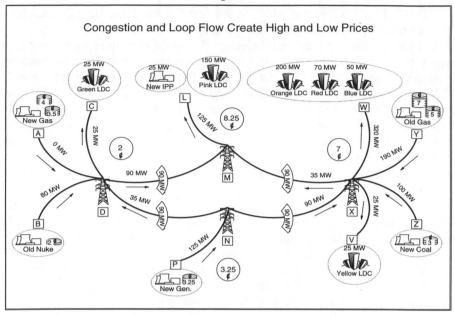

Congestion and Loop Flow Create High and Low Prices

Figure 9

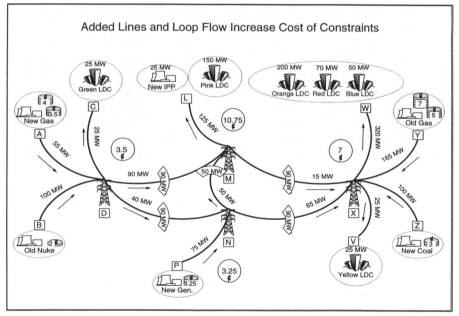

Added Lines and Loop Flow Increase Cost of Constraints

Figure 10

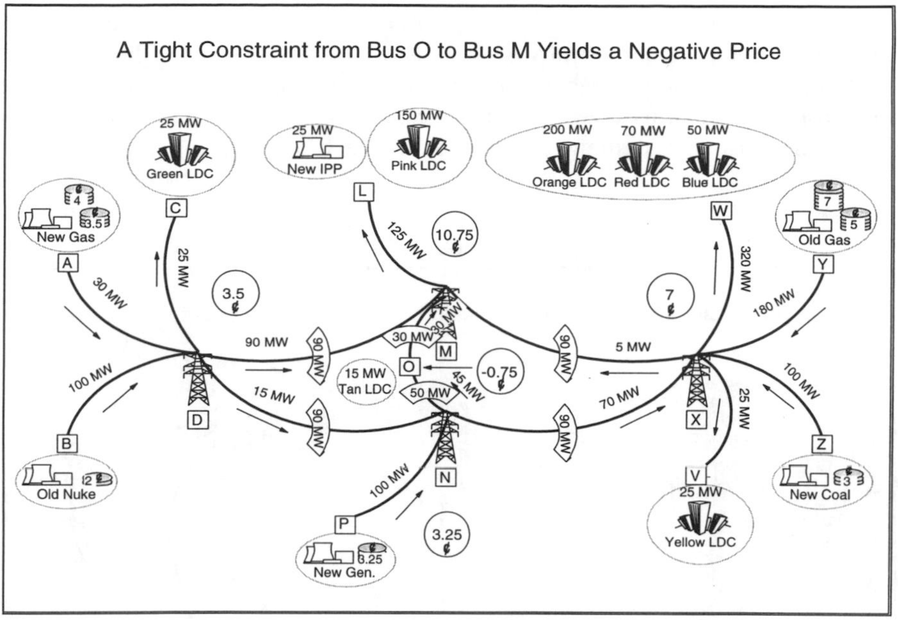

A Tight Constraint from Bus O to Bus M Yields a Negative Price

equivalent to the marginal costs for the least-cost dispatch, can include simultaneously at different locations prices higher than the cost of the most expensive generation and lower than the cost of the cheapest generation source. Application of the principle of locational pricing implies that transmission congestion would lead to many prices. Even with only a single constraint, there could be a different price at each location.

Zonal Versus Nodal Pricing

The use of locational prices has been described as being too complex, with the implication that an alternative approach would produce a simpler system. A common response to this assertion has been to recommend a "zonal" approach that would aggregate many locations into a smaller number of zones. The assumption has been that this would tend to reduce complexity. However, in the presence of real constraints in the actual network, the zonal approach may not be as simple as it might appear without closer examination.[5]

Complications created by a zonal approach may be greater than any complications existing with a straight locational approach to pricing and transmission charging.

The difficulties would arise in the context of a competitive market where participants have choices. If the actual operation of the network system does not conform to the pricing and zonal assumptions, there will be incentives created to deviate from the efficient, competitive solution. In the presence of a vertical monopoly that can ignore the formal pricing incentives, this has not been a problem. But under the conditions of a market, where participants will respond to incentives, the complications created by a zonal approach may be greater than any complications that would exist with a straight locational approach to pricing and transmission charging.

Figure 11

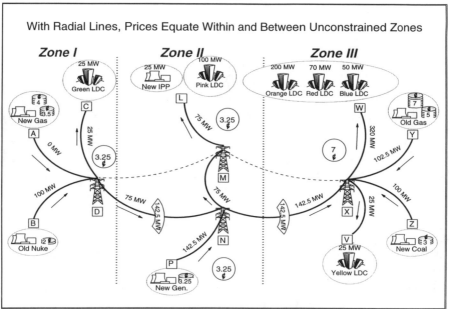

Consider the simplified example in Figure 11. The network has been constructed so that there are only radial connections. With strictly radial connections, locations within and between unconstrained zones would have a common price. Hence, aggregation of locations offers an apparent simplification by reducing to a few distinct zones. This motivation from a typical radial example leads to the assumption that in general there could be areas in a real network that would have the same prices and, therefore, these locations could be aggregated into zones that would be simpler for participants in market operations.

There are two problems with this line of argument. First, if the multiple locations truly do have the same prices, then there is no need to aggregate into zones. The point of the aggregation was to reduce the number of prices, and in the case where the assumption of common prices holds, aggregation would be unnecessary.

Second, the definition of a zone, which appears easy in the case of a radial network, becomes more problematic in the case of a more realistic network with loop flows. The radial examples can be a poor guide to thinking about interactions in networks. For example, it is often argued, or assumed, that congestion or differences in prices between zones would be caused only by transmission constraints that could be defined for lines that connect the zones. Furthermore, it is often assumed that differences in prices within zones can only be caused by congestion on lines within the zone. Under these simplifying assumptions, therefore, it is assumed that zones can be well defined and that what happens within a zone can be treated independently of what happens between zones, or independently of what happens in other zones. When we move beyond the radial examples, however, these assumptions and the associated conclusions can be false.

Figure 12

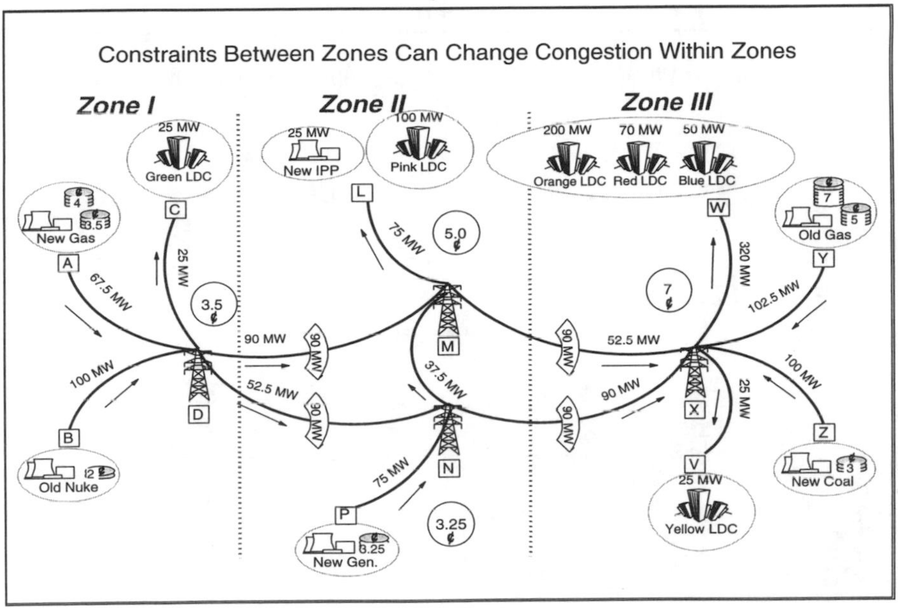

Constraints Between Zones Can Change Congestion Within Zones

With the more typical case of loops in a network, prices could differ within and between "unconstrained" zones due to the indirect effects of "distant" constraints. Consider the slightly modified example in Figure 12. In this case, the zones developed from the radial analogy produce a very different outcome from the assumptions derived from the radial case in Figure 11. In this example, the prices within "Zone II" differ, but there is no binding constraint in the zone. The lines within the zone are operating below their thermal limits. The difference in prices between buses M and N arises not due to constraints within the zone but because of the loop flow effects interacting with the binding constraints between the zones. Apparently the determination of prices within a zone cannot be made independent of the effects on constraints outside the zone.

Aggregation into zones may add to complexity and distort price incentives.

A symmetric result appears in Figure 13 with a different pattern of loads and flows. In this case, there is no constraint binding between Zones II and III, but the price in Zone III differs from the prices in Zone II. Again this effect cannot be seen in radial networks, but it is easy to create in real networks with loop flow. The price in Zone III differs from all the other prices in part because of the interaction with the constraints in Zone II. In a sufficiently interconnected network, these examples suggest that a wide variety of pricing patterns would be possible. In fact, with loop flow, it is possible for a single binding constraint to result in different prices at every location in the system, reflecting the fact that every location has a different impact on the constraint.

Figure 13

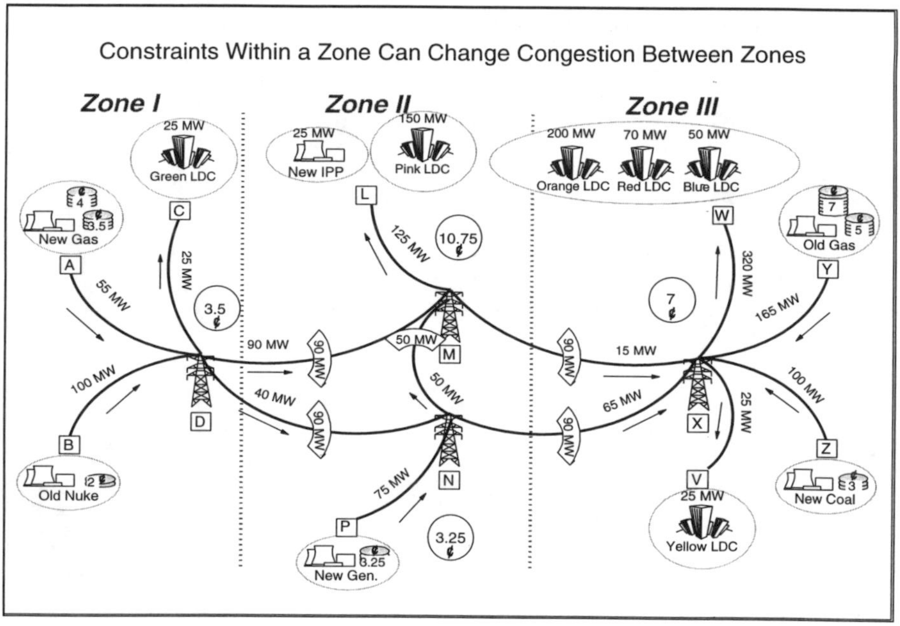

Constraints Within a Zone Can Change Congestion Between Zones

Aggregation into zones may add to complexity and distort price incentives. The assertion that conversion to zones will simplify the pricing problem is not supported by analysis of the conditions that can exist in a looped network. Furthermore, aggregating networks presents a number of related technical problems that follow from the fact that exact aggregation requires first knowing the disaggregated flows. In other words, the first step in calculating consistent aggregate flows and prices is to calculate the disaggregated flows and prices. Hence aggregation produces no savings in computation, and no additional simplicity. If no price dispersion exists, no aggregation is necessary. And if price dispersion does exist, aggregation only sends confused price signals. In the end, the simplest solution may be to calculate and use the locational prices at the nodes, without further aggregation.

Nodes And Zones For Short-Run Pricing

With this somewhat tedious review of locational pricing principles available, we can turn to the issue of the "simplification" offered by the proposal to implement short-run pricing by aggregating into nodes into zones. The approach is to postulate and then examine a series of canonical arguments or questions.

If Zones are Defined by Nodes with Common Prices, Why Bother?

The definition of a zone is sometimes offered as a group of locations that would have the same locational price. As we have seen from the above examples, for this to be literally true the connections must be radial connections. In a sufficiently interconnected system, with parallel flows, there will be different prices across any collection of locations, even with constraints that appear to be external to the putative zone. Hence, the case of true equality of the locational prices would be a limited and special set of conditions.

The more general argument would be to aggregate locations where the locational prices do not differ by very much. There may be collections of such locations, but with this definition the natural question arises: What is the need for the zones? If the locational prices differ by only trivial amounts, then locational pricing and zonal aggregation produce the same end result. There would be no need to aggregate.

Hence, it appears that the real application of zonal aggregation must be in situations where the underlying rationale is compromised. In other words, zonal aggregation would be interesting only in those situations where the aggregation results violated the premise of the creation of the zone. In particular, zonal aggregation produces a material difference from locational pricing only in those cases where the locational prices being aggregated are materially different, in contradiction to the original justification for the definition of the zone.

How Would We Define the Zonal Prices?

If the real application of zones is important only when there is a material difference in the locational prices, then there must be some rule specified for determining the price in the zone. The answer is not obvious. Here the intuition derived from the analysis of the single radial transmission line connection can mislead. Contrary to the case of the single line, the price in the zone is not determined by the highest cost generator operating in the zone. Rather, as illustrated above, it is entirely possible for the true price to be more than the operating cost of the most expensive generator in the zone, driven by the effects of loop flow and the interaction with transmission constraints.

The usual proposals for price aggregation involve some form of averaging. A typical approach, as in England and Wales, is to determine a hypothetical unconstrained price in the zone, which is then charged to all customers and paid to all generators. For those generators that are needed but operate at locations with truly higher prices, they would be paid their opportunity costs. The difference above the "unconstrained" price is collected in an uplift that is averaged over all customers.

Any such rule immediately raises the question of what happens to the constrained-off generators, those that would have run at the unconstrained price but whose true locational value is less than the unconstrained price. Clearly they would want to operate, but they cannot be allowed to run because of the transmission constraint.

The solution to this problem in England and Wales has been to pay the generators the profit they would have made if they had run and received the unconstrained price, with the costs added to the uplift and collected again from all customers. This adds to the total cost as seen by all customers and has the perverse effect of providing an incentive to build or maintain generation in locations where there is excess capacity.

In addition, the English pool prohibits bilateral transactions to avoid the problem of the constrained-off generators going around the price averaging system. This obviously limits the flexibility of the market and has been a principal source of complaint by market participants in that system. However, the importance of such rules was dramatically illustrated by the events in the Pennsylvania-New Jersey-Maryland Interconnection (PJM) system during June of 1997.

During June, the PJM system was operating under an interim tariff provision that followed English zonal model with two critical exceptions. The PJM market was treated as one zone, with a hypothetical unconstrained dispatch setting the so-called market clearing price. In the event of transmission congestion, some generators bidding into the pool were constrained on while others were constrained off. The cost of the more expensive generation was rolled into an average congestion charge that applied to all loads. So far this was the same as the English system. The difference is that constrained-off generators were not compensated for their lost profits, and non-firm bilateral transactions were allowed at only the price of the average congestion cost uplift.

When the system became constrained, the result was predictable and predicted. Some low cost generators bidding into the pool were constrained off. The corresponding loads would then be charged the "unconstrained" price of 2.9 cents plus the uplift. However, the marginal cost of the constrained-off generators was as low as 1.5 cents. If the same loads arranged a bilateral transaction with these constrained off generators, who would now withdraw from the pool dispatch, the loads could have the energy for this 1.5 cents price plus the same uplift. Given this incentive, this is precisely what happened. The loads and constrained-off generators arranged bilateral transactions that brought the generators back on line. This, in turn, forced the ISO to back off other generators, who then faced the same incentive to leave the pool and schedule themselves.[6]

The end state of this downward spiral was that the ISO was left with virtually no controllable generation to redispatch in order to respect the transmission constraints. Under the existing tariff provisions, there was nothing the ISO could do to correct the perverse pricing incentives. Hence, the ISO invoked a "temporary fix" by immediately modifying the rules to prohibit such bilateral transactions, which it did with subsequent FERC approval.[7]

The net effect was to subsidize consumers in the high price areas by charging more to consumers in low price areas, and to remove the flexibility for bilateral transactions that was an objective of the market restructuring and would be a natural result of locational pricing. Apparently, the zonal simplification contained a hidden complexity.

Would Locational Prices Be Hard to Calculate and Come from a Black Box?

The locational prices would be determined by the actual dispatch, which makes the problem simple. The computations are easy, and have been available for years in power pools; they just haven't been used for pricing purposes. Calculating locational marginal costs for the actual dispatch is easier than the familiar and widely used split-savings methodology. Furthermore, since locational pricing is already done (almost in full) in Argentina, Chile, New Zealand, and Norway, there is a demonstration that the technical computation is straightforward.

Once the method is explained, system operators always say the prices could be computed easily. Part of the misunderstanding on this point is the distinction between determining an economic dispatch (difficult) and determining the prices given the dispatch (easy). The hard part in dispatching is both unavoidable and already done. The easy part of calculating the prices is a detail. At a recent FERC Technical Conference, the ISO for PJM explained how to calculate the prices and described the software which is operating in parallel to determine the prices.[8] An independent auditor verified that the system was understood and auditable.[9]

This brings us to the issue of the perception and comprehension of the market participants. At the moment the majority of market participants would claim that the idea of using locational prices is too complicated. However, the view of the moment should not be all that concerns us. So far, every simple alternative proposed has turned out to be pretty complicated, once the implications of the full package unfolded to include the extensive regulatory rules needed to negate the incentives of incorrect prices.

Would It Be an Easy Matter to Set and Later Change the Zonal Boundaries?

The rationale for zones rests in part on the assumption that the zones would be easy to define and would be stable for long periods. However, when conditions changed, the zones would be redefined to come back into compliance with the original definition that there would be no difference in locational prices within the zones.

Each of these points raises a number of complications that must be recognized. First, it is not so obvious where the zonal boundaries should be set. For example, recent PJM "[O]perating data show that, during the past 14 months, 70 percent of the out-of-merit costs for transmission control in PJM resulted from thermal contingencies."[10] These thermal limits are exactly the type of constraints that create the looped interactions as illustrated in the previous sections by the numerous examples. They are not typically radial lines, and the impact of the constraints give rise to different prices throughout the system.

If the zones are not stable, then there would be again little or no distinction between the prices reported by a locational pricing system and the zonal prices. In Norway, for example, the system is described as a zonal system, but the system operator can and does change the definition of the zones daily or hourly. Hence, the Norwegian system is more like a locational pricing system.

If the zones are intended to last for extended periods, but change when there is a material and sustained difference in locational prices within the zone, then a number of other complications arise. For instance, it would still be necessary to calculate the locational prices on a regular basis just to evaluate the suitability of the zonal definition. This means that there will be regular information available that some people are being subsidized and other people are paying the subsidy required by the zonal configuration. The reconfiguration step, by definition, amounts to rearranging the pattern of these subsidies just when the threshold criteria indicates that the reconfiguration really matters.

Since establishment and reconfiguration of the pattern of subsidies will depend on extensive analysis of prospective conditions, there will be many assumptions and points of debate about what the appropriate boundaries should be next week or next year. Although the computational challenge of computing locational prices for the actual dispatch is trivial, the process of forecasting these prices is another matter entirely, one that promises to be controversial. At the risk of understatement, there is little in past regulatory experience that gives confidence that this creation and rearrangement of subsidies will be either swift or simple. Policy makers who think that zonal aggregation and cross subsidies will simplify the process should look again.

Is Transmission Congestion a Small Problem?

To argue that transmission congestion is and will be minor is to argue that there should be no interest in gaining transmission rights. Given the keen interest in tradeable transmission capacity rights, the behavior of the market participants already contradicts the assertion that this is a minor issue. Furthermore, if it is a minor issue, then the locational prices will not differ most of the time, except for losses, and nothing could be simpler than this outcome. Even if congestion costs were small in the past under the regime of vertically integrated utilities, the incentives will be different in the competitive market where customers have choices. As seen elsewhere, small differences in costs could be a large part of the profit on a transaction, and would lead to substantial differences in behavior. If we give market participants choices, such as between pool and bilateral transactions, it will be important to get the prices right.

Furthermore, the improving understanding of the importance of this matter indicates that when the constraints do apply, the price differences can be surprisingly large. In August for example, the reports were that PJM single zone again was operating with "dispatch rates," which would be similar to the locational prices if they were being charged, that were 8.9 cents in the constrained-on regions and 1.2 cents in the constrained-off regions of the zone. The "widely differing dispatch rates were repeated for several days last week."[11] When constraints bind, therefore, the incentives created can be much larger than most people imagine. If participants were given the choice and flexibility that we think of as appropriate for the competitive market, these incentives would overwhelm the system as long as the prices charged diverged from the underlying locational marginal prices.

Would Zonal Pricing Mitigate Market Power?

To the extent that there is a high concentration of control of generation or load, there will continue to be a potential for an exercise of market power. This potential creates demand for continued regulatory oversight. The analysis of market power in the face of significant transmission constraints is a broader subject.[12] However, an advantage of the market model with opportunity cost pricing at locations is the ability to expand the range of options available to address potential problems of market power without compromising other goals in the development of a competitive electric market.

This argument appears counterintuitive at first glance, and there would appear to be advantages to aggregation into zones. As the argument goes, the use of locational pricing would imply small local markets. By contrast, it seems logical that aggregation into zones would expand the geographic scope of the market and bring more actors into competition, thereby mitigating market power.

If the separation into local markets and locational marginal cost differences were simply an artificial institutional constraint, there might be something to this story, especially if the local generators were not competing with other generators in the network. In the present case, however, the facts are different. The constraints are real, and aggregation into zones would not remove the transmission constraints. Aggregation into zones would be likely to hide the market power and remove some of the most important limitations on market power; namely, the demand side response and the ability of new entrants to challenge the dominant generator.

Under locational pricing, the ISO provides open access to the grid at opportunity cost prices. This unbundles the system and eliminates vertical market power. Horizontal market power arises from concentration of ownership of generation plants. The auction mechanism in the bid and dispatch system does not create market power; a dominant firm would not need the auction to manipulate market prices. Furthermore, compared to charging locational marginal cost prices, all the alternatives involve some form of price averaging, which would both enhance and hide horizontal market power.[13] With locational pricing, customers at the location would face the higher price and this would create two beneficial incentives. First, customers would have an incentive to reduce their demand and thereby weaken the power and profits of the dominant firm.   Second, customers would have an incentive to sign long-term contracts with new entrants that would support entry and mitigate market power.   With zonal aggregation, however, these incentives would be removed or substantially attenuated.   The generator with market power would still be paid a high price.   Customers would not see the high price, they would see only an average price spread across those at other locations.   In fact, the generator with market power would benefit from this disguise.   By confronting a less responsive demand curve, the generator would see its market power enhanced within the zone.   With zonal averaging, new entrants would face the problem of entering a market that was subject to manipulation by the dominant generator but would have no customers prepared to sign a long-term contract, because no individual customers would see the higher price.   Hence, zonal aggregation would increase the need for regulation.

Zonal aggregation would not expand the real geographic scope of competition unless the aggregation rule implied setting all prices at the price of the dominant firm, which would create another set of problems.   Hence, locational marginal cost pricing would reduce market power relative to the common zonal alternatives, and locational pricing would make the exercise of market power more transparent.

Can the Market Operate With a Simpler System?

Locational marginal cost pricing lends itself to a natural decomposition.   For example, even with loops in a network, market information could be transformed easily into a hub-and-spoke framework with locational price differences on a spoke defining the cost of moving to and from the local hub, and then between hubs.   This would simplify without distorting the locational prices.   As shown in Figure 14, a contract network could develop that would be different from the real network without affecting the meaning or interpretation of the locational prices.[14]

With the market hubs, the participants would see the simplification of having a few hubs that capture most of the price differences of long-distance transmission.   Contracts could develop relative to the hubs.[15]   The rest of the sometimes important difference in locational prices would appear in the cost of moving power to and from the local hub.   Commercial connections in the network could follow a configuration convenient for contracting and trading.   The separation of physical and financial flows would allow this flexibility.

The creation or elimination of hubs would require no intervention by regulators or the ISO. New hubs could arise as the market requires, or disappear when not important. A hub is simply a special node within a zone. The ISO still would work with the locational prices, but the market would decide on the degree of simplification needed. However, everyone would still be responsible for the opportunity cost of moving power to and from the local hub. There would be locational prices, and this would avoid the substantial incentive problems of averaging prices. The hub-and-spoke approach appears to give most of the benefits attributed to zones without the costs, and it implies that the ISO works within a locational pricing framework.

Figure 14

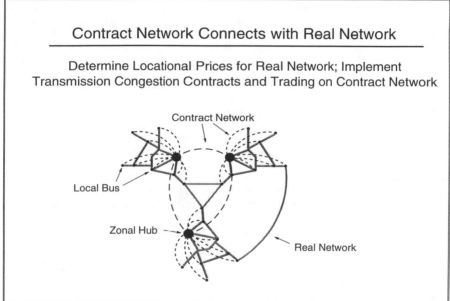

Contract Network Connects with Real Network

Determine Locational Prices for Real Network; Implement Transmission Congestion Contracts and Trading on Contract Network

Contract Network

Local Bus

Zonal Hub

Real Network

Conclusion

Efficient marginal-cost pricing in competitive electricity markets implies sometimes substantial locational differences in the presence of transmission constraints. Aggregation of individual nodes into zones for short run pricing appeals as a putative simplification. However, in a sufficiently dense network, zonal aggregation provides less simplification than meets the eye. Zonal pricing itself would be controversial and complicated, more complicated in practice than straight locational pricing. Furthermore, locational pricing would avoid perverse incentives that lead to restrictive rules. The path to greater flexibility in commercial transactions, therefore, is through locational pricing. And the hub-and-spoke approach that can evolve as the market requires, can obtain the simplification hoped for with zones while avoiding the restrictions and regulation that zonal approaches would require. It would be better if the world were less complex, but the reality of the electric network cannot be avoided if we want to have a competitive market with a maximum degree of flexibility. To support choice, as always it is important to get the prices right. And in electrical networks with transmission constraints, there is an essential and significant locational element that can be accommodated, but not easily suppressed.

Notes

1. Lucius N. Littauer Professor of Public Policy and Administration, John F. Kennedy School of Government, Harvard University, and Senior Advisor, Putnam, Hayes & Bartlett, Inc. This paper draws on work for the Harvard Electricity Policy Group and the Harvard-Japan Project on Energy and the Environment. Many individuals have provided helpful comments, especially Robert Arnold, John Ballance, Jeff Bastian, Ashley Brown, Michael Cadwalader, Judith Cardell, John Chandley, Doug Foy, Hamish Fraser, Geoff Gaebe, Don Garber, Scott Harvey, Stephen Henderson, Carrie Hitt, Jere Jacobi, Paul Joskow, Marija Ilic, Laurence Kirsch, Jim Kritikson, Dale Landgren, William Lindsay, Amory Lovins, Rana Mukerji, Richard O'Neill, Howard Pifer, Susan Pope, Grant Read, Bill Reed, Joseph R. Ribeiro, Brendan Ring, Larry Ruff, Michael Schnitzer, Hoff Stauffer, Irwin Stelzer, Jan Strack, Steve Stoft, Richard Tabors, Julie Voeck, Carter Wall and Assef Zobian. The author is or has been a consultant on electric market reform and transmission issues for British National Grid Company, GPU Inc. (and the Supporting Companies of PJM), GPU PowerNet Pty Ltd, Duquesne Light Company, Electricity Corporation of New Zealand, National Independent Energy Producers, New York Power Pool, New York Utilities Collaborative, Niagara Mohawk Corporation, PJM Interconnection LLP, San Diego Gas & Electric Corporation, Trans Power of New Zealand, Williams Energy Group, and Wisconsin Electric Power Company. The views presented here are not necessarily attributable to any of those mentioned, and any remaining errors are solely the responsibility of the author. (http://ksgwww.harvard.edu/people/ whogan).
2. These examples illustrate the elements of locational marginal cost pricing. They are adapted from Hogan (1992), Hogan (1995), Hogan (1996), and Harvey, Hogan and Pope (1996).
3. The welfare maximizing formulation is the natural extension of traditional least-cost dispatch to include flexible demand. See Schweppe, Caramanis, Tabors, and Bohn (1988). On the same point, but with examples to illuminate the critical importance of the phenomenon of loop flow in interconnected electrical grids, see Hogan (1992), and Chao and Peck (1996).
4. Walton and Tabors (1996).
5. For a similar analysis with similar conclusions, see Stoft (1996).
6. PJM Supporting Companies (1997), p.5.
7. PJM Interconnection, Inc. (1997a).
8. Pennsylvania-New Jersey-Maryland Interconnection (1997).
9. Price Waterhouse (1997).
10. PJM Supporting Companies (1997), p.30.
11. Power Markets Week (1997).
12. Cardell, Hitt and Hogan (1997) and Hogan (1997).
13. If locational prices differ in a zone, the rule might be to charge all customers and pay all generators the highest price in the zone, allowing the scope of the generators market power to expand. However, most zonal proposals are based on some form of averaging to soften the impact of higher prices.
14. For further details on long-run transmission congestion contracts, see Harvey, Hogan and Pope (1996).

15. For a similar argument, see Walton and Tabors (1996).

References

Cardell, Judith B., Carrie CullenHitt and William W. Hogan. 1997. "Market Power and Strategic Interaction in Electricity Networks." *Resource and Energy Economics* 19: 109-137.

Chao, Hung-po and Stephen Peck. 1996. "A Market Mechanism for Electric Power Transmission." *Journal of Regulatory Economics* 10 (1): 25-29.

Harvey, Scott M., William W. Hogan and Susan L. Pope. 1996. "Transmission Capacity Reservations and Transmission Congestion Contracts." Harvard University.

Hogan, William W. 1992. "Contract Networks for Electric Power Transmission."*Journal of Regulatory Economics* 4 (3): 211-242.

Hogan, William W. 1997. "A Market Power Model with Strategic Interaction in Electricity Networks." *Energy Journal* 18 (4): 107-141.

Hogan, William W. 1995. "A Wholesale Pool Spot Market Must BeAdministered by the Independent System Operator: Avoiding the Separation Fallacy." *The Electricity Journal* (December):26-37.

Hogan, William W. 1996. "Transmission Pricing and Access Policy for Electricity Competition." Harvard University.

Pennsylvania-New Jersey-Maryland Interconnection. 1997. Responses toFERC's March 28 Questions on Implementation of Locational Marginal Pricing. FERC Docket Nos. OA970261-000 and ER97-1082-000 (April 14).

PJM Interconnection, Inc. 1997. FERC Section 201 Filing. (June 27).

PJM Supporting Companies. 1997. "Motion to Intervene and Comments of the PJM Supporting Companies in Support of PJM Interconnection, Inc. Filing. FERC Docket No. ER97-3463-000. (July 2).

PJM Supporting Companies. 1997a. Motion to Intervene and Motion to Reject CCEM Filing Submitted by the PJM Supporting Companies. FERC Docket Nos.OA97-261-000and ER97-1082-000 (July 23).

Power Markets Week. 1997. (September 1): 13.

Price Waterhouse. 1997. Comments, *FERC Technical Conference, Docket Nos.* OA97-261-000 and ER97-1082-000

Schweppe, F.C., M.C. Caramanis, R.D. Tabors, and R.E. Bohn. 1988. *Spot Pricing of Electricity*. Kluwer Academic Publishers.

Stoft, Stephen. 1996. "Analysis of the California WEPEX Applications to FERC. "PWP-042A, University of California Energy Institute.

Walton, S. and R. Tabors. 1996. "Zonal Tranmission Pricing: Methodology and Preliminary Results From the WSCC."

4 OWNERSHIP STRUCTURE, CONTRACTING AND REGULATION OF TRANSMISSION SERVICES PROVIDERS[1]

Paul R. Kleindorfer

Introduction

This note considers a number of questions arising out of the EPRI-sponsored MEET Workshop on challenges associated with restructuring of the U.S. electric power industry. Restructuring objectives include transparent and efficient markets for both long-term and short-term transactions, dynamic efficiency and innovation, customer-focused operations, and system integrity. After a brief review of unbundling strategies intended to implement these objectives, I structure and pose some of the key questions (I call them MEET questions) which are currently "center-stage" in the debate. This note focuses primarily on questions related to the ownership structure and regulation of the ISO (and related other institutions such as the Power Exchange), including necessary incentives for the ISO to promote efficiency in financial and physical contracting, as foreseen and partially prescribed in FERC Order 888. The required contracting includes financial instruments (spots, forwards, futures, and performance contracts) encompassing long-term and short-term energy contracts, asset-use and resource supply contracts, ancillary service contracts, investments in generation and transmission assets, load-management and demand-side management contracts, and contracting for other market-mediated services required for the efficient configuration and operation of the power market.

In the transmission area, most attention has been focused in the U.S. on the issue of pricing. However, pricing is arguably less significant than the issues of ownership and decision rights for access to transmission capacity. For one thing, transmission costs are only 10-15% of the total retail costs of power. For another, almost all of these costs are fixed and therefore efficient (i.e., marginal cost-based) prices signals for transmission are hardly noticeable relative to other components of energy cost related to generation and to fixed cost components of transmission, which are driven by investment and contracting decisions of transmission service providers. In any case, transmission is critical in assuring open and nondiscriminatory access and with it in enabling wholesale and retail competition in generation and between generation, transmission and distribution. For these reasons, transparency, simplicity and system integrity must the initial guiding principles of transmission service provision and regulation, followed by efficiency in transmission investment and lastly efficiency in short-term pricing. How to achieve a balance among these principles is the challenge which we briefly discuss in the following comments.

Unbundling and Rebundling

What gets *unbundled* to promote transparency and competition must be *rebundled* to provide effective power services. In this process, ownership and contracting are central issues to the efficiency of investment and the transactions costs of rebundling. Unbundling occurs at two physical levels: (1) between generation, transmission and distribution; and (2) within generation, between the provision of energy and various other ancillary services

Ownership and contracting are central issues to the efficiency of investment and the transactions costs of rebundling.

In addition there is a separation of physical products and financial services as is apparent from the Figure below. The benefits of unbundling are to clarify for competitive reasons the cost and value of each of the separate elements of the value chain for creating electric power. The problem created by unbundling is that these separate elements must be rebundled, via contracting or spot markets, in an on-going fashion to (re-)create from these elements desired services and end outputs.

Figure 1 provides a snapshot of the physical functions provided by the electric power system and the financial decisions and instruments which complement and parallel the physical. We structure the physical system *functions* and the financial market *decisions/contracts* as they occur in 4 time frames, Long-Term, Medium-Term, Short-Term and Real-Time.

Long-term Functions and Decisions: Physical: Technology planning and acquisition, human resource planning and development, to build and operate assets to support generation, transmission and distribution (GTD). Financial: Secure required capital, technology and human resources to accomplish the physical functions.

Medium-term Functions and Decisions: Physical: Schedule and implement system maintenance of GTD assets.   Financial: Forward contracts and bilateral agreements are negotiated for power delivery and contracts for load management, for transmission constraint payments, and for delivery of ancillary generations support are determined.

Short-term Functions and Decisions: Physical: Forecast and schedule near-term power demand. Unit commitment decisions and other set-up decisions to enable economic dispatch are made. Financial: Execution of medium-term contracts (e.g., forwards); spot markets and economic dispatch provide clearing mechanisms for residual supply and demand.

Real-time Functions and Decisions: Physical: Network coordination occurs to assure system reliability, security and stability, through spinning reserves, Automatic Generation Control (AGC) and ancillary generation support providing frequency and voltage support.   Financial: Execution of medium- and short-term contracts for interruptible loads, VAR contracts and other support services.

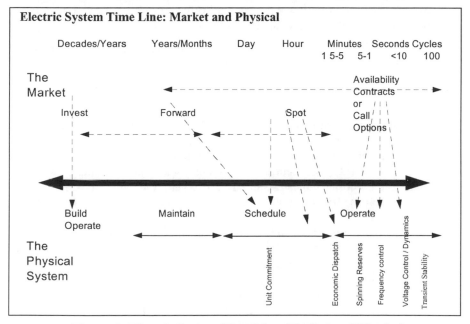

Figure 1: Electric System Time Line: Market and Physical

In terms of organizational boundaries, the natural demarcation is between the organization(s) controlling long- and medium-term transactions, and those occurring in the short-run or in real-time. The latter transactions are the purview of system operations and organizationally will be the responsibility of the Independent System Operator (the ISO), coupled with a "Power Exchange", which will also have responsibility for bilateral contracting at various temporal levels (monthly, daily, hourly).   The longer-term functions and decisions are the responsibility of Generation, Distribution and Transmission Asset Providers (I refer to the last-named as TAPs). Concerning transmission service and network coordination, the key is the organization and ownership boundaries of the ISO and the TAPs. I discuss this in the next Section in more detail, but it should be clear right away that two general possibilities exist: either the ISO and the TAPs are brought under the control of one (presumably regulated) company, or the ISO and the TAPs remain under separate ownership and control.

Structure and Ownership of the ISO and TSPs

From the above sketch, the reader should have no problem imagining a number of different approaches to organizing and regulating the ISO and Transmission Service Providers (TSPs) and their relationship to facilitating long-term markets (between Gencos and Discos) and short-term markets (e.g., forward markets and the residual "Pool"). Indeed, a variety of ISO models are technically possible, differentiated in broad terms by the following (inter-linked) factors:

1. Involvement of the ISO in the energy market (e.g., procedures for contracting for reserves and managing congestion costs);

2. The scope of commercial activities undertaken by the ISO, including the extent of support functions bundled within the ISO;

3. Structure (e.g., profit or non-profit), ownership and control of assets by the ISO.

Rather than use the limited space available here for a detailed treatment of this subject, let me just summarize a few of the on-going "experiments" internationally, which show considerable variation in the institutional realization of the above factors (see Table 1).[2] A recent survey of U.S. States and regional power pool approaches and proposals indicates similar variety w.r.t. the dimensions indicated in Table 1.[3] Given this array of existing alternatives, it is natural to pose the following MEET questions:

Question: What are the likely effects on efficiency (including financial performance for TSPs) and quality of transmission service of alternative approaches to ISO structure (e.g., w.r.t. ownership, profit-orientation, rights and responsibilities to contract for ancillary generation support and for wires use and maintenance, etc.)? What has the experience been internationally with various approaches to the ISO and which of the factors (1)-(3) above (or others) are critical success factors?

Question: What should the relationship be between the ISO and the institution/organization responsible for managing price-determination, contracting and settlements in the short-term power market (the Power Exchange in the California Market or the Pool Administrator in the England/Wales Pool)? Are there any findings which can be drawn from international experience to date?

Question: What technical, demand and supply factors are likely to determine the looseness or tautness of pool rules relative to approval and acceptance of physical bilateral contracts by the ISO? What findings are there in international experience and in regional power pools to date about what is feasible/desirable in assuring an efficient confluence of (physical or financial) bilateral agreements with the Pool?

To make matters specific enough to go on, I will assume below that the ISO is allowed to enter into commercial transactions related to its primary role in balancing supply and demand in real time and in managing congestion. I will also assume that some flexibility exists for allowing bilateral contracting between supply aggregators/discos and generators, with the Power Exchange or Market Clearing-house Function being organizationally separated from the ISO. Given these mild assumptions, we now consider questions related to the organization and regulation of the ISO and its relationship to Transmission Asset Providers (TAPs).

Efficient Organization and Regulation of Transmission

Scope and Organization of Transmission Service
Figure 2 illustrates the components of transmission service. At a primary level, generators and loads will gain access to the market through a connection to the transmission grid, and their supply and demand gives rise to the electricity marketplace. Transmission of energy from generators to wholesale customers is the quantity or energy side of the transmission service. The other side of transmission service is the quality or system support side, which is concerned with ensuring security of supply and voltage and frequency standards.

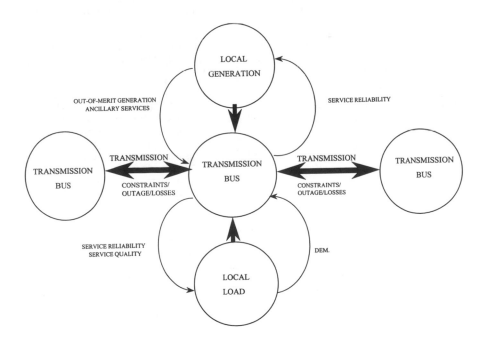

Figure 2: Transmission Service

Table 1a: Transmission Issues for Selected Electric Power Markets
Contracting and ISO Structure

Country	Types of Transactions, i.e., Pooling vs. Bilateral	Involvement of the ISO in the Commercial Market
Argentina[4]	GENCOs can either sell into a pool or enter into private contracts with customers whose load exceeds 1MW; buyers (i.e., large customers or DISCOs) pay a contractual price, or a seasonal price, and/or spot price which is then used by the Power Exchange (CAMMESA) to reimburse generators.	The NIS coordinates the generation, transmission, and distribution of electricity. CAMMESA is responsible for managing the Wholesale Electricity Market (WEM), for publishing seasonal and spot prices, and for performing least cost dispatch. Balancing is performed using an hourly spot price.
Australia (New South Wales)[5]	Generally pooling, though about 10,600 customers with annual consumption in excess of 160 MWh per annum will be eligible for retail access in July 1998. Spalding reports that there are proposals in place for full retail access beginning July 1999.	Transgrid (Market and System Operator) is responsible for both managing the commercial market and for performing the role of a system operator, i.e., least cost dispatch.
Chile[6]	Both, even though contractual amounts might be satisfied via a combination of actual generation and spot purchases. Bilateral contracts are generally limited to customers with a demand for capacity of greater than 2 MW.	Two CDEC's perform economic dispatch in two interconnected systems, SIC and SING. The CDEC's compute seasonal and hourly spot prices to enable balancing by GENCOs for deliveries that are different from contractually agreed upon amounts.
New Zealand[7]	Voluntary pooling though the market tends to be generally dominated by bilaterals.	EMCO is responsible for managing the market; EMCO and Transpower are responsible for performing least cost dispatch
Norway[8]	Generally voluntary pooling with bilateral contracting between sellers and buyers	NordPool (50% owned by STATTNETT) is responsible for managing the commercial market and overseeing daily (i.e, spot), weekly (i.e., hedging instruments), and balancing (i.e., deliveries different from contractual amounts) markets. STATTNETT is responsible for ensuring reliable delivery of power to the final destination.
Peru	Identical to Chile, except that customers with demand in excess of 1 MW can enter into bilateral transactions.	Identical to Chile; two dispatchers in two interconnected systems, i.e., SICN and SIS.
UK (England & Wales)[9]	Voluntary Pooling with bilateral contracting allowed for (large) customers.	The National Grid Company (NGC) is responsible for: a) managing the market, i.e., pool operations; b) operating the 275kV and 400kV transmission system; and, c) for performing least cost dispatch.

Table 1b: Transmission Issues For Selected Electric Power Markets
Ownership and Pricing

Country	Ownership of Transmission Assets & Construction of New Transmission	Transmission Cost Allocation & Pricing
Argentina	Multiple private owners operating under regulated prices; expansion of grid decided and paid for by users	Multiple TAPs. Transmission tolls paid by GENCOs or DISCOs are based on a marginal cost approach and consists of a connection charge, a volumetric charge, and a charge to cover losses. Large users having bilateral contracts with GENCOs pay the DISCOs a toll for transmission.
Australia (New South Wales)	Generally, the high voltage transmission is state owned and operated; the state is responsible for constructing new transmission.	Transmission pricing is regulated by IPART which determines a total allowable annual network revenue requirement. Generators pay the cost of connecting to the network and common service charges are averaged over all customers. Recovery of costs is based on a 3-part tariff; 50% fixed, 25% demand, and 25% based on energy.
Chile	Multiple private owners providing access at regulated prices; grid extensions can be funded by any player.	Based on a location based ("nodal") marginal approach plus additional charges to cover losses and congestion.
New Zealand	State Owned (Transpower) and operated; Transpower is responsible for constructing new transmission.	Similar in concept with the system in NSW, Australia except that Transpower uses a 2-part tariff (fixed and variable) to recover its allowed revenue requirement from DISCOs (or ESA's).
Norway	State Owned (STATTNETT) and operated; Stattnett is responsible for constructing new transmission.	Transmission pricing is fixed for each local distribution area regardless of the source of the power, i.e., postage-stamp in nature. A Stattnett Transmission Charge consists of 4-parts; charges for connection, power, energy, and capacity.
Peru	Identical to Chile.	Transmission is divided into principal and secondary systems; all GENCOs can access principal lines in exchange for connection and volumetric tolls. Secondary lines are accessible only by certain generators. Pricing is similar to that in Chile.
UK (England & Wales)	Owned by the NGC which provides all generators with open access. NGC is responsible for expansion of transmission capacity.	Charges for the use of the transmission system are split into two elements; connection, and use of the system. Connection charges are levied on any user directly connected to the transmission system. Use of system charges are paid by suppliers or generators who connect with and use the grid. Charges vary across 14 zones.

As set out in the framework shown in Figure 2, the quality side of the transmission service would include the procurement of Out-of-Merit (OOM) generation services for constraint control and ancillary services from generators (and other suppliers of these services). The provider of transmission service may also acquire the right to interrupt loads and In-Merit (IM) generation through interruptible service contracts.[10] The other key aspect of the quality side of the transmission service is the security or insurance value of the network, which is assured by appropriate network investment and maintenance. The point here is that all participants in the energy market acquire through their transmission grid connection a valuable option to generate or consume electricity. This option is made valuable by the additional investments (e.g. reserve lines) and operational decisions (e.g. scheduling generation reserve) undertaken by the transmission provider. Hence, the transmission grid is both a medium for transportation/trading, as well as a security network. The key MEET question arising from this is the following:

> Question: What regulatory or ownership incentives will assure (at least rough-cut) efficiency for both the quantity and quality sides of transmission service? In particular, what property and decision rights should be internalized within the ownership boundaries of the transmission provider to assure efficiency?

Given the importance of centralized operations in accomplishing real-time functions, a key question is how many ISOs are needed and what their boundaries should be. Clearly, however the boundaries are drawn, a communication infrastructure and close interaction between ISOs will be required to maintain system reliability and efficient operation. Focusing on a specific ISO, the needs for real-time control strongly suggest that the ISO must be located within the organizational boundaries of a single economic entity. This leads to one obvious classification of possible ownership structures for transmission: (a) either the same entity which houses the ISO owns and operates other transmission assets; or (b) this entity consists only of the ISO and does not own these assets but leases/contracts for these from other transmission asset providers (TAPs); or (c) the TAPs lease their assets directly to the users (generators and loads) and the ISO sets the rules of trade and usage and has responsibility for real-time operational requirements. Using comparative institutional economics[11], it is not possible to rule out either of these approaches as *prima facie* inefficient. Approach (a), which sets up a single company, which I call the "TransCo", would give rise to the problem of providing regulatory incentives through performance-based regulation to assure that the TransCo, a regulated monopolist, undertook its responsibilities in a manner which promoted system-wide efficiency. Approach (b), the ISO+TAPs, could yield clearer information on the value of transmission assets and services (the former provided by TAPs and the latter by the ISO), but would lead to transactions costs between the ISO and the TAPs in contracting for and maintaining transmission assets. A hybrid approach might create a single organizational entity, the TransCo, but require it to have two separate divisions, TransCo-Wires and TransCo-ISO, to create transparency in cashflows and value-added resulting from the asset management and system operation functions of the TransCo. Under approach (c), the ISO keeps track of transmission credits and debits and specifies trading rules, but it is the TAPs and market participants who trade these rights in a decentralized fashion, e.g., as in Chao and Peck (1997). Since even in this decentralized approach, it will be necessary for the ISO to control real time operations, and therefore to contract for ancillary generation and load balancing assets, we will treat approach (c) as a special case of (b). It should be noted, however, that (c) has additional problems of assuring that the ISO is properly motivated to monitor transmission credits and debits and to establish and operate an efficient and responsive trading center. In any of these cases, note further that the resulting ISO could be for-profit or not-for-profit. Let us consider these options in more detail.

In the single, unified TransCo option, a regulated monopolist would be given responsibility for universal transmission service. To assure clarity in its motives and some incentives for X-efficiency, this TransCo would probably be best structured as a for-profit, regulated monopoly (as in the case of the National Grid Company in the UK). As noted above, it could be required to keep separate books on its ISO and its TSP operations. The TransCo would then face various forms of profit and price regulation. Such regulation should be performance-based to assure an outward-looking (or customer-focused) TransCo as opposed to an inward-looking, asset-directed company. Revenues for the TransCo would come from two types of services:

a   Monopoly or reserved services, such as those associated with managing system operations.

b   Contestable services, such as connecting new loads or generators to the system, which could be provided by a number of third parties.

Ideally the price and/or revenue for contestable services would not be regulated, but would be determined by an open market in these services. For services of type (a), prices and revenues would be derived from the three traditional elements of transmission pricing (see Fernando and Kleindorfer (1997) for details):

• Access charges levied against wholesale customers on either a lump-sum or an energy-supplied basis;

• Energy injection and capacity (or demand) charges levied against generators on the basis of either injections into the transmission system or the total capacity of the generator connected to the grid;

• Energy charges to reflect marginal transmission costs (congestion plus losses).

The total of these transmission charges would cover (for reserved services) asset costs, system operation costs, congestion costs and losses.

Under the ISO+TAPs option, asset providers and TSPs would be separated. Here the ISO must deal with the added complication of negotiating with independent asset owners (the TAPs) for continuing use, enhancement and maintenance of their assets. If, as envisioned in several recent Regional Transmission Group proposals, the ISO itself were set up/owned or otherwise not independent of these TAPs, then additional problems of assuring uniform and fair treatment for all comers (including the TAPs) through a committee decision-making process involving all the TAPs presents additional opportunities for transactions costs and organizational inertia. Presumably, the same guidelines on reserved and contestable services would hold for the ISO+TAP approach as for the TransCo approach. However, if the ISO is owned by the TAPs, additional monitoring and oversight will no doubt be called for to assure that the ISO fulfills its market facilitation role in an objective fashion. The following MEET questions seem appropriate here:

> Question: What are the consequences of alternative corporate forms for the ISO (including the for-profit question)? What are the consequences of alternative ownership and contracting boundaries for the ISO? In particular, what are the relative merits of asset ownership by the ISO versus contracting with TAPs? If the ISO does not own transmission assets, what should the relationship be between the ISO and TAPs and how can the ISO assure effective control and maintenance of these assets? Similarly, what forms of contracting should be allowed/encouraged for the ISO (e.g., contraint management—OOM and IM interruptibles; ancillary generation support; granting of firm transmission rights for execution of physical bilateral contracts12) and how will alternative ownership structures affect the likely efficiency of these contracts.

Regulation--Appropriate regulatory scenarios will depend on which of the organizational alternatives sketched earlier is chosen. In the event that an asset-thin ISO is set up with no "wires" ownership, the central problem will be to provide incentives to the resulting ISO to properly contract for use of assets, since the cost of such use would be largely outside of the ISO's control, and if asset costs are simply passed through the ISO will have no particular reason to make or encourage investments which would maximize total transmission network value added.[13] On the other hand, in the event of a TransCo (with, say, an asset-holding division TransCo(TA) and a transmission service division TransCo(ISO), the key regulatory issue will be to assure that the TransCo faces the proper incentives to avoid inefficient strategies such as asset-padding. Exploring these two cases further, we note the following.

Regulating a TransCo's Revenues -- A TransCo's revenue stream could be regulated through cost of service, price caps or various other incentive regulation schemes. A pure cost of service scheme is probably not appropriate in a setting where TransCo's cost side is subject to significant uncertainty, especially in the case of constraint control costs. The two key criteria for regulatory governance structures for a TransCo are:

1. Provide TransCo the correct incentives to invest and operate the transmission system. For example, a price cap applied on a kWh basis for the energy components of the TransCo's services would cause the TransCo to confront the correct incentives for investment and contracting if TransCo has to cover all energy costs (losses and congestion costs) of transmission.

2. Provide TransCo a means of passing through risks that it is not equipped to manage (for example, a substantial change in constraint costs as a result of a change in the relative coal/gas price).

Regulating ISO+TAPs (e.g., an RTG's) Revenues -- The same principles as above apply to the determination of the aggregate revenue requirement. In the case of an unbundled TSP with multiple TAPs, revenue allocation mechanisms to asset owners should provide proper signals to these owners of the value of their existing assets and the incremental value of various options for expanding transmission capacity. This is complicated both by the complexity of marginal cost measurement in transmission and the fact that the large proportion of these costs are not variable in the short run, so that breakeven operations and marginal-cost pricing are in tension.[14] Assessing insurance and quality benefits of assets (e.g., contingency lines) provides further problems in valuation.

> **It is important that transmission pricing and service delivery be kept sufficiently simple to assure transparency and open access.**

The issue of multiple TAPs and a correct valuing of their assets for quantity and quality of service remain an open issue. It points to the key difficulty with the ISO+TAPs model, the level of contractual transactions costs with TAPs and the related issue of control of asset quality by the ISO. From the TAP's point of view, there are problems of assuring that their assets are valued correctly in contracts with the ISO and that the assets are properly maintained. To the extent that the TAPs jointly own the ISO, there would also be problems of assuring even-handedness in the provision of transmission service to non-TAP users. In all of this, it is also very important to remember that transmission costs are typically only 10-15% of the total costs of delivered retail power.[15] Moreover, as noted in Fernando and Kleindorfer (1997), it is the total price and quality of delivered power (and not the transmission price) to which wholesale and retail customers react. Thus, it is important that transmission pricing and service delivery be kept sufficiently simple to assure transparency and open access for the rebundling process that will provide the ultimate bundled good to consumers—delivered power.[16] The fundamental value of transmission is to connect cheap energy sources to loads and to restrain market power by providing the potential to do so. These considerations give rise to the following MEET questions:

Question: What are the appropriate tradeoffs between transparency, simplicity and efficiency in transmission pricing and regulation? How should Transmission Asset Providers (TAPS) and the ISO be remunerated and who should determine which transmission assets are to be constructed and under what conditions these will be brought on line by the ISO?

Question: What review procedures should be implemented to assure appropriate quality and insurance standards are met by the transmission network, while avoiding overbuilding transmission? How should total system transmission costs (congestion costs, losses and operating and maintenance costs) be measured and monitored and by whom? What incentives will various ownership and regulatory structures provide for the ISO and TAPs to minimize total system transmission costs through their investment, operating and contracting options?

Conclusions

The above sketch of the unbundled electric power industry suggests several critical issues which will need to be resolved in the area of ownership and property rights related to the ISO and other transmission service providers and TAPs. The key issue arising from the above discussion revolves around the following summary MEET question:

Question: Will the ISO be only a non-profit market "facilitator" which controls the Network (the real-time functions noted above) and the voluntary pool(s), while contracting for (or buying in spot markets) all assets and support services with other market participants? Or will the ISO be a profit-oriented, regulated commercial entity with some assets (e.g., wires, control systems and possibly generation plant) of its own? Or will some other, e.g. distributed, form of ownership and control develop for the ISO?

Key regulatory issues of transmission pricing, investment, and contracting for services will depend very much on how this question and the other questions in this note are answered.

Notes

[1] This note is a follow-up to a meeting of the EPRI-sponsored Workshop "Markets for Electricity: Economics and Technology (MEET)", Stanford University, March 7-8, 1997. The author acknowledges helpful discussions with Don Anderson, Chitru Fernando, Shmuel Oren, Nagendra Subbakrishna and MEET Workshop participants, none of whom are to be held responsible for the views presented here. Additional details on many of the ideas presented here are available in Fernando and Kleindorfer (1997). For a detailed discussion of issues of governance and contracting in the electric power restructuring area, see also Joskow (1997).

[2] For further details on potential alternatives for structuring the ownership, contracting and investment rights of the ISO, see Fernando and Kleindorfer (1997).

[3] This statement is based on a survey undertaken for the author by Linda K. Johnson, "Survey of States: Status of Electric Utility Restructuring", March, 1997. The details of this survey suggest both different perspectives across the States, but also very different stages of readiness to implement unbundling, restructuring and various ISO proposals.

[4] As of January 1992, the Argentine Electricity Act divided the electricity industry into three sectors: generation, transmission, and distribution. Though there are multiple owners of transmission, such owners are required by law to provide open access at regulated prices. In addition to its market making responsibility, CAMMESA performs optimal dispatch taking into account the security of the system and the quality of the supply of electricity, and acts as a long term planning agency to plan for the needs of power and energy.

[5] Both the New South Wales and Victorian markets in Australia are similar in design. While generation is competitive in both markets, ownership of transmission, dispatch, and market management are in the state domain. Economic dispatch in New South Wales is performed by TransGrid and in Victoria by the Victoria Power Exchange (VPX) using generators bids as the criterion. The markets in both states are designed to allow for both spot and contract trading. The

situation in Queensland, which is large and sparsely populated, is quite different as reported in Anderson et al. (1997).

[6] By law, generators in Chile can sell their output pursuant to short or long term contracts; they are also free to determine whether and with whom to contract, the duration of contracts, and the amount of electricity to be sold. The transmission sector consists of companies that transmit electricity at high voltage from generators to distribution companies. The Chilean Electricity Law states that to the extent that a company's transmission assets were constructed pursuant to concessions granted by the Chilean government, open access should be provided to the use of such assets. Economic dispatch of generating resources in each of the two major interconnected transmission regions is coordinated by autonomous generating industry groups. Currently, the Chilean system consists of 5 major private generation owners with about 3,300 MW of generating capacity (predominantly hydro), three transmission regions, and 16 distributors. (Bacon and Thobani, 1996)

[7] The Electricity Market Company Ltd. (EMCO), New Zealand's version of a power exchange, reported that as of October 1, 1996, there were 20 registered generators, purchasers, and traders.

[8] The current number of players in the Norwegian market include about 94 wholesale and generating utilities owning and operating about 600 power stations with installed capacities of 1 MW or more and about 205 utilities distributing the power from the generators to consumers. The main Norwegian grid is owned and operated by a state enterprise (STATTNETT) which also owns the power transmission lines and/or undersea cables connecting Norway with Russia, Finland, Sweden, and Denmark. A subsidiary of STATTNETT, NordPool, provides a forum for the sale (by producers) and purchase (by distribution utilities) of electricity in the form of an (hourly) spot market, weekly market, and a regulating market; the regulating market covers adjustments to the sale and purchase of electricity over the grid. EnFO notes that since 1994, contracts for the sale and/or purchase of electricity have been traded in privately owned market places as well. (EnFO, 1997)

[9] Newbery (1995) reports restructuring of the electric power industry in England and Wales began with the Electricity Act of 1989 which divided the Central Electricity Generating Board (CEGB) into four units; Powergen, National Power, Nuclear Electric, and the National Grid Company (NGC). These four were vested as public limited companies on March 31, 1990 at the same time as the 12 distribution companies (or Regional Electricity Companies [REC's]). In December of 1990, the NGC was transferred to the joint ownership of the REC's and the REC's were sold to the public. About 60% of National Power and Powergen were sold to the public in March 1991 with the balance sold in 1995. Nuclear Electric continues to remain in the public domain.

[10] See Kleindorfer, Fernando and Wu (1997) for a discussion of such contraint contracts in the England and Wales context.

[11] For an introduction to instititional assessment procedures in the context of network industries, see Crew and Kleindorfer (1986), *opus cit.*, Chapter 7. See also Williamson (1996).

[12] Interestingly, PJM and NEEPOOL are both currently beset with problems related to mechanims for approving and allocating transmission capacity for execution of bilateral contracts. In the case of PJM, the current system is essentially first-come, first-served with consideral uncertainty and no underlying economic logic. In the case of NEEPOOL (and also of PJM) who has initial property rights to the transmission capacity is currently under dispute at the FERC. In some areas of the country, these issues of transmission capacity allocation and valuation have yet to be structured. Clearly, this is an area very much in need of study if the MEET objectives (of a functioning market) are to be met.

[13] Further complexities on the incentives for efficient investment in transmission are provided in Bushnell and Stoft (1996), Chao-Peck (1997) and Oren (1997).

[14] The recent work by Chao-Peck (1997) and Oren (1997) and the earlier work of Hogan (1992) examine a number of possible approaches to value-based allocation, but there are clearly still more questions than answers in this area.

[15] Note also that only a fraction of this 10-15% is variable in the short run so that if single-part tariffs are used, fixed component markups will typically swamp the SRMC portions of transmission tariffs, whether these markups are added to the transmission tariff itself or are collected as "energy taxes" from generators or distributors. Of course, two-part tariffs can still allow efficient signals to be passed on to customers, but then other complexities enter into the discussion relating to how the fixed charge portion of the two-part tariff is to be collected. See Table 1 for an indication of the gay profusion which international experience has produced on this point to date.

[16] As is apparent from Table 1 at the end of this paper, this has given rise in many jurisdictions to rules such as zonal, marginal-cost based pricing which attempt to provide a balance between the complexity of "true" (i.e., nodal, real-time varying) marginal-cost based transmission pricing and the dictates of full-cost recovery and approximate signals to transmission system users of the congestion and loss costs they cause. See Anderson et al. (1997) for a discussion.

References

Anderson, D., P. Moy and D. Price, "Delivering Efficient Regulation: Issues in Electricity Transmission Regulation in Australia", Department of Commerce, University of Queensland, April, 1997.

Bacon, R. and M. Thobani, "Restructuring the Power Sector—The Case of Small Systems", Finance and Private Sector Development Division, The World Bank, 1996.

Bushnell, J. B. and S. E. Stoft, "Elecrtric Grid Investment under a Contract Network Regime", *J. of Regulatory Economics*, 10: 61-79, July, 1996.

Chao, H-P and S. Peck, "An Institutional Design for an Electricity Contract Market with Central Dispatch," *The Energy Journal*, Vol. 18, No. 1, 1997, 85-110.

Crew, M. A. and P. R. Kleindorfer, *The Economics of Public Utility Regulation*, MIT Press, Cambridge, MA, 1986.

Einhorn, M. and R. Siddiqi (Eds.), *Electricity Transmission Pricing and Technology*, Kluwer Academic Publishers, Boston, 1996.

Electricity Association (UK). The UK Electricity System. Description available at EA's web-site - http://www.electricity.org.uk/uk_inds/how_work.html, 1997.

Electricity Corporation of New Zealand (ECNZ). ECNZ and the Competitive Market. Information on ECNZ's web-site - http://www.ecnz.co.nz/, 1997.

Electricity Market Company (EMCO) of New Zealand. 1996. Occasional Publication.

Fernando, C. S. and P. R. Kleindorfer, "Integrating Financial and Physical Contracting in Electric Power Markets" in S. Awerbuch and A. Preston (eds), *The Virtual Utility*, Kluwer Academic Publishers, Boston, 1997.

Hogan, W., "Contract Networks for Electric Power Transmission," *J. of Regulatory Economics*, 4(3): 211-242, 1992.

London Economics, Overview of Nordpool. Draft Paper prepared for the Western Power Exchange (WEPEX), February 1, 1997.

Joskow, P. L. "Restructuring, Competition and Regulatory Reform in the U.S. Electricity Sector", *The Journal of Economic Perspectives*, Summer 1997, Volume 11, No. 3. pp. 119-138, and This Volume, Chapter 2.

Kleindorfer, P. R., D-J. Wu and C. S. Fernando, "Strategic Gaming and the Evolving Electric Power Market", Paper presented at the Spring INFORMS Meeting, San Diego, May 4-7, 1997.

Newbery, D. M. "Power Markets and Market Power", *The Energy Journal*, Vol. 16, No. 3, 1995, pp. 39-68.

Norwegian Electricity Federation (EnFO). Description of the Market Structure, Power Generation, Distribution, Consumption and Statistics in Norway. Also available at EnFO's web site http://web.sol.no/enfo/english/energy/, 1997.

Oren, S. S. "Economic Inefficiency of Passive Transmission Rights in Congested Electricity Systems with Competitive Generation", *The Energy Journal*, 18(1): 63-84, 1997.

Pontifica Universidad Catolica de Chile. "Briefings on Argentinian and Chilean Electricity Law." Escuela de Ingenieria, Departmento de Ingenieria Electrica, Santiago, Chile. Information on Electricity in other Latin American countries is also available at PUC's web-site: http://www.ing.puc.cl/~power/, 1997.

Rudnick, H. "Latin American Experience in the Restructuring of Electric Power." Pontificia Universidad Catolica de Chile, Escuela de Ingenieria, Departmento de Ingenieria Electrica, Santiago, Chile. January 1996.

Spalding, B. "The New South Wales Wholesale Electricity Market: A Valuable Experience." Paper presented at the Annual Conference of the Electricity Supply Engineers' Association, Wellington, New Zealand, August 1996.

Williamson, O. E., *The Mechanisms of Governance*, Oxford University Press, New York, 1996.

5 AUTHORITY AND RESPONSIBILITY OF THE ISO: OBJECTIVES, OPTIONS AND TRADEOFFS[1]

Shmuel S. Oren[2]

"The significant problems we face cannot be solved at the same level of thinking we were at when we created them" Albert Einstein

Background

The widespread movement toward deregulation of the electric power industry around the world and in the US is fueled by technological and social changes that led to a fundamental reexamination of conventional wisdom concerning natural monopolies and economies of scale in this industry. The central planning paradigm and vertical integration in that industry rationalized by the conventional wisdom has led to inefficient investment policies and high electricity prices. The primary objective of deregulation in the electric power industry has been to promote long-term efficiency through prudent investment and technical innovation by unleashing competitive forces in the electricity market. While there is little disagreement with regards to this long-term goal, alternative implementation proposals differ radically with respect to the immediate approach and the short-term objectives that must be pursued for achieving the long-term goal. A major area of dispute is the extent of centralized control and "market management" that is needed to assure system reliability and that is desirable from a social efficiency perspective. There is general agreement that the physical characteristics of electricity impose requirements for real time central coordination in order to assure reliable service. It is also agreed upon that decentralized decision making is an important element of competitive markets and as such is a desirable goal in a restructured electricity industry. The dispute center on the "how much" questions, on what is essential and what is optional, on the relationship between short-term and long-term efficiency and on the tradeoffs involved in short-term policy choices. The objective of this paper is to articulate the range of options available, underlying assumption and tradeoffs involved in choosing among the available options and raise questions that need to be addressed in making such choices.

There is general agreement among academics practitioners and policy makers that direct access to the transmission grid is the essential centerpiece for a competitive electricity market. Order 888 and Order 889 of the Federal Regulatory Energy Commission (FERC) reflect the role of direct access as the foundation for the electric power industry restructuring. These orders provide guidelines for nondiscriminatory transmission pricing and mandate timely disclosure of available transmission capacity but do not prescribe a particular approach to the institution of direct access. However, the prevailing restructuring paradigm being adopted in many states in the US has two key features: functional unbundling of generation transmission and distribution and the transfer of control over the transmission system to an Independent System Operator (ISO).

Some basic principles underlying the ISO function are:

- Fair and non-discriminatory governance

- Fair representation of stakeholders

- Financial neutrality with respect to users of the transmission system[3]

- Provide open access and other services under a single tariff

- Ensure short-term reliability of grid operation

- Control regional interconnected transmission facilities

- Relieve constraints

- Enforce trading rules

- Have incentives for efficient management

- Provide guidance for transmission investment

- Promote efficient resource utilization

- Coordinate with neighboring control areas

- Establish dispute resolution protocols.

In order to understand the latitude in defining the authority and responsibilities of the ISO it is useful to classify the potential functions of the ISO into three broad categories.

System security:

- Security, voltage stability through reactive power control

- Dispatch, load following, frequency regulation through AGC control
- Transmission constraints relief

Service quality and operational efficiency:

- Allocate transmission capacity rights and coordinate their use
- Scheduled congestion management
- Ancillary services: reserves, VAR support
- Schedule balancing

Short-term economic efficiency:

- Unit commitment
- Organizing the spot market: running an energy auction, setting locational energy prices, setting transmission charges, setting regulation charges.
- Administering uplift charges: transition charges, transmission access charges, revenue reconciliation payments.
- Supervising transmission contracts and secondary transmission capacity markets.
- Management and compensation of transmission property rights [e.g. Transmission Congestion Contracts (TCCs)]

Flexibility in Defining the Role of the ISO

System security functions have system-wide impact, they must be performed in "real time" which spans a time framework ranging from single cycles to minutes. While technological advances are like to reduce this time span there is general agreement that system security functions must be closely coordinated by the ISO. On the other hand the ISO itself could be distributed among multiple control centers coordinated through protocols and communication facilities. Current operation of the US electricity system proves that indeed system security can be maintained through a network of control centers.

Service quality and operational efficiency functions have system-wide aspects and require central oversight; however, they can be decentralized with proper market incentives and with the ISO playing a coordinating role. For instance, spinning reserves and VAR support requirements can be self-provided by the users to ISO specifications or alternatively purchased from the ISO who could operate an ancillary service market. Likewise, scheduled congestion can be self-managed based on congestion forecasts and power flow sensitivity information provided by the ISO or can be relieved by the ISO who may operate a congestion relief market.

Short-term market efficiency functions can be fully decentralized, with regulatory oversight over market power. Advanced metering communication and electronic markets technology can facilitate decentralization. However, the extent of such decentralization is a policy decision that must be based on realistic assessments of achievable objectives and tradeoffs.

From a technical feasibility perspective it is possible to have an ISO with minimal responsibilities that cover only system security functions with limited oversight of service quality functions, but with no authority or responsibilities with regard to short-term market efficiency. By contrast one could conceive of a fully centralized market structure in which the ISO has full authority and responsibility for the three function categories outlined above. These two extreme visions of the ISO to which we will refer as the MinISO and MaxISO[4] are motivated by opposing views of the "ideal" market structure and the short-term means for achieving the long-term efficiency goal. Thus, in order to evaluate these opposing visions and any hybrids we need to ask two basic questions:

Are the short-term goals, important, necessary and desirable given the long-run objectives?

Are the short-term means implementable and their objectives achievable?

Because of the divergence in motivation and perspective underlying theses two extreme vision of the ISO it is difficult to provide a parallel discussion of the two concepts. Instead we will examine each vision in terms of its own objectives and evaluate separately the objectives themselves in terms of the generally agreed goals of the industry restructuring.

The MinISO

The MinISO paradigm is based on the notion that customer choice and long-term efficiency goals are best served by minimal intervention and the short-term objective of maximal decentralization. The basic motivation underlying this objective stems from the premise that the primary drivers toward long-run efficiency are technological innovation and prudent investment fueled by market forces and direct interaction between buyers and sellers. The vision of a fully decentralized market originates with the ideal of an *infinite-capacity-open-access bus*, which would be an appropriate representation of a system with no transmission constraints. In such a system power transaction could be handled through bilateral and multilateral trades with the ISO functioning as a "traffic cop" whose job is to monitor the state of the system, establish and enforce the "rules of the road" and provide (in a nondiscriminatory fashion) real time information and forecasts that facilitate market transactions and economic efficiency. Such information may also include capacity planning and investment guidelines for generation and transmission. However, the MinISO does have neither the authority nor the responsibility to displace one generator by another for economic reason. Initiating such transactions is left to the market participants.

The MinISO paradigm is based on the notion that customer choice and long-term efficiency goals are best served by minimal intervention and the short-term objective of maximal decentralization.

The MinISO would intervene, physically, only as a last resort when market fails to respond (or such response is not feasible,) in order to mitigate contingencies, rectify supply and demand imbalances or take preventive actions. Such intervention can be based on curtailment protocols or dispatch of emergency resources. The cost of such mitigating actions (with possible penalties) can be recovered from the responsible parties or through some form of transaction insurance paid for by the market participants. Under this open access paradigm, ownership of transmission assets would be compensated as a regulated monopoly whereas transmission access charges, property rights, and any type of settlements will be handled among the market participants as in any other common carrier system (e.g. telecom) subject to antitrust rules. It is the prerogative of the market participants to establish voluntary market institutions such as exchanges or over the counter trading floors that will facilitate trading. However, the MinISO, by definition, would be excluded, from offering such services[5].

When transmission capacity is constrained the infinite capacity open bus paradigm need to be supplemented by institutions that allocate capacity rights and coordinate their use. Whether this function needs to be part of the MinISO is an open question. However, even if the ISO is given that responsibility, the minimal intervention philosophy may still be applied in expanding its role. Capacity constraints in the transmission system result in congestion and hence the responsibilities of the MinISO must include real time congestion management. Economic efficiency not withstanding, congestion management can be achieved by means of rules and protocols. Air traffic control procedures, metering lights on bridge access roads and packet switching protocols are classic examples of congestion management approaches that are not based on economic considerations.

In the context of electricity there have been several proposals outlining congestion management protocols based exclusively on network feasibility (but not economic information). In the Chao and Peck[6] approach, congestion management take the form of trading rules enforced by the ISO which require that energy transaction be "covered" by appropriate transmission capacity permits on the links impacted by the transaction. Varaiya and Wu[7] propose an iterative scheme where the ISO curtails transactions to meet feasibility constraints and provides sensitivity information that guides traders in configuring feasible incremental multilateral transactions. In either case the ISO neither elicits nor uses economic information but provides information to the market participants that can instigate profitable trading which improves economic efficiency within the limits prescribed by the transmission constraints.

The feasibility and desirability of a MinISO approach hinges on several key questions which we will discuss below.

How prevalent is congestion?

Since the objective of the MinISO is not to intervene, its ability to meet this objective is diminished as congestion becomes more prevalent. Frequent congestion amplifies the need for supplemental institutions that will allocate scarce transmission capacity and coordinate their use and also raises the bar for the required precision of the allocation mechanisms.

How efficient is the market in exploiting gains from trade without central intervention?

This is a fundamental question that underlies any competitive market. The motivation of traders to exploit potential trading gains must be taken as an axiom. However, to make this a reality price discovery and access to crucial information in real time by all market participants are essential. Furthermore, the market must have well designed incentives, a built in review mechanism to revise these incentives in case of unforeseen problems and a guaranteed trial period in order to work out early-stage efficiency problems. With proper market design, the competitive advantage that trader would gain from real time information and the potential gains from timely response to such information are likely to fuel developments in communication, real time metering and electronic markets.

What is the magnitude of efficiency losses due to market imperfection?

That is an important issue that might tip the scale against a MinISO. While this issue is seldom raised in other commodity markets, the tradition of public scrutiny through regulatory commissions in the electric power industry are likely to bring to the forefront any evidence of "waste" due to lack of central market coordination. The possibility that such short-run waste might stimulate entry and strengthen long-term competitive forces might be ignored if short-term inefficiency losses prove to be excessive.

How important is short-term operational efficiency for long-term efficiency?

In theory, short-term efficiency is important in the sense of providing correct price signals for investment. However, this relationship is more anecdotal than based on scientific proof and the effect of short-term price signal may be dominated by other factors such as technological change. Entry and product/service design decisions are determined by "total cost and total revenue" whereas output adjustments and other short-term decisions are determined by marginal and unit price. Thus, getting the unit price precisely equal to SRMC may not be the central issue; the central issue may well be providing adequate total compensation for innovation and entry. In the

A major breakthrough in power electronics or in storage of electricity may revolutionize the definition of transmission capacity.

context of electricity a major breakthrough in power electronics or in storage of electricity may revolutionize the definition of transmission capacity. Such a change will overwhelm the effect of fine tuning the locational marginal cost of generation to account for transmission constraints. Experience from the restructuring of other regulated industries such as airlines and telecom suggest that much of the gains have resulted from redefinition of the product to better meet customer needs and from technological innovation and not necessarily from short-term efficiency improvement. For example, duplication of long distance telephone lines by the major phone companies would be hard to justify from a short-term efficiency perspective. It would also be more socially efficient (in the short run), and it would certainly reduce congestion if airlines would pool their customers and share planes while restricting their distinct operation to booking reservations.

How precise do short-term price signals have to be in order to prompt efficient investment?

This is an empirical question worth further research. It is conceivable that the correct "sign" or relative magnitudes of the short-term price signal are sufficient to prompt efficient investment and entry.

How important is customer choice and product diversity?

The ability to exercise free choice in arrangements between buyers and sellers is a key motivation for a MinISO. It is impossible to predict how much choice and product diversity is enough or desirable without providing the opportunity. It is also difficult to measure the value of customer choice since such value would occur on the benefit side of the equation and we tend to measure efficiency gain by focusing on the cost side. Product diversity manifests itself in the financial terms of a contract and in the physical delivery specification. The MinISO will attempt to accommodate any physical delivery specification as long as there is no conflict among transactions. This becomes important for niche markets where there are gains from matching supply and demand characteristics (e.g. wind power generation with battery charging). How important are such transaction and the extent to which physical delivery specification can be met with a standardized commodity needs further investigation. The product diversity accommodated by the MinISO also facilitates and encourages intermediation, whether by established players or new ones, and this can be an effective lubricant to market development and efficiency. The natural gas market discussed in Doane and Spulber[8] is a good example of such development.

The MaxISO

The MaxISO paradigm is based on the notion that resource allocation in a constrained environment is best done in a centralized fashion and on the premise that the primary drivers toward long-term efficiency are short-term operational efficiency and accurate short term price signals which will guide resource utilization and investment. Consequently, this approach is centered on the short-term goal of minimum generation cost. The Vision of a centralized physical market operated by a MaxISO originates with the ideal of a perfectly informed central welfare maximizing authority. With sufficient computational power, such an entity would solve an optimization problem that would determine the optimal generation and load level at each bus, as well as the corresponding shadow prices of each resource constraint and the marginal

> *The MaxISO paradigm is based on the notion that resource allocation in a constrained environment is best done in a centralized fashion.*

cost or benefits at each bus. The role of the MaxISO is to emulate the ideal welfare maximizing authority. So even in the absence of contingencies or congestion, the MaxISO plays an active role in regulating generator output in an attempt to reduce total generation cost or equivalently to equalize marginal costs and benefits at all busses. From this perspective, the primary objective of direct access, functional unbundling, transmission tariffs and ISO protocols are viewed as means for mitigating "obstacles" to the central welfare maximization ideal, such as incentives problems, imperfect information, market power etc.

In order to understand the intended role of the MaxISO it is useful to first review its ideal task of short-run welfare maximization. Current technology used by vertically integrated utilities approximates this task by treating demand as inelastic and performing the optimization into two stages. The first stage is a unit commitment phase that is typically solved on a rolling horizon basis for 168 hourly interval to determine which generation units should be on or off. This problem has roughly the following general structure:

$$\underset{\{State,Output\}}{Minimize} \sum_{Time} \sum_{Resource} [\text{ On/Off cost} + \text{Energy cost}]$$

Subject to:

Demand constraints

Spinning reserves requirements

Intertemporal constraints (e.g. Ramping rate constraints)

Commitment/Availability constraints.

This is a difficult mixed nonlinear-integer optimization problem which simultaneously determines the binary On/off state of each resource in every time period and the corresponding output level of each resource on line. Due to their computational complexity such problems can only be solved approximate by heuristic approaches. Because of their computational difficulty current versions of the unit commitment problem ignore geographical distribution of resources. Current, research grade software for "multi-area unit commitment" is capable, however, to account for geographic distribution of resources and for transmission constraints.

Taking the unit commitment as given an optimal power flow problem is solved in real time to determine the economic dispatch. The general structure of this problem is:

$$\underset{Buses}{Maximize} \sum [\text{Benefit- Energy cost}]$$

Subject to:

Generator limits

Demand constraints

Power flow constraints

Thermal line limits

Voltage line limits

System security constraints

This is a convex nonlinear continuous optimization problem, which is easily solvable for realistic size systems.

The simplest implementation of MaxISO takes the form of a power pool in which the dispatch of generation resources and dispatchable loads is determined by the MaxISO using conventional unit commitment and optimal power flow algorithms. The cost, benefit and operational constraints data needed for such optimization are replaced with corresponding information specified as multipart bids while the social welfare maximization objective is replaced with the surrogate objective of maximizing gains from trade. The marginal energy prices at the various buses corresponding to the optimal power flow define "locational" market clearing prices for energy. These prices are used by the MaxISO to compute the energy component of the settlement with suppliers and buyers at each node (settlement may include other components such as capacity payments, transition charges etc.). The locational prices also provide a consistent framework for accommodating bilateral transactions among non-pool participants and for defining and compensating transmission rights[9]. According to this paradigm, the price for transmission of a MW from bus A to B is defined as the opportunity cost of selling a MW at bus A and buying it back at bus B at the corresponding locational pool prices. This approach effectively assimilates all nonpool transactions into the pool by making a bilateral transaction from A to B equivalent to bidding the supply schedule into the pool at bus A with price zero (to guarantee dispatch) and withdrawing the corresponding amounts at bus B. This equivalence requires, of course, that a bilateral transaction can be fit or decomposed into the standardized commodity molds allowed by the pool. Then, any financial arrangement among the trading parties can be emulated by a combination of settlements with the MaxISO and a contract for differences stipulating side payments relative to the locational pool prices.

Point to point transmission rights are defined in this framework in terms of transmission congestion contracts (TCC), which entitle (or obligate) the right holder to receive (or pay) the locational price difference between the two points. This arrangement again assimilates physical transmission rights into the pool by making the physical exercise of such a right for a bilateral transaction from bus A to bus B equivalent to trading with the pool at the respective locational pool prices and settling the TCC financially. The MaxISO has the authority to issue TCCs, distribute them to owners of physical transmission assets or historical rights and auction them off on behalf of their owners. The MaxISO is also responsible for the ex-post financial settlements with the TCC holders.

The ability of the MaxISO to emulate the short-term central welfare maximization goal hinges on a number of approximations and behavioral assumptions. Furthermore, the centralization of the market making authority under the MaxISO places some restrictions and imposes some standardization on physical transactions. How sensitive is the MaxISO performance to the various approximations and assumptions and how significant are the restrictions imposed by a centralized "visible hand" approach? We focus on these question by examining the ideal conditions that would enable the MaxISO to meet its short-term goals.

Suppliers provide truthful cost and constraints bids.

Market power and strategic behavior by bidders is a reality of the electric power industry. Even the most optimistic predictions acknowledge that market power might be reduced but not eliminated. Furthermore, congestion effects, environmental constraints on new generation and locational market power due to reliability considerations provide ample opportunity for strategic behavior by generators. The repetitive nature of electric power auctions also facilitates tacit collusion. All these factors make it unrealistic to expect that generators will bid their marginal cost. The problem gets compounded with multipart auctions in which bidders also specify operational constraints, on/off switching costs and available capacity. Empirical evidence suggests that such auctions can be "gamed" and the theory of multidimensional auctions is not sufficiently developed to provide guidance on how to prevent such gaming[10]. In view of these considerations we need to ask to what extent does the strategic bidding compromise the short-term efficiency objective. Is pursuing central optimal dispatch with distorted cost information still serving a meaningful purpose given that one could hope for a second or third best outcome. While there have been several studies examining the potential for strategic bidding, little attention has been paid to the robustness of central dispatch in the presence of such bid distortion.

*MaxISO can solve and implement optimal unit commitment
and optimal power flow.*

Setting aside the issue of imperfect information the next issue to be considered is the implementability of central optimal unit commitment in a decentralized ownership environment. Simulation experiments[11] indicate that due to nonconvexities, the unit commitment problem may have multiple solutions which have virtually the same cost but which dictate different dispatch schedules. From the perspective of welfare maximization such a phenomenon is of no importance. However, in a system with competitive generation different schedules often imply that some suppliers will have their units turned on and make a profit while other will be turned off. The different solutions may also be supported by different prices, which affect the distribution of social welfare between buyers and sellers. What we are facing here is an equity problem, which can not be solved on the basis of short-term efficiency considerations. One could argue that some sort of random draw among the dispatch schedules tied for the same cost could resolve this problem. Unfortunately, it is not practical to search for all such solutions. In the simulation experiments cited above the switch from one solution to another was triggered by very subtle changes in the search method. Thus any particular implementation of a unit commitment algorithm may be systematically biased in favor of some market participants. The phenomenon discussed above is just one of several adverse outcomes resulting from the nonconvexities and intertemporal dependencies characterizing the production cost function for electricity. How important are such complications in the big picture is an open question whose answer might have strong implication regarding the legitimacy of the MaxISO as an impartial institution.

Performance criteria for ISO provide incentives for its efficient
and impartial operation.

Financial neutrality is not a guarantee for efficient operation. Unlike the MinISO whose success could be gauged by how little it does, The MaxISO has extensive and complex responsibilities. Regulating or auditing the MaxISO would be much more complicated than regulating a vertically integrated utility in terms of the information and technical expertise needed for such oversight. Many of the inputs to the unit commitment optimization and to the optimal power flow calculation, particularly inputs associated with system security, are highly subjective. Hence a financially neutral MaxISO might have strong incentives to sacrifice efficiency for excessive security. A bias in favor of security might favor some market participants at the expense of others. We need to question the validity of financial neutrality as the foundation for the ISO incentives to meet its efficiency goals and examine alternative governance approaches.

All desired transactions can be decomposed into or assembled
from standard commodities (e.g. time specific energy blocks)
without efficiency loss.

Standardization of the commodity is inevitable in a centralized market. It has been argued that such standardization doesn't affect customer choice, which can be accommodated through a combination of transactions with the pool and bilateral financial contracts. This argument hinges on the premise that any physical transaction can be decomposed into or assembled from the standardized pool commodity (e.g. time specific blocks of energy). Even if a transaction does not fit into the rigid framework of scheduled pool transactions it can be accommodated as an imbalance. One question that comes to mind is whether such a "melting pot" treatment of nonconforming transactions comes at some efficiency loss. One suspects that in view of the nonconvexities and intertemporal dependencies in the production and consumption of electricity commoditization is not free. The more important question from a long-term efficiency perspective is whether standardization of the commodity inhibits innovation in services and technology. The desirability of standardization and the tradeoff between the short-run efficiency goal vs. the open bus goal hinges on the impact of commodity standardization inherent in the MaxISO paradigm.

Issues and Remedies

Some of the issues and questions raised above have prompted various hybrid proposals that offer compromises between the two extreme ISO visions outlined above. We will discuss these options within the context of the specific issues they address.

*Price based congestion management without economic
dispatch*

This is an amendment to the MinISO design, which is intended to provide an economic rational for real time congestion management when such intervention is called for. Variants of this approach are used in the Norwegian system and in the California ISO design. The basic concept is to create a market for congestion relief while minimizing centralized intrusion into the workings of a free energy market. For that purpose a unit of congestion relief service between two busses can be defined as a unit of counter-flow between the buses. Such counter-flow can be supplied by injecting and withdrawing power at the respective buses in the direction opposite to the congestion or by reducing the injection and withdrawals at the corresponding busses in the congested direction. The MinISO can solicit bids for such congestion relief service from market participants engaged in bilateral transactions and use this information to relieve congestion at least cost. Alternatively, the MinISO may solicit bus specific bids for incremental changes to the scheduled transaction and use those bids to relieve congestion at minimum cost. The distinction between congestion relief and energy trading is maintained by constraining the incremental changes to be balanced within each balanced schedule (i.e. the schedule should remain balanced with injections equal withdrawals plus losses). This approach guarantees efficient congestion relief in the sense that the marginal cost of congestion relief is equalized across all the perturbed transactions. The objective of minimal intervention by the MinISO dictates that the MinISO will not engage in generation displacement beyond what is needed for congestion relief. Such additional efficiency motivated transactions are left to the market. The MinISO could facilitate such transaction by publicizing the bids for congestion relief, which will reveal to the market participants' profitable trading opportunities.

Self-commitment and energy only auctions

The problems with obtaining truthful information for central unit commitment and the difficulty of achieving an equitable implementation of an optimal unit commitment can be addressed by relieving the MaxISO (or a mandatory Power exchange authority) of the unit commitment responsibility. The basic idea here is to have an "energy only" auction leaving it up to the bidders to make their own scheduling decisions. In this scheme it is up to the generators to pick a schedule and energy bids so that their operational constraints are met and the energy revenues covers all the costs (including startup, ramping, no load and capital costs). While this may sound as a revolutionary concept for the electric power this is the reality in any other industry. It is always the producers' responsibility to decide how to schedule operations and utilize its resources and then recover its costs and profits by selling its product (in our case energy). The tomato grower does not charge separately for maintaining the land, watering and harvesting.

In the long run one may expect that generators will learn how to schedule and price their energy offers so as to be profitable. To the extent that such self-dispatch becomes two risky we may expect to witness mergers that will enable generators to bid as one entity and diversify their dispatch risk. Properly designed auctions could also simplify generators' task (under self-commitment) of internalizing in their energy bids the effects of nonconvexities and intertemporal dependencies in production costs. One approach is to define the tenders and auction rules so as to match the bid structure to the cost structure and thus eliminate the nonconvexities. A discriminatory auction in which the tenders are units of capacity committed to a posted schedule would enable generators to collapse their offers into a single price, which accounts for all the fixed costs and state transition costs associated with the schedule.

An alternative approach adopted by the California Power Exchange is a simultaneous multi-round auction for a block of time intervals (e.g. 24 hourly intervals) where the tenders are quantities of energy offered in each time interval and corresponding energy prices. All successful tenders in each time interval are paid the market-clearing price. The multiple rounds allows the bidders to internalize the fixed and On/Off costs into their energy bids and adjust their bids so that their schedule meets their operational constraints. A set of activity rules forces early price discovery and speedy convergence.

The complexity of the auction design accompanying the self-commitment concept is justified if we believe that nonconvexities and intertemporal dependencies in generation cost play an important role and their effect on the auction results cannot be adequately predicted by the generators. One could argue that the repetitive nature of power auctions would enable generator to anticipate their winning dispatch schedule and therefore a single round of energy only bids should suffice[12]. An empirical study comparing alternative ISO design could shed light on this issue.

Regulating the ISO

While there is agreement that the ISO should operate in an efficient and impartial way little attention has been given to the design of governance procedures and incentives that will assure its efficiency and impartiality. A complete treatment of this topic is beyond the scope of this article. Paul Kleindorfer[13] provides an excellent discussion and further references on this subject highlighting the implications of possible alternatives ownership and control relationships between the ISO and the transmission assets providers. The discussion below is limited to the control functions of the ISO and the quality assurance of these functions. The principle of financial neutrality that is taken for granted as a fundamental principle of the ISO does not guarantee neither its impartiality nor its efficiency. Even if the incentive is not monetary, any performance measure or reward structure not properly conceived could result in adverse behavior. For instance, a financially neutral ISO that is held responsible for system reliability would tend to operate the system in an overly conservative fashion. In California the governing board of the ISO is a conglomerate of stakeholders which are supposed to insure impartiality. However, this arrangement has been criticized for giving a say to market participant that will benefit from the inefficiency of the ISO. Then who should regulate and oversee the ISO, perhaps FERC? This might raise jurisdiction conflicts with the states. It is inevitable that an oversight mechanism for the ISO will be at a cost and it will incur an efficiency loss. Any quality control procedure is costly and when a product is perfect its inspection may be perceived as a waste. Unfortunately, that is the only way one can find out that the product is perfect. Likewise, a governance mechanism designed to regulate the MaxISO may be perceived as wasteful to one who equates the MaxISO to its ideal- the social welfare maximizer. The mechanisms described below fall into this general category. The research questions in this area should focus on the tradeoff between the efficacy of the governance mechanism and the efficiency loss. Consideration should also be given to the impact of alternative governance approaches on long-term efficiency.

Separation of authority and competitive market making

This approach which has been adopted in California separates the power exchange from the ISO with an arms length arrangement that levels the playing field for system coordinators to compete with the power exchange. This arrangement puts the ISO in a position of supplying information to the power exchange and the system coordinators that would allow them to self-manage congestion, self-provide their ancillary services and identify profitable trading opportunities. In principle the power exchange could be a voluntary organization and there is no reason why there should only be one exchange. Competition among the exchanges and system coordinators subject to antitrust rules takes care of the governance issue with regard to the market making functions.

The question that has been raised is why should the ISO be prohibited from providing economic dispatch services to willing customers. Clearly such a constraint is costly in terms of short-term efficiency. It is conceivable that in real time some trading opportunities go to waste because the market participants cannot respond in a timely fashion. The response to that question is that permitting the ISO to offer economic dispatch could create a conflict of interest with its responsibility to provide timely and unbiased information to market participants who would essentially compete with the economic dispatch function of the ISO. Such a conflict may arise when managing congestion. The main dilemma for the ISO in such a situation would be how to integrate and prioritize quantity transactions submitted by independent marketers along with price-based transaction requesting economic dispatch from the ISO. Using the zero bid approach for quantity transactions amounts to a PoolCo model, which deprives the marketers of the opportunity to mitigate their congestion charges by self-managing congestion. Furthermore if the ISO is engaged in economic dispatch any sensitivity information that could guide the marketers in identifying opportunities for profitable arbitrage and self-management of congestion would be used internally before the marketers had a chance to act on such information. While it might be possible to design protocols that could address the issues associated with merging quantity and price transactions in an equitable fashion, separating the voluntary pool from the ISO is an expedient governance approach that will avoid actual, potential or the perception of conflict of interest. Ideally, decentralized trading among market participants guided by information provided by the ISO will approximate the economic dispatch equilibrium so the efficiency loss due to such separation are likely to be small. Nevertheless the costs and benefits of such an approach need be carefully assessed. Since California and the eastern power pools have taken opposite sides on the issue of separating the ISO from the power exchange, a downstream assessment of these systems could illuminate this issue.

Franchising the ISO

An alternative approach to ISO regulation is to create a for-profit entity[14] which accepts schedules from market participants and offers insurance against deviation from schedules due to real time contingencies, imbalances and congestion. Under such an arrangement the ISO is self-regulated since it would have financial incentives to be efficient in its congestion management, contingency handling and reconciliation of imbalances. The ability of the market participants to self-provide such services and avoid imbalance by more accurate scheduling (aided by improvement in metering and communication technology) places natural boundaries on the ISO market power.

Conclusion

The physical characteristics of electric power systems require central coordination of real time security related functions. However, even with current technology it is feasible to decentralize the market-related activities in the electricity system and to minimize the need for ISO intervention in the competitive electricity market. The work by Chao and Peck, cited above, demonstrated the feasibility of defining property rights and ISO protocols that can induce operational efficiency in a decentralized market structure with an ISO whose role is limited to enforcing trading rules and provision of information to the market participants. Advances in metering, communication and electronic market technologies will further improve the operational efficiency of decentralized electricity markets.

How much market authority should be given to the ISO and the extent to which a competitive electricity market should be centralized are policy decisions and not unambiguous consequences of technical realities. The desirability of a centralized or decentralized short-term electricity market depends on fundamental tradeoffs that are not well understood and on philosophical views concerning the ideal market structure. There is a need for thorough examination of the feasible options and better understanding of the tradeoffs. In particular it would be useful to explore alternative technological and economic scenarios projecting the evolution of the electricity market under alternative market organization option.

Notes

1. The material contained in this chapter is based largely on collaboration and discussions with Pravin Varaiya, Felix Wu and Pablo Spiller. The concepts of MinISO and MaxISO were described by Varyia and Wu "MinIso: A Minimal Independent System Operator", Proceeding of the 30th Hawaii International Conference on System Sciences, Vol. V, pp. 602-607 (January, 1997). These ideas were also discussed in a workshop organized by the Power System Research Center (Pserc) and EPRI at the University of Arizona, (March, 1996). A workshop summary is described by Robert Thomas and Thomas Schneider "Underlying Technical Issues in Electrical Deregulation" Proceeding of the 30th Hawaii International Conference on System Sciences, Vol. V, pp. 561-570, (January, 1997). See also the article by FernandoAlvarado, Robert Camfield and Rajesh Rajaraman, "Open Transmission Access: An Efficient Minimal Role for the ISO", Proceeding of the 30th Hawaii International Conference on System Sciences, Vol. V, pp. 571-580 (January, 1997).
2. Department of Industrial Engineering and Operations Research, University of California at Berkeley.

3. Under current proposals the ISO is envisioned as a nonprofit entity with no physical assets. However, as will be discussed later, the ISO could function as a franchised or regulated transmission monopoly with or without ownership of transmission assets.

4. This categorization provides a useful frame of reference and is not intended to prejudice the discussion or to represent particular implementations or proposals under consideration although the MaxISO paradigm contains many elements of the Poolco model.

5. The question of whether the ISO should be allowed to engage in providing trading services will be raised when we discuss issues of governance and conflicts of interest.

6. Hung-po Chao and Steven Peck, "A Market Mechanism for Electric Power Transmission",*Journal of Regulatory Economics*, Vol. 10 (July 1996).

7. Felix Wu and Pravin Varaiya, "Coordinated Multilateral Trades for Electric Power Networks: Theory and Implementation," POWER Report PWP-031, University of California Energy Institute, June 1995

8. Doane M. J.and D. F. Spulber, "Evolution of the U.S. Spot Market for Natural Gas,"*J. Of Law and Economics*, Vol. XXXVII No. 2, (1994).

9. These ideas are due to William W. Hogan, "Contract Networks for Electric Power Transmission," *Journal of Regulatory Economics*, Vol. 4, (1992) pp. 211-242.

10. Of course market power and pricing above marginal cost can exist under a MinISO as well. However, as indicated earlier the later approach is more conducive to the emergence of arbitrageurs and intermediaries who will actively engage in the discovery and exploitation of market inefficiencies and in the process will improve system efficiency.

11. Raymond B. Johnson, Shmuel S. Oren and Alva J. Svoboda, "Equity and Efficiency of Unit Commitment in Competitive Electricity Markets," *Utilities Policy*, Vol. 6, No 1, (1997) pp. 9-19.

12. The Victoria Pool in Australia employs a single round energy only auction.

13. Paul R. Kleindorfer, Chapter 4, This Volume.

14. Hung-po Chao and Steven Peck, "An Institutional Design for an Electricity Contract Market with Central Dispatch", *The Energy Journal*, Vol. 18, No. 1 , (1997) pp. 85-110.

References

Alvarado, Fernando, Robert Camfield and Rajesh Rajaraman, "Open Transmission Access: An Efficient Minimal Role for the ISO", Proceeding of the 30th Hawaii International Conference on System Sciences, Vol. V, pp. 571-580 (January, 1997).

Chao, Hung-po and Steven Peck, "A Market Mechanism for Electric Power Transmission", *Journal of Regulatory Economics,* Vol. 10 (July 1996).

Chao, Hung-po and Steven Peck, "An Institutional Design for an Electricity Contract Market with Central Dispatch", *The Energy Journal*, Vol. 18, No. 1 , (1997) pp. 85-110 and This Volume.

Doane M. J.and D. F. Spulber, "Evolution of the U.S. Spot Market for Natural Gas," *J. Of Law and Economics*, Vol. XXXVII No. 2, (1994).

William W. Hogan, "Contract Networks for Electric Power Transmission," *Journal of Regulatory Economics*, Vol. 4, (1992) pp. 211-242.

Johnson, Raymond B., Shmuel S. Oren and Alva J. Svoboda, "Equity and Efficiency of Unit Commitment in Competitive Electricity Markets," *Utilities Policy*, Vol. 6, No 1, (1997) pp. 9-19.

Paul R. Kleindorfer, Chapter 4, This Volume.

Thomas, Robert and Thomas Schneider "Underlying Technical Issues in Electrical Deregulation" Proceeding of the 30th Hawaii International Conference on System Sciences, Vol. V, pp. 561-570, (January, 1997).

Varaiya, Pravin and Felix Wu "MinIso: A Minimal Independent System Operator", Proceeding of the 30th Hawaii International Conference on System Sciences, Vol. V, pp. 602-607 (January, 1997).

Wu, Felix and Pravin Varaiya, "Coordinated Multilateral Trades for Electric Power Networks: Theory and Implementation," POWER Report PWP-031, University of California Energy Institute, June 1995.

6 PRICING ISSUES

Robert Wilson

Introduction

This chapter elaborates three pricing issues that arise in decentralized markets for power. One concerns the design of pricing rules for ancillary services to promote an efficient allocation of resources between primary energy markets and reservations of capacity for ancillary services. A second, the role of allocation rules for assigning transmission charges. And a third, the design of bid formats for energy markets that allow recognition of the start-up costs incurred by thermal generators.

All three stem basically from decentralization, including "self-scheduling" of capacity in the first and third, and "self-management" of transmission congestion in the second. The first two are peculiar to the sequencing of markets. In the California restructuring, for instance, the day-ahead markets for energy, transmission, and ancillary services operate in sequence, and this is repeated on an hour-ahead basis. The efficiency of these markets depends on traders' accurate prediction of prices in subsequent markets, and on measures to ensure that commitments made in earlier markets do not impair the contestability of later markets.

Selection and Pricing of Ancillary Services

> All three (issues) stem basically from decentralization, including "self-scheduling" of capacity in the first and third, and "self-management" of transmission congestion in the second.

Ancillary services include various generation resources in the form of quickly dispatchable generation capacity, and some curtailable loads, reserved by the system operator (SO) to meet real-time contingencies. A typical example is spinning reserve, which is capacity that can be ramped quickly to meet a surge in demand or to cover a loss of generation or transmission capacity. Others are non-spinning reserve and replacement reserve, each with corresponding minimal ramping rates and required durations of sustained production, as well as AGC, VAR, and black-start reserves. The ancillary services comprise a cascade of resources that can be invoked to meet load and stability requirements. This cascade can be interpreted as providing successive caps on the real-time price. Decentralized markets also require negative spinning reserve, in the sense of curtailable generation, to bound the price below, but this consideration will be ignored here.

On the supply side, ancillary services are priced in two parts: one part is a capacity reservation fee paid in advance, and the second is a price paid for ordered energy generation. Offers of capacity reservations are accepted according to one merit order up to a level specified by the SO to maintain security; and similarly energy generation is ordered as needed based on a second merit order. Two aspects need not be addressed in detail here: one is the design of auction markets to select resources, and the second is the construction of an overall merit order that takes account of the features unique to each service; e.g., spinning reserve that is used incurs the cost of replacements to maintain the required reserve margin, and automatic generation controlled (AGC) units are usually required to return to their set points periodically so their net energy variation is nearly nil.

The aspect addressed here is the proper formulation of the SO's objective in selecting and using ancillary services. A key feature of decentralized designs is some separation between the SO and the energy markets. That is, the SO's role is confined to management of the transmission system and maintenance of system security, typically on a short time frame measured in minutes and hours. Separate forward markets for trading energy establish the main allocation of supplies to demands on longer time frames, such as day-ahead or hour-ahead transactions. This functional separation creates a problem peculiar to ancillary services.

For suppliers who are infra-marginal in the energy markets, reserving capacity for an ancillary service such as spin substitutes for energy sales that could be made at the market price. Consequently, when the SO acquires capacity reservations from these infra-marginal suppliers, they are replaced in the energy market by other suppliers who would otherwise be extra-marginal, which raises the energy price. But it is precisely these infra-marginal energy suppliers who can provide incremental energy at least cost when ordered by the SO. This poses the problem:

the SO cannot minimize its cost without raising the energy price. This shows that in the case of ancillary services there is an inherent conflict between the objectives of cost minimization by the SO and allocating resources efficiently for the system as a whole.

One way to resolve this conflict is to impose a priority pricing scheme for the selection of capacity reservations and incremental generation. In such a scheme, the merit order for resource selection is based on the suppliers' offered prices for capacity reservations, and similarly the merit order for energy generation is based on the reserve prices for energy offered by those suppliers whose capacity reservations have been accepted. (Prior screening of offered capacity reservations is required for full efficiency: this excludes an offer, taking account of both the capacity and energy bid, that is not least-cost for any duration of called generation.) The key feature that makes this work is that settlements for delivered energy are based solely on the real-time price, not the supplier's lower reserve price. If markets for ancillary services are fully competitive then this scheme allocates resources efficiently; in particular, it encourages a supplier to offer its marginal generation cost as its reserve price. Maintaining competitiveness requires interventions by the SO; e.g., it must reserve enough spinning and replacement capacity to ensure that there is no gap between their merit orders for generation, since otherwise suppliers of spin can raise their reserve prices to exploit this gap.

Priority pricing is only one way, however, and other approaches have not been thoroughly studied. The flaw in this approach is evident from the fact that the two separate merit orders are *imposed* on the SO to promote efficiency. On the other hand, under most organizational designs the dominant incentive of the SO will remain to minimize its own cost of the ancillary services it acquires – implying that it wants to take some account of the energy cost associated with a capacity bid. Over the long run it will be difficult to force the SO to undertake actions that are costly for itself but benefit demanders in the energy markets. This problem is indicative of the more general problem of designing an organizational structure for the SO that provides incentives to pursue policies that promote efficiency of the overall system.

The general form of the problem spans other concerns. For instance, one is whether the SO's security standards are too loose or too tight, taking account of both the costs of managing the transmission system and the effects on suppliers and demanders in the energy markets. The initial study of the general problem is by Chao and Peck (1997). They show that one means of providing the correct incentives is for the SO to be operated as a franchise that, as part of its contract, is liable for costs imposed on traders through its actions. In effect, traders pay for insurance against interference in their energy transactions, and as insurer the SO is liable for compensatory payments. This is one way to internalize in the SO the full benefits and costs of its actions in the overall system. Further studies are needed to elaborate the range of organizational designs that can eliminate conflicts between the incentives of the SO and the objective of overall efficiency.

Allocation of Transmission Charges

The basic theory of transmission pricing is based on a price for energy and prices for directional links that are converted into bundled prices at nodes (or zones) using the pattern of power flows. In this view, energy prices are quoted as delivered prices at some particular node chosen as a reference point. For any pair of injection and extraction nodes, the difference (possibly negative) between the nodal prices represents the transmission charge, which can be interpreted as the cost of transporting energy from the injection node to the reference node, and then from there to the extraction node.

When energy markets are separated from transmission markets, this scheme can be interpreted as an allocation rule for assigning transmission charges to traders. If the reference zone is an import zone then in an export zone each supplier is charged the cost of transmission to the import zone, and each demander is subsidized by the transmission charge to the import zone. This is just one of many allocation rules that have the requisite properties that (1) transmission charges are fully covered by the assignments, and (2) each trader's marginal incentives for efficient energy trading are preserved. It is (2) that requires that every charge imposed on a supplier is matched by a subsidy to a demander in the same zone.

In practice the allocation rule should be designed to meet additional criteria. A simple scheme uses as a reference zone a fictitious one constructed so that the resulting energy price is the average of the delivered prices among all zones – but one can imagine other criteria. One way or another it is of some importance to fix the allocation rule so that the resulting energy price has an explicit interpretation that facilitates its use for other transactions, such as QF contracts.

There is a deeper problem of economic substance. If only nodal or zonal prices are used then all transmission charges are bundled into energy prices. This leaves no well-defined energy price. Indeed, the pure energy price can be whatever the traders think it is. This is harmless if they share the same interpretation, but if different traders assign different interpretations then an inefficient allocation can result. This is the basic problem that arises in markets dependent on "rational expectations," which is inherent in all designs relying on a sequence of markets. If all traders know, expect, or predict correctly the subsequent interzonal transmission charges but interpret observed prices in pure energy markets differently, then some gains from trade can be missed. This problem is obviated by simultaneous markets for energy and transmission, but it is fundamental in other designs in which the energy and transmission markets occur sequentially. When the markets are sequenced, at the very least the imputed price for pure energy should be specified in a way that facilitates accurate prediction of congestion charges. Using a reference zone, such as a zone that is typically an importer or an exporter, need not be optimal for enhancing the predictability of congestion charges, since it does not take account of the intrinsic negative correlation between the zonal prices in import and export zones, whereas a zone defined as a fictitious average delivered price does.

There are several additional complications. One arises when an energy market is organized solely to obtain market clearing, as in California's power exchange (PX).

The PX cannot trade for its own account or take a net position, and therefore it cannot participate effectively in trading adjustment bids (or transmission reservations in other designs) with other market makers in the transmission market. Because of this restriction, its energy traders are likely to submit their adjustment bids into other markets, leaving the PX as simply a price-taker with respect to transmission charges. Absent this restriction, a second problem appears. If the PX or any other energy market self-manages congestion then for efficiency it will do this by imposing zonal prices, with the result that it will collect a substantial surplus of revenue that would otherwise have gone to the owners of transmission assets or TCCs. But this raises anew the allocation problem, because if the surplus is refunded pro rata then the incentive effects of zonal prices are impaired by traders' anticipation of refunds.

Load-Slice and Load-Profile Pricing

A pervasive feature of energy markets is that a substantial proportion of demand is expressed on a time-of-day basis but supply is based on load-duration. The latter reflects mainly the requirement of thermal generators that in order to economize on start-up costs (and meet technical requirements for ramping up and down, and warming up and down) they must schedule operations over a sequence of consecutive hours. Moreover, they have no particular preference about the start and stop times themselves, caring only about the duration of the operating run. This difference creates difficult problems in organizing markets; e.g., if the energy markets are specified by time-of-day then suppliers face inherent problems identifying the optimal start and stop times for their thermal generators. In the California design this problem is eased by conducting the day-ahead energy market iteratively so that suppliers can develop reasonable expectations about the pattern of prices over the hours of the next day.

An alternative proposed by Elmaghrabi and Oren (1997) allows the demand and supply sides of the market to use different bid formats. (Actually, each trader can participate on either side: a hydro supplier can bid a negative demand, and a demander with a load-duration requirement can bid a negative supply.) The key to making this design work is to recognize that there are standard formulas for translating any pattern of time-of-day prices into load-duration prices (the price for a MW of power delivered for some specific number of consecutive hours, starting from a particular time), and vice versa. In effect, load-duration prices are bundled time-of-day prices, and vice versa, and each provides sufficient information to unbundle the underlying prices of the other type.

This proposal indicates that there are opportunities for designing energy markets to take account of the differing technical characteristics of the traders. No complete design has been worked out, but it seems clear that the Oren proposal has a substantial chance of being viable, with much reduced incentive problems (mostly because iterations can be dispensed with) and potentially greater efficiency (because the start-up costs of generators are fully accounted for by the bid format).

These considerations are also relevant to the design of retail pricing. There is a long-standing presumption in the U.S. that efficiency depends ultimately on real-time pricing, in which customers pay the spot price over each short interval. This presumption is wrong in theory, in practice, and in the prevalence of retail pricing based on load-profiles. In theory, a Wright tariff that assigns charges based on the duration that each increment of load is used is equivalent to spot pricing. It also reflects more accurately the long-term cost structure of generation and it simplifies metering. In practice, Wright tariffs have been very effective in France, where EDF's tariffs are based on duration-dependent charges per kW. The net effect is to charge each customer for its actual load-duration profile – not its predicted profile, as often assumed by those who criticize load-profile pricing. It may be that the development of retail markets will encourage the use of Wright tariffs in the U.S., but in any case it seems desirable to examine this and other forms of retail pricing that can provide better signals to customers about the long-term costs their demands impose. It remains unclear how to integrate the effects of these retail pricing schemes into the design of wholesale markets. If the wholesale markets are short term forward markets (rather than long term contract markets) then power marketers cannot realize the advantages of Wright tariffs unless they are prepared to assume substantial financial risks purchasing power daily to meet demand loads that are priced to establish long-term incentives for efficiency. Because short-term forward markets place risks on demanders, the solution must lie in developing markets for financial instruments that hedge against price risks.

Conclusion

The three issues addressed in this chapter indicate that the decentralized markets introduced in restructuring the power industry bring new problems of optimal pricing. The long history of regulation based on vertically integrated monopolies left these problems unexamined. They were not anticipated because few expected that restructuring would result in a sequence of separate forward markets for energy, transmission, and ancillary services. Based on the UK model, the prevailing presumption in the U.S. was that a single integrated market for all these components would be adopted, and little account was taken of the quite different market structures developed elsewhere, such as Scandinavia and Australia, that have become models for restructuring in California and perhaps in some other states later. The fundamental pricing problem is to ensure the overall efficiency of this sequence of separate markets.

The problems of coordinating a sequence of markets seem fundamental. As implementation of restructuring proceeds it becomes increasingly clear that the technology of electricity makes it advantageous to use a hybrid market structure. Corresponding to the long-term, short-term, and real-time perspectives, the market allows bilateral contracting, day-ahead trading in a power exchange, and spot markets for system balancing and load following. Melding these temporally differentiated markets for energy together with similarly differentiated markets for transmission and ancillary services yields inevitably a sequence of markets in which the key to efficiency is tight linkage among the several components.

References

Chao, Hung-po and Stephen Peck, "An Institutional Design for an Electricity Contract Market with Central Dispatch," *Energy Journal*, Vol. 18, No. 1, January 1997, and This Volume, Chapter 12.

Elmaghrabi, Wedad and Shmuel S. Oren, "Efficiency of Multi-Unit Electricity Auctions," *Proceedings of the IAEE Conference*, San Francisco, California, (September 1997) pp. 458-462.

7 DEREGULATING ELECTRIC POWER: MARKET DESIGN ISSUES AND EXPERIMENTS

Stephen J. Rassenti and Vernon L. Smith

Part I. Key Issues in Mechanism Design

In this section we will articulate our view as to what are the key issues in the design, behavior and performance of deregulated competitive electricity markets. These issues arise from two prominent distinguishing characteristics of electricity markets: Energy is injected and withdrawn for consumption at various nodes of a network with limited ability to control the energy flows; coordination is necessary to achieve balance, reliability and frequency control. The nonstorability of electricity, often listed as a distinguishing characteristic, is neither unique nor critical, as all transportation and accommodation (hotel/motel) industries have this property, and where they are competitive engage in time of use pricing without having to be ordered to do so by a regulatory commission. This is because peaking capital requirements will not be supplied without an incentive return, and competition responds to all relevant margins of cost in space and time.

The essential design considerations as we see them are the following: (1) coordinated dispatch based on decentralized generators and buyers; (2) bilateral contracting via financial futures markets to hedge spot market volatility; (3)

defining divisible rights to indivisible facilities; (4) pricing and property rights in the transmission network; (5) competition in local distribution.

Coordination dispatch based on decentralized generators and buyers

Electric power systems the world over, whether regulated or government owned, have been based on central coordination and control using economic dispatch algorithms. Beginning with the discovery of the marginal cost load balancing rule by engineers in the 1920s, and its extension in the 1930s to include transmission line losses, economic dispatch technology has become increasingly sophisticated. (Funk and Ralston, 1923; Steinberg and Smith, 1943). More recently innovation has impacted automatic generator and load control, metering, and more flexible voltage, reactive power metering and wave form control. Much of this technology, though available, is not widely installed although it can be expected that, assuming an appropriate market design, the altered incentive environment created by deregulation is likely to accelerate its implementation.

Historically, in vertically integrated power systems whether regulated or government owned, central economic dispatch allowed short-run cost minimization to be effected in response to the pattern of demand and changes in this pattern. Political considerations biased system investment toward supply side adjustments to avoid "losing lights." Hence, demand was inelastic by institutional design because little or no provision was made for price-based voluntary interruption of demand where buyers were able and willing to reduce demand contingent on price increases. Reliability and reserves were treated exclusively as supply side problems under inflexible must-serve demand requirements. This situation was inevitable given the politicized incentives of American style regulation and foreign government ownership organizations. Albiet with low probability, this system sometimes failed, and every local utility company has a priority system for shedding load involuntarily in the event of emergency, with hospitals, street lights, public parking areas, etc. having the highest priority for continued service.

With deregulation, it is natural to think in terms of a spot market in which economic dispatch remains in place except that instead of centrally provided generator costs based on fuel prices and heat rates, we substitute location specific generator willingness-to-accept (WTA) offer (supply) schedules submitted by decentralized generator owners. These WTA schedules need not, nor should they, correspond to generator marginal cost schedules. Thus, it may pay the owner of a baseload unit to run it at outputs below marginal cost at night time spot prices to avoid shut down and restart costs. A well-designed spot market will also require bulk buyers to forecast their own demand, and submit location specific willingness-to-pay (WTP) bid schedules. The "must-run" portion of any demand is bid "at market," paying whatever uniform price clears the market at each node adjusted for marginal transmission losses. Errors in forecasting demand, as we see it, should be subject to penalties as a means of incentivizing the demand side, modifying the policy that the cost of contingencies in demand must be absorbed exclusively by the supply side. This design specification provides buyers with an incentive to explore interruptible demand technologies to increase control over demand. This in turn sets the technological stage for increased demand side bidding with step functions indicating the schedule of prices above which buyers are prepared to interrupt corresponding quantities of demand. Those willing to interrupt demand at higher prices would be freed from the need to pay for spinning reserve, the burden of which would be born by the must-serve buyers who are the ones for which spinning reserves are needed. Spinning reserve requirements for stability and response to unplanned outages would simply be added to expressed bid demand, the required additional costly generators brought on line at less than capacity, and the higher resulting price would be paid by the must-serve buyers only.

By instituting demand side bidding, and its concomitant time-of-day pricing, the cost of new generators, transmission lines, reserves and reliability are traded off, through the market, against the cost of demand interruption. The potential is to provide a far more cost efficient pattern of investment in hardware and software, than is achievable under either political regulation or government ownership. Also of importance is the need to price nodal reactive power in the spot market where the cost of control and meter support is justified by the efficiency savings. Some power lines have such high and variable reactive power absorption characteristics that in order not to restrict unduly the lines' real power delivery capacity, it is necessary to excite a generator near the delivery end to produce mostly reactive power. Properly priced and metered reactive power would be delivered where and when needed.

Bilateral contracting via financial futures markets to hedge spot market volatility

It is reasonable to expect some, perhaps many, buyers and sellers of spot power to want to hedge financially against spot market volatility. Hence, the need for futures markets in which a buyer and seller can lock in some fixed contract price in advanced, say Pf. Each party to such a contract would still be required to submit a location-specific bid or offer schedule into the spot market if they wish to buy or sell spot power. If the spot price is Ps > Pf, then under their futures contract agreement, the seller, who receives price Ps from the exchange, reimburses the buyer for the difference, Ps - Pf. If the spot price is Ps < Pf, then the buyer reimburses the seller for the difference Pf - Ps. In this way the original futures contract price, Pf, is assured for both parties whatever the spot price, Ps. These contracts can be long term or short term as negotiated. Such multilateral futures contracting could be run off the algorithms used by the dispatch/exchange system, with a single market clearing price on the reference node, as has been proposed for Australia, but could be effected on a bilateral basis at higher individual transactions cost.

What should *not be acceptable* in a properly designed market is *bilateral contracts* for *physical delivery*, which force the system to be constrained by purely financial contracts rather than only the physics of alternating current power systems. All the advantages to be achieved by bilateral physical contracts can be obtained in financial futures markets, with none of the artificial externality costs imposed on others by contracts for physical delivery. Short-run efficiency which minimizes energy expenditure cannot be achieved by adding unnecessary physical flow constraints dictated by financial considerations.

In foreign countries where privatization coincided with the institutionalization of a spot market, as in the United Kingdom, it was easier to avoid the demand by agents for bilateral delivery contracts. But in the United States, liberalization and trading yielded bilateral contracting within the framework of regulation before robust well designed spot markets were forthcoming. Hence, spot market design has been subjected to the political demand by market makers for a continuation of these bilateral arrangements in which prices are secret and only the exchange quantities are reported to the exchange/dispatch center.

All the advantages to be achieved by bilateral physical contracts can be obtained in financial futures markets, with none of the artificial externality costs imposed on others by contracts for physical delivery.

Imagine the outcry if anyone proposed to run the NASDQ stock exchange without publishing the prices of market makers. Forcing load flows to be constrained by the contracting patterns (assuming that in the aggregate they are even feasible), independently of location-specific WTP/WTA information, guarantees higher cost, inefficient dispatch. The political pressure is to average the higher loss transmission costs over all customers independently of individual differences in marginal impact. Such a system creates externalities that are easily avoided by computing all nodal prices and flows simultaneously, because then each agent bears the marginal cost of the losses the agent imposes on all others. The same considerations apply to congestion pricing when one or more transmission lines are constrained. Efficiency under such physical constraints is preserved via the dispatch center accepting only the lowest cost offers of generators who are on the upstream side of a constrained line.

To illustrate these issues, here is an example of how bilateral transfer arrangements are currently effected. Suppose 100 MWh of power for a one half-hour period is to be injected in dispatch control area A for delivery in control area C, with control area B standing between A and C. Each of the three control area centers are alerted to the transfer. The seller in area A injects 100 MWh at his node in A, the coordinator in A balances all other generator outputs in A so that they supply the demand plus transmission losses in A. This causes 100 MWh of power, after losses are made up, to be forced over the interties between A and B. Coordinator B balances all generators in B so that supply equals demand plus losses in B. This in turn forces the original 100 MWh after losses to be exported on the intertie busses connecting areas B and C.   Finally, coordinator C balances all generators and loads in C so that the transferred power, after all losses are made up, arrives at the destination node C for withdrawal.

Note that this physical transfer of power from A to C, constrains physical flows in all three regions so as to assure the contracted delivery in area C. The customer in C pays for the 100 MWh plus an estimate of its losses to areas A, B and C. This contrasts with how the desired 100 MWh are delivered to the appropriate node in area C in coordinated spot markets run in areas A, B. and C. The buyer in C simply places a bid for the 100 MWh, at whatever bid price represents his maximum WTP. Assuming the bid is accepted in full, this impacts all nodal prices in area C; prices rise on the area C side of the interties between B and C. The spot market coordinator in B, responding to all bid and offer schedules in B, finds it optimal to export power from B to C. The same response occurs in area A and power is optimally exported from area A to B. All nodal prices in areas A, B and C reflect the total pattern of bids, offers, and purely physical constraints throughout the system. If the nodal price at the customer's delivery node in C is $30/MWh, this is the price paid by the customer, and that price reflects all incremental loss costs imposed on all nodes throughout the system, consequent to that customer's bid for the delivery of 100 MWh. At this node price, he pays for his marginal effect on all other buyers and sellers, with all power flowing to optimize total energy management in the three systems combined. Where does the power come from? It comes from all the lowest cost sources of generation through the three systems. In fact the selling generator in area A in the bilateral contract example may find that his offer to sell at his node, at the contract price in the original example, is not even accepted in the spot market in area A. Alternatively, it, or a portion thereof, may be accepted because the offer price is submitted at a lower level than the original contracted rate. The point is that each party in the spot market example, pays (receives) prices that reflect their marginal impact on the system, given all other bids and offers and only the physical flow constraints on the system.

The bottom line is that, except in very special and unusual circumstances, the spot market solution will be more efficient than the bilateral contract example. The efficiency of the former can never be less than that of the latter, and will regularly and normally be greater than the latter.

Defining divisible rights to indivisible facilities

A power transmission network should be conceptualized as a production joint venture in the sense that all energy is commingled, information (WTP/WTA) is node specific, and allocations that maximize the gains from exchange require nodal prices and network flows to simultaneously honor all network physical constraints (Kirchhoff's laws, ohms/impedance laws, and thermal, voltage and stability line capacities). Consequently, the paths of power flow through a network from generator injection buss nodes to load withdrawal nodes cannot be defined in advance of calculating a dispatch program based on the pattern of current WPT/WTA information and the current physical state of the transmission network. (Hogan, 1997, discusses the mischief this does to misguided attempts to aggregate nodes into zones; such zones can only be defined expost dispatch). These flow patterns change hourly, daily and seasonally. To demand rights to paths in advance is to demand rights whose opportunity cost is unknown, and may not even be feasible under some conditions of capacity constraint. Capacity on any line or any sequence of lines depends upon what is the economical way to maximize system surplus, which simultaneously minimizes energy loss in transmission, given the pattern of WTP/WTA schedules and system constraints. Where contrary arrangements prevail it is the political power of those who demand and hold such rights that are served, without an account of the costs that must be borne by other users at the time of dispatch.

What rights can exist and be recognized in transmission networks? Only two: node specific rights to submit (1) bid schedules to withdraw power from specified nodes up to their maximum withdrawal consumption capacities, and (2) offer schedules to inject power into specific nodes up to their maximum injection production capacities; where "maximum capacities" are determined by the capacity of installed equipment to withdraw or inject power at each node, whether or not such capacities have often been utilized, or are even achieved, given the characteristics of the network and its pattern of usage. Rights cannot be defined in terms of paths through the network because these can only be defined expost by the economic dispatch center. Even New Zealand, where the predominant flow is from the South Island to the North Island over a bipolar DC link, has experienced the necessity for economic reverse flows due to South Island droughts that reduced reservoir levels to unprecedentedly low levels.

Thus at demand node i, suppose the historically defined physical capacity of the buss, transformers, and loads is 800 MW. Then one can define rights, which might be held by many agents, to submit bid schedules for various amounts of power, at various prices, up to and not exceeding a total withdrawal rate of 800 MWh. Thus eight agents might each submit a bid schedule truncated at 100 MWh. What portion of these bids are filled at any particular spot time of day depends upon the bids and offers of all other agents, and the physical state of the network. Similarly, at generator injection node j, if four generators at that buss each have a physical nameplate capacity of 250 MW, then one can define rights at node j to submit offer schedules that do not exceed 250 MWh for each generator unit. (Units could have cotenant owners, as is common, e.g. two cotenants could each own half the capacity of unit #1). Whether and how much of each offer is accepted is up to the dispatch center given all its decentralized information. Thus, unit #1 might be loaded at 250 MWh, unit #2 accepted for spinning reserve at a commitment level of 50 MWh and so on.

Rights must be defined in terms of nodal capacity opportunities, never outcome quantities. This is because in a transmission network it is impossible to make outcome guarantees without physically constraining the opportunities of others. Rights must always be defined in terms of actions that agents are allowed to take, not outcomes that might result from such actions. This "equal opportunity" design requirement for a property right governed competitive power industry stands in sharp contrast to what has existed in the past, and what exists in the current transition period in the United States. Currently and in the past, "fair" rates of return on "prudent" investments have been guaranteed, with prices adjusted so as to meet the guarantee, and all risk borne by final consumers. Conceptually, the new system must be one in which risk is borne by firms and investors. Naturally, the latter want to limit that risk with long-term rights to deliver power to certain customers. That is not possible in the new regime without infringing on the rights of others caused by network interdependence. Rights to take certain actions – submit bids (offers) to buy (sell) up to a maximum, with no guarantee of acceptance – must now replace rights that guarantee certain outcomes. The transition is sure to be chaotic and political, tending to favor those with the most influence on mechanism design, and who do not want to give up interim "defacto" rights that are inconsistent with, and inefficiently constrain, the new regime of open competition, decentralization, and economic coordination.

Although networks are interdependent, indivisible entities, rights to use them are definable in terms of node injections or withdrawals, that are as divisible as a unit of energy. Such rights can be widely dispersed to achieve competitive surplus maximizing policy objectives, but must be defined in terms of what can and cannot be done in the context of a network dispatch engineering economic system.

Pricing and Long-term Property Rights in Transmission

Given how spot market rights to act can feasibly be defined in a power network, how can transmission be priced and property rights in the network itself be fined? In particular how can investment be incentivized in transmission systems subject to the realities used to define nodal rights as discussed above? Here is an answer proposed by one of us for New Zealand in 1991 (Smith, 1991; also see Smith, 1988, 1993, 1996 for a discussion of general cotenancy issues and the New Zealand proposal in particular).

All users jointly own the transmission network and its dispatch center, under cotenancy property right rules specified by the government upon divestiture. The transmission network, and its support, is a co-owned operating company, not a profit center. It is a property right creature of the state, not a corporation free to vote its own policies. Call the resulting entity a "competitively ruled joint production venture." Each user – bulk buyer or generator owner – acquires rights to and pays for the network in proportion to his capacity rights to submit bids (offers) to buy (sell) at specific nodes. How these historical costs are borne are largely irrelevant for efficiency, because they do not affect marginal WTP and WTA, but this proportionality rule based on nodes and historical capacity, which is use related, is natural and more or less likely to be perceived as fair and reasonable. What is crucial is that one acquires nodal rights to an existing network as defined in the section above. Nodal pricing by the dispatch/exchange center is then used throughout. Hence, the price difference between any two nodes is determined by the marginal energy loss based on the flows consequent to dispatch. Since losses are approximately a quadratic function of power injected into a line, the marginal loss on the line is roughly double the average loss. (In New Zealand from the bottom of the South Island to the top of the North Island, the highest on-peak price difference would be some 43% of the delivery price). Where a line constraint must be honored by dispatch, the line produces congestion prices that exceed these marginal loss prices. In this pricing system, buyers pay more than sellers receive because each pays (receives) his opportunity cost (value). The difference in total revenue goes to the node rights holders in proportion to their capacity to submit bids (offers). All transmission maintenance and operating costs are also borne by the rights holders in proportion to these capacities.

Suppose it is economical and desirable to expand capacity by constructing a new link. Here are competitive rules for governing such an expansion. Any consortium of existing rights holders, or any outsider or combination of outsiders, are free to conduct simulation studies using historical dispatch data. Based on such studies they site a line and its capacity. The simulations indicate the range of expansions in specific node capacities to inject or withdraw power over and above the historical capacities installed at the indicated nodes. The consortium pays for the increase in capacity, and obtains tradable rights to the increased nodal capacities made possible by the investment. Those incurring the investment cost enjoy rights to the new injection/withdrawal capacities that the investment makes possible. Such simulation studies are estimates only, and actual use capacity at specific nodes may vary with economic and network conditions which may not have been incorporated into the initial simulations. Those risks are borne by the investors without recourse. They can install new injection or withdrawal capacity and submit bids (offers) but without guaranteed outcomes, or sell the new capacity rights to others under contractual agreements mutually negotiated. Some existing rights holders may be negatively impacted by a new investment. They bear this risk without recourse much as the carriage industry was displaced by the invention of the automobile. Existing rights holders are free to join the investment consortium, and benefit from increased capacity rights elsewhere, much as the carriage makers one hundred years ago were free to invest in, and convert to, automobile manufacture.

Suppose, as is possible, that a new line between nodes i and j redirects flows so that some generators are negatively impacted at node k; this provides reason for those affected at node k to join the consortium to build the line from i to j to acquire new unfettered rights. Suppose the negative impact at node n was not anticipated by the computer simulations? Do those affected have recourse? No. If the invention of the automobile, and expanding automobile production, causes a reduced demand for carriage manufactures, the latter have no recourse because new entry in one segment of the economy may require a redirection of resources – a fact which is transmitted through the pricing system to decentralized decision makers.

In large systems such as the United States, the proposal might be applied to regional grids (small or large) whose control centers export or import power to or from interconnection points depending upon intertie price differences between the two regions.

The bottom line is that rights and any inherent ambiguities, should only be defined in terms of the physical and economic realities of alternating current networks. The present system in the United States is an artifact of regulation based on "control areas" across which power can be made to flow artificially by adding constraints which in turn become the basis of trade in the absence of well-functioning spot markets. Such constraints necessarily must reduce (weakly or strongly) energy efficiency.

Competition in local distribution

Local distribution systems, whether for delivering the mail, or electricity, have been habitually declared to be natural monopolies ever since the claim by John Stuart Mill (1848) that duplicate mail carriers would be wasteful; nor could Mill imagine the need for two parallel railroad tracks connecting two cities. If, however, local distribution is truly a natural monopoly the common practice of granting exclusive (legal monopoly) franchises is without merit; only a few cities have nonexclusive distribution systems. Lubbock, Texas is the best known example of a city with two parallel local power distribution companies. In other retail trades, such as automobile service stations, supermarkets, drug stores, shopping malls, etc. it is common for competing facilities to serve overlapping territories, in spite of abstract arguments that such services involve wasteful duplication. "What value is choice?" is the question unanswered by these arguments.

What can be said about mechanism design for local retail distribution? Several alternatives merit consideration.

As in the United Kingdom and New Zealand, the wires business can be required to be separated from the energy delivery business, with the services of wires paid for by a monthly charge depending upon capacity and any special service features, while energy is priced separately. The latter could be at a fixed price per KWh, at various block rates throughout the day, at time-of-use rates, with seasonal variation, and so on depending upon customer choice among contracts offered by competing retail energy merchant suppliers. The latter should submit location-specific bids to buy in the bulk spot power market, and resell this power to their customers, passing through any monthly charge for the local wires service, but in the U.K. no provision has yet been made for demand side bidding.

In the U.K. the wires service business is subject to price cap regulation, adjusted for inflation less an X factor for postulated increases in productivity. Savings within these constraints can be retained as profits. In New Zealand a more innovative experiment has been implemented. There is no regulatory office for controlling the wires' charge. Local distributors are free to set their own prices. But any customer can challenge such prices under the New Zealand commerce laws. Evidence relevant to a challenge would be to show that the price in your local area is higher than prices in another area with comparable service densities and conditions. Also, entry by a competing wires business is not excluded, because distributors do not have an exclusive local franchise.

In principle, local wires can be structured as a property right joint venture creation of the state, similar to transmission as indicated above. Since withdrawal nodes are more homogeneous in local distribution than transmission, one could conceive of a small number of "hook-up" classes: apartments, single family residences, and commercial customers. The local distribution system, its maintenance and operations is structured as an operating company – a cost center – which is owned jointly by 3-4 competing retail power merchants. Each merchant receives hook-up rights (customers) in proportion to his share of the capital cost of the local grid. Excess capacity rights, in unoccupied homes and new development houses under construction can be exercised anywhere in the territory served, as merchants compete on price and contract terms. Hook-up rights can be transferred by sale or lease, and created by expansion, as one or more of the merchants expands hook-up capacity in a new home development area, or in new apartment construction projects. By investing in time-of-day meters a merchant can provide such services by contract with individual customers. But commercial customers, neighborhoods, home owners associations, and apartment complexes would be free to bypass the system by installing local generation (gas, solar, fuel cell, wind, as allowed by local codes).

What would be desirable is to see local communities experiment with alternative mechanisms for structuring their distribution systems.

Part II. What is the relevant learning to date from laboratory experiments?

In what follows we will focus largely on what we see as the role of live laboratory experiments in mechanism design. (There is some role for computer simulations, but simulations require assumptions to be made about behavior – assumptions with which we are not comfortable. For example one sided markets are often studied by simulating fully revealing buyers, which is not what live buyers do. In general, a crucial part of the uncertainty in how alternative systems would work has to do with the behavior of the participants). The subjects can of course be industry people – we have used many – but they present both advantages and disadvantages over the computer savvy generation of undergraduates who have little motivation to strategically serve political ends that reduce their profit earnings in an experiment.

Generally, we have known for some time that the class of mechanisms known as smart computer assisted markets show promise in allowing previous systems that were hierarchically organized to be decentralized and marketized. Experiments have already influenced policy in the Australian and New Zealand electricity privatization, in the design of U.S. emissions rights markets, and in spectrum rights markets. There are many more examples, but often they are proprietary and/or hidden in consulting reports. Thus, the New Zealand government has used combinatorial auctions for allocating cutting rights on Crown timber lands although the methodology was originally motivated by airport runway rights (Rassenti, Smith and Bulfin, 1982).

Here is a summary outline of some of the learning from electric power or potentially related experiments. We will not pretend that it is very comprehensive.

1. Smart vs Non-Smart Auctions

In papers discussing combinatorial auctions (Rassenti, Smith, Bulfin 1982) and composite good auctions (McCabe, Rassenti, Smith 1990) it has been shown that short of providing a mechanism by which a coordinator considers the explicit needs of all decentralized agents simultaneously, as expressed in their bids to buy and/or offers to sell, it is difficult (sometimes impossible) to achieve high levels of allocative efficiency even ignoring the higher transactions costs associated with bilateral bargaining for direct exchange. In such environments it sometimes is a relatively simple matter to create a coordinating exchange center which finds a Pareto superior improvement for all segments – buyers, sellers, transporters --based on decentralized WTP/WTA information, compared to bilateral bargaining in private with limited information dissemination.

2. Effect of transmission line constraints.

Nodal pricing theory is based on incremental loss pricing in unconstrained networks with congestion rents added to loss prices to reflect the shadow value of line constraints. This comes from optimization theory, not equilibrium theory. In fact there is no equilibrium theory to support the former in realistically complicated networks. Hence, the important question is whether the congestion rents created by transmission constraints will actually be collected as a shadow *residual* by passive line owners. This is a behavioral question, and would still be so even if we had an equilibrium theory that supported optimization theory. Do generator sellers of energy upstream from a line constraint raise their asking prices, and do wholesale buyers on the downstream side of the constraint lower their bids in comparison with control experiments with no line constraint? The answer is "yes" for sellers, and "slightly" for buyers in the context of a three-node radial network with stationary supply and demand: efficiency is significantly reduced, and generator profit significantly increased under the treatment with a binding line constraint. (See Backerman, Rassenti and Smith, 1997).

> **Do generator sellers of energy upstream from a line constraint raise their asking prices, and do wholesale buyers on the downstream side of the constraint lower their bids..? The answer is "yes" for sellers, and "slightly" for buyers.**

Another interesting behavioral result can occur even when there is no transmission constraint but high nonlinear losses. Buyers and sellers can both be better off by transacting less quantity at prices favorable to each. Again the passive transporter loses loss rents that would otherwise be his if values and costs were completely revealed.

3. Comparison of alternative spot market rule systems.

Many alternatives to the continuous double auction have been explored experimentally. These are all variants of call markets which have two important features: they compute a uniform price for the good being transacted, and with nodal pricing of losses and constraints can accommodate network externalities. The uniform price double auction (UPDA) (McCabe, Rassenti, Smith 1993), in which continuous feedback of bid changes is provided in real time, has many implementational variants. Of particular note is whether the rules allow any new bid (offer) to displace a currently transacting bid (offer), or whether the new bid (offer) must meet the terms of the first extramarginal offer (bid) before being sorted into the current set of accepted bids and offers. These are known as the "both sides" and "other side" rules respectively. The "both sides" rule is the intuitive and less restrictive version of UPDA. The "other side" rule brings a stronger element of continuous double auction trading incentives to UPDA and is better at overcoming off-equilibrium price inertia, called "stuttering" in Wilson (1997) and Plott (1997). The end rule can also affect the performance of UPDA. An endogenous close, which is triggered after a period with no volume increase, and performs more efficiently than a time clock, but at a cost of lengthier auctions. There are many versions of end-rules which can be implemented, including a random close, to induce better revelation properties. The Arizona Stock Exchange uses the "both sides" rule with an increasing commission scale over the call period to encourage earlier submission of bids and offers.

Wilson (1997) and Plott (1997) address these incentive issues using a multiround sealed-bid auction with activity rules. We would be cautious about any rule which supports unilateral bid withdrawal *after* it is accepted. In stressful conditions where one side of the market is much more inelastic than the other, sophisticated subjects are likely to discover the value of late withdrawal of marginal units to manipulate price.

Also, most of the Wilson/Plott experiments occur in a highly competitive (12 agents) one sided sellers' auction. This leads to downward price movement as sellers compete to satisfy the prescribed demand. The hazards of allowing sellers to be active as unconstrained price quoters were reported in McCabe, Rassenti and Smith (1991). This study led us to discover that under such conditions an extremely efficient and much simpler institution is provided by the multiple unit English clock (McCabe, Rassenti and Smith, 1990). In a seller auction the clock price starts at a high price with every seller declaring his maximum provision of units. As the clock ticks down, sellers withdraw units until the supply exactly matches the declared demand: the auction is over, the price determined, and message passing minimized. Manipulation is reduced because bidders have no control over the price through their choice of asking prices. An individual's only recourse in preventing a price decline is to withdraw capacity which benefits all others who do not reduce their capacity offered. Bernard, Mount and Schulze (1997) have extended these multiple unit English auction results to very simple electricity-like markets, and report very high final (eighth) round efficiencies (96 to 100) percent. But the results are not directly comparable to Wilson/Plott because of several differences in the environment. So, there is plenty of work left to answer the obvious questions.

Instead of eliminating the capacity of sellers to quote price (by using an English clock), Wilson/Plott deal with this incentive problem by limiting the right of subsequent bid adjustment by bidders who are not in the cross early. The proposed Australian system requires capacity commitment at the beginning, which cannot be subsequently withdrawn, whatever the price(s) at which the capacity is offered.

There is a natural two-sided extension of the English auction: Double English (McCabe, Rassenti and Smith, 1992). Although the efficiency of the one-sided English clock has been replicated many times in various environments, Double English performs very poorly. Why? You have two clocks. The seller's clock starts at a high price, the buyer's clock at a low price. Whichever side is long at any given pair of prices, say the supply, you move that clock until there is excess demand, then switch to the other side, and so on until the clock prices are equal to each other, with a rationing rule if supply ≠ demand. Unlike the one sided English clock, with the demand (or supply) quantity announced in advance, in the two-sided version quantity is determined endogenously, and this invites strategic manipulation on both sides. In English clocks the terms of trade always move against the decision maker, so that the only way of getting a favorable price is to reduce one's quantity offer and stop the clock. In Double English, each side tends to do this and the resting (price, quantity) pair tends to end up inside the true supply and demand cross, and is inefficient.

What is the fix? One is Double Dutch. Now the buyer's (seller's) clock starts high (low), and the clock that moves switches back and forth depending on which side is long. Incentives are better because Dutch clocks move so as to improve the terms for the decision maker. This yields much better revelation than in Double English. Behaviorally, almost as good as Double Dutch is the two sided Dutch English (or English Dutch) auction. There is just one price from one clock, which is a Dutch clock for buyers and an English clock for sellers (or the reverse). Price falls until the expanding demand quantity equals the declining supply quantity.

All these mechanisms share the feature that agents make only capacity commitment decisions, and can only influence price through such decisions. It is not known how clock auctions might be implemented in nodal network pricing in which the transmission loss factors are computed endogenously.

4. Comparing UPDA with the sealed-bid-offer (SBO) market rules.

When buyers face penalties for not delivering in full to their "must serve" clients, sellers face penalties for not meeting "must run" minimum base load generator conditions, and demand cycles dramatically from peak to off peak, a very stressful trade environment is created (Backerman, Rassenti and Smith, 1997). Under these conditions the Sealed Bid Offer (SBO) and UPDA rules were compared as possible mechanisms for trading electric power. Considering its history for underperforming other institutions (such as DA and UPDA) in the homogenous, single good environment, SBO was found very efficient, and tracked the equilibrium well. We conjecture there were two reasons for this: under must serve and must run penalty costs buyers and sellers have better incentives to reveal values and costs, and with much more experience (80 periods) than traders in other sealed bid experiments, trader behavior began to reflect the risk inherent in trying to manipulate the spot price.

Surprisingly, UPDA, in the version tested, did not perform as efficiently even with our super experienced subjects. It did, however, accurately track equilibrium price changes with its good price discovery properties. The shortfalls on volume were probably due to a number of reasons which have implementational fixes. The "both sides" rule (discussed in 3) was used rather than the "other side" rule for ease of explanation to subjects in an otherwise complicated electric power environment. Also, in that implementation, there was no way for a subject to know, given the nonlinear losses being recomputed instantaneously, exactly how much to bid and offer to trade an entire block. This becomes extremely critical as time winds down, and marginal losses increase. It could be alleviated by quoting bids and asks that reflect the discrete losses implicit in block bids and offer quantities instead of only marginal losses as used in the baseline experiments. It could also be alleviated with an endogenous close to the auction depending on lack of new activity, a random closing rule, or higher bid submission fees for later rather than earlier submission.

5. Effect of demand side bidding.

In experiments in which the demand side is simulated by fully demand revealing buyers, 6-7 generator sellers raise their asking prices over time, capturing much of the surplus that would be attributed to buyers at the competitive equilibrium. This effect is especially prevalent when the supply side has competing producers who each have a mix of baseload, medium and peaking units, and can afford to manipulate the margin at which higher cost units are supplied. Divestiture often requires a mix of base, medium and peak load capacities to be owned by each generator company. This invites locking in the base and medium load capacities at low offer prices and using peaking units to manipulate the spot price. This appears to be the strategy used in the U.K. by the two companies who own all the load following capacity. (A better policy might be to have at least two generator companies that own only peaking generators who thereby face Bertrand style competition.) But if there is free entry, as in the U.K., new capacity is encouraged to enter forcing the two firms with load following capacity to withhold increasing amounts of production if price is not to fall. This hypothesis is supported in data reported by Littlechild (1995, Table 1, p. 102 and Table 2, p. 105) showing that over time the two dominant firms share of production has declined more than their share of capacity. Clearly, this cannot continue to occur without substantial erosion of the incumbents' profits, as new entrants free-ride on the price umbrella held up by bid withholding.

Part III. Core Issues Requiring Experimental Investigation

As we see it there are currently several types of experiments which could enlighten and inform the policy debate concerning the design of the electric power market. They are:

1.   Comparison of institutions which explicitly consider the intertemporal constraints on buyers and sellers versus those that decentralize the responsibility by allowing financial futures instruments to develop to satisfy the needs of agents to protect themselves against financial risk and assist them in intertemporal planning. It is questionable how far one should go in burdening the exchange/dispatch center with central treatment of nonconvexities. The inflexible baseload units inherited from the past are very likely to be replaced with smaller more flexible cost efficient technologies, thereby reducing the nonconvexity problem.

2.   In principle any bilateral contracting for physical delivery must weakly reduce market efficiency. This is because increasing the number of constraints on choice in a maximum problem can never improve the maximum. Comparing spot markets with and without such constraints enables one to determine empirical measures of the efficiency loss from contracting for physical delivery. Using this baseline comparison one could then introduce bilateral financial futures trading to test the hypothesis that such contracting produces no loss in efficiency comparable to what occurs under bilateral contracting for physical delivery. Such comparisons could also be made in networks with or without a transmission constraint.

3.   A second issue arises when traders are free to leave the spot market and trade bilaterally. It concerns the resulting effect on spot market price volatility. As trades are diverted from the spot market the latter becomes thinner and more volatile, increasing the motivation for bilateral contracting.   This was the lesson in Campbell, LaMaster, Smith and Van Boening (1991) when off-floor exchange was permitted as an alternative to spot electronic trading. In this study off-floor bilateral traders free-ride on the public bid/ask spread. As off-floor trading increases, the bid/ask spread widens, prices become more volatile and efficiency declines.

4.   Comparison of institutions in which the cost of maintaining and upgrading the transmission system is achieved through rate-of-return, or price cap, regulation, versus providing an opportunity for agents to expand capacity and increase their nodal injection/withdrawal right as indicated in Part I above. Other possible implementations of transmission pricing schemes include those presented by Chao and Peck (1996).

References

Backerman, Steven, Stephen Rassenti and Vernon Smith, "Efficiency and Income shares in High Demand Energy Networks: who Receives the Congestion Rents When a Line is Constrained?" Economic Science Laboratory, University of Arizona, June 25, 1996 (Revised April 3, 1997).

Backerman, Steven, Michael Denton, Stephen Rassenti and Vernon Smith, "Market Power in a Deregulated Electrical Industry: An Experimental Study," Economic Science Laboratory, University of Arizona, February 1997.

Bernard, John, Timothy Mount and William Schulze, "Auction Mechanisms for a Competitive Electricity Market," Department of Agricultural Resources and Managerial Economics, Cornell University, 1997.

Campbell, Joseph, Shawn LaMaster, Vernon Smith and Mark Van Boening, "Off-Floor Trading, Disintegration and the Bid-Ask Spread in Experimental Markets," Journal of Business, October 1991.

Chao, Hung-po and Stephen Peck, "An Institutional Design for an Electricity Contract Market with Central Dispatch," Electric Power Research Institute, June 17, 1996.

Funk, N. E. and F. C. Ralston, "Boiler-Plant Economics," American Society of Mechanical Engineers Transactions, XLV, 1923, pp. 607-641.

Hogan, William, Chapter 3, This Volume.

Littlechild, Stephen, "Competition in Electricity: Retrospect and Prospect," in M. E. Beesley (editor) Utility Regulation: Challenge and Response. London: Institute of Economic Affairs, 1995, pp. 101-114.

McCabe, Kevin, Stephen Rassenti and Vernon Smith, "Auction Design for Composite Goods: The Natural Gas Industry," Journal of Economic Behavior and Organization, September 1990.

_____, "Auction Institutional Design: Theory and Behavior of Simultaneous Multiple Unit Generalizations of the Dutch and English Auctions," American Economic Review, December 1990.

_____, "Testing Vickrey's and Other simultaneous Multiple Unit Versions of the English Auction," Research in Experimental Economics, Vol. 4 (edited by R. M. Isaac), 1991.

_____, "Designing Call Auction Institutions: Is Double Dutch the Best?," Economic Journal, January 1992.

_____, "Designing a Uniform Price Double Auction: An Experimental Evaluation," in D. Friedman and J. Rust (eds.) The Double Auction Market: Institutions, Theories and Evidence. Reading: Addison-Wesley/SFI, 1993.

Mill, John Stuart, Principles of Political Economy, 1848, reprinted, London: Colonial Press, 1900.

Plott, Charles, "Experimental Tests of the Power Exchange Mechanism," Report to the California Trust for Power Industry Restructuring," January 9, 1997.

Rassenti, Stephen, Vernon Smith and Robert Bulfin, "A Combinatorial Auction for Airport Time Slot Allocations," Bell Journal of Economics, Autumn 1982.

Smith, Vernon L., "Electric Power Deregulation: Background and Prospects," Contemporary Policy Issues, 6 no. 3, 1988, pp. 14-24.

_____, "Transpower Separation and Restructuring: A Cotenancy Approach," C. S. First Boston Consulting Report, August 13, 1991.

_____, "Can Electric Power – A 'Natural Monopoly" – Be Deregulated?" in H. H. Landsberg (editor) Making Natural Energy Policy. Washington, D. C.: Resources for the Future, 1993, pp. 131-151.

_____, "Regulatory Reform in the Electric Power Industry," Regulation, No. 1, 1996, pp. 33-46.

Steinberg, Max J. and Theodore H. Smith, Economy Loading of Power Plants and Electric Systems. New York: John Wiley, 1943.

Wilson, Robert, "Activity Rules for the Power Exchange," Report to the California Trust for Power Industry Restructuring, March 3, 1997.

8 BINDING CONSTRAINTS ON ELECTRICITY RESTRUCTURING: *An Inventory*

Edward P. Kahn

Introduction

Electricity deregulation is increasing around the world. While there is some general agreement about the drivers and nature of the process (Perl, 1997; Gilbert, Kahn and Newbery, 1996), it is much less clear how much learning is possible from the growing international experience (Ruff, 1997). This paper adopts an approach that emphasizes limits on learning due to the presence of initial endowments that constrain deregulation. It is the purpose of this discussion to classify these constraints and identify the extent to which they are amenable to amelioration.

The transformation of electricity markets from vertically integrated monopolies to more competitive structures has been studied from an industrial organization perspective (Hunt and Shuttleworth, 1996). The institutional constraints on this process, however, are much less well understood. These constraints take a variety of forms depending upon the initial conditions in particular markets. Much of the discussion concerning electricity competition focuses on technical constraints associated with the particular properties of electricity production and trade, and how these affect the structure of trading. While these issues are certainly important, they are potentially more amenable to economic and commercial innovation than other constraints arising out of ownership issues.

The inventory presented in Section 2 differentiates between technical and ownership issues, illustrates the role of each kind of constraint with reference to particular examples, and argues that ownership constraints are much less tractable than technical constraints.

The Inventory

Table 1 summarizes the inventory that will be discussed in this paper. It concentrates on issues associated with the bulk power system (either generation or transmission). Issues associated with distribution and retailing are not considered.

Table 1. Seven Constraints on Electricity Restructuring

Case	Type	G or T	Region	Constraint	Origin	Solution
1	Technical	T	California	Transmission congestion	Regional resource cost differences	Transmission congestion contracts
2	Ownership	T	Central US	Transmission rate pancaking	Contract path pricing	Midwest ISO Proposal
3	Technical	G	All thermal markets	Start-up and no load costs	Fixed operating costs	Forward markets; Dutch auction
4	Ownership	G	Argentina; British Columbia	Market power/ collusion	Cascading with mixed ownership on rivers	Water value bidding (as a function of head height)
5	Ownership	G	Spain; Australia	Excess Zero Bids	Supply entitlements	Negative bids
6	Ownership	G	Ontario	Bond financing	Stranded costs	
7	Ownership	G	Hungary	Expropriation	Price suppression	

Ownership vs. Technical Types of Transmission Congestion

A useful place to begin drawing out the distinction between ownership and technical constraints is by focusing on the two cases involving transmission in Table 1. There is a large literature emerging on the role of transmission system congestion in electricity markets. The reason that congestion occurs is the existence of persistent differences in electricity production costs in different regions. Most commonly, large load centers have higher electricity production costs than remote sources of generation. These differences can be due either to the high environmental mitigation costs associated with production in dense urban areas, the low resource costs of remotely located coal or hydro plants, or a combination of the two. When there is a geographic asymmetry between the demand and supply regions, there is the potential for transmission congestion. In Table 1 this case (#1) is identified with California because it is widely believed to be a problem that will need management in the emerging California market.[1]

Case 2, listed in connection with the Central US, involves a very different form of transmission congestion; I will call it pricing congestion. In this case, it arises from the standard US transmission pricing regime which imposes a tariff on all transactions that nominally cross any utility service territory. So if two utilities chose to transact, but they were separated by two intermediate utilities, the total transmission tariff would involve three or four separate charges. This phenomenon is known as "pancaking" and it arises in the Midwestern US, particularly because there are a large number of moderately sized and some geographically large utilities in the region. There is no physical congestion problem restricting transactions, indeed, the geographic distribution of loads and resources is quite symmetric. The restraint on trade is the financial barrier posed by high non-economic transaction costs. This problem arises from the multiplicity of network ownership and the absence of a pricing policy that would induce efficient trade.

The solution to the barrier that transmission rate pancaking imposes on electricity trade is a regional tariff administered by an entity serving all utilities in the Midwest. American Electric Power has proposed this approach, known as the Midwest ISO (Independent System Operator) (Falcone, 1996). It has yet to be implemented, because an appropriate compensation scheme is difficult to devise for the large number of firms (on the order of 25) with substantially different historic transmission cost structures.

Technical vs. Ownership Barriers to Efficient Dispatch

One goal of electricity competition is efficient dispatch. Decentralized electricity trade encounters both technical and ownership barriers to this objective as well as problems that are particular to different kinds of power generation technology. Case 3, the start-up and no-load cost problem, is a technical issue for all steam power generation. Start-up and no-load costs are essentially fixed costs of operation that must be recovered in addition to marginal energy costs. In the UK Pool, these costs are explicit and separate parts of the generator's bid prices. The Pool uses standard unit commitment software to select the least cost schedule from the bids, taking the complex bid prices plus operating constraints into account. Then it adjusts the peak period prices upward so that all scheduled generators receive enough revenue on peak to cover their start-up and no load bid prices. This price formation process is not particularly transparent, and involves less decentralization of decision-making than is common in other markets.[2]

Recent proposals to decentralize the bidding process, while still meeting the start-up and no-load cost constraint have been made based on a "Dutch auction" procedure (Wilson, 1997). The basic idea is to use energy only bids which start at a sufficiently high level to guarantee adequate supply, but which are subject to downward price revision in subsequent iterations of the bidding. This price revision rule coupled with restrictions on withdrawing and renominating capacity appear to result in price convergence (LE, 1997). In this fashion, bidders can satisfy themselves that prices are adequate to meet all costs without having to rely on a central market-maker to make that determination.[3] In Australia, bidders are required to "self commit" on the basis of simple, energy only bids, without elaborate bidding rules (Wolak, 1997).

There are short-term forward markets available there to help generators manage the price risks of this process.

Hydro generation does not involve fixed operating costs. On river systems it is typical, however, for there to be upstream and downstream water availability linkages due to the presence of multiple dams and reservoirs. Water becomes available downstream after it is released upstream. Where all of the dams, reservoirs and powerhouses on a given river are under common ownership, these "cascading" linkages are internal production issues for the single owner. Where there is diversity of ownership on such river systems, efficient coordination of operation can be construed to be collusive exercise of market power. Thus the distribution of ownership creates a regulatory problem in the case of multiple ownership (#4) where it does not exist in the case of common ownership. Even where the collusion issue does not arise, spot market pricing under diverse ownership creates conceptual difficulties due to the water availability linkages.[4]

Table 1 identifies the cascading problem under diverse ownership with two particular electricity markets: Argentina and British Columbia. These are polar cases. Argentina illustrates a potential solution to the market power and pricing dependence problem; British Columbia is a jurisdiction where the problem has been argued to be a barrier to competition. Let us first consider the positive example. In Argentina, hydro owners bid water values as a function of how much water is in their reservoirs. These bids are made for 6 month forecast periods and are revisable once during each period. On the basis of these bids, the actual amount of water in each reservoir, and the bids of other generators, the market maker will dispatch the hydro resources to minimize total cost. This technique reduces the potential for collusive behavior, particularly because the forecasts must be made at times of relatively little knowledge about hydrologic conditions. On the other hand, it is not at all clear that this approach results in particularly efficient dispatch. In Argentina there are also thermal generation resources which compete with hydro, so the market does not depend completely on solving the cascading problem. In British Columbia, however, hydro resources in two river basins dominate the generation mix. This makes it all the more important to have confidence in a decentralized solution.[5] As yet, the provincial government of British Columbia has not taken the step toward restructuring and competition. Sweden is an intermediate case; where River Management Authorities coordinate the bidding and operation of hydro resources in a given river basin. Since there are a number of such basins and not all participants belong to these associations, the benefits of coordination can be achieved without any particularly large loss in competition.

This discussion does not exhaust the issues associated with achieving efficient dispatch under competitive restructuring. Joskow (1997) gives a useful overview of these problems in the U.S. context.

Ownership Disincentives to Electricity Trade

The final category addressed here I call ownership disincentives to electricity trade. In each of these cases, barriers to trade arise due to the definition of property rights by public authority. These affect private incentives to participate in electricity markets.

Case 5 represents a certain kind of excess participation; Case 6 represents a refusal to participate. Case 7 also involves withdrawal issues, but arising in quite a different way. In each case, particular features of the ownership regime create dis-incentives to participate in electricity trade on a purely commercial basis.

The situation characterized in Case 5 represents electricity markets in which the overwhelming fraction of suppliers has an entitlement of one kind or another to supply the market. Therefore, they do not really offer prices in any conventional sense; they simply offer quantities on a must-take basis. In Table 1 we refer to resources of this kind as "zero bidders." In a bid price pool, any supplier who wants to be dispatched at any price simply bids zero. As a practical matter, nuclear production is effectively a must-take resource and hydro typically functions similarly. Supply entitlements of different kinds exist in any number of markets. Various commercial arrangements (such as take-or-pay fuel contracts) or technical constraints on generators (such as minimum stable generation levels) can also induce zero bidding. Other forms of supply entitlement are less common.

The electricity market in Spain illustrates a situation of large scale supply entitlements.[6] In this market, nuclear and hydro supply about 50% of demand. There are entitlements for indigenous coal that amount to another 25-30% and a large class of self-producers that account for another 10%. This leaves a free market of only about 10-15%. The task of liberalization under these conditions amounts to reducing the magnitude of these supply entitlements.[7]

In Australia, the case of excess zero bidding has arisen in Victoria, where it appears to be due not to supply entitlements so much as to technical constraints. Most of the generation is lignite-fueled and exhibits considerable inflexibility of operation. It is quite simply difficult to start-up such units, so operators prefer to keep them running, even at a zero price. An interesting solution has been proposed for this situation. It is quite simple, namely allowing negative bids for the right to run during periods of excess supply. At present this approach has been incorporated into the market rules for the national market. The proposal in that case is to use the revenue generated to reduce ancillary services costs, although it could also be returned to consumers.[8]

Case 6 represents the opposite of excess non-competitive participation, namely a refusal to participate. This is a case where stranded costs are unavoidable and difficult to mitigate. In this case, participation in electricity trade may threaten the recovery of sunk costs by exposing the demand served by an integrated supplier to competition. In this situation, the constraint is financial in essence. The costs sunk in uneconomic assets have not been paid for as incurred, but deferred through long-term debt. In the case of government ownership, bond financing can represent 100% of the capital. Table 1 identifies Case 6 with Ontario, Canada (although similarities with France are also apparent). The government of Ontario, responding to pressures for competition in electricity, commissioned a study of the opportunities in the province (Advisory Committee, 1996). The financial constraint is discussed in this committee's report, where a write-off of $10 billion (Canadian) was thought necessary to establish viable commercial ventures. This would represent about 30% of invested capital at historic costs. Despite recommendations by the committee to go forward with the introduction of competition, the provincial government has taken no action to date. It is ultimately the provincial government which is responsible for the sunk cost debt in Ontario, through debt guarantees on the utility's bonds. One must interpret the reluctance of the government to proceed with competition as a recognition of the unavoidable stranded cost risks. In this situation it appears as if prudence has been determined to be the better part of valor.

It is also fair to say that Ontario's situation is strongly conditioned by the dominance of nuclear assets in the generation mix (and financial asset base). The safety and waste disposal issues posed by nuclear power put this technology in a class by itself. Finding an acceptable solution to managing these issues under private ownership is as much a social and political challenge as a technical one. The questions involved go beyond most ordinary commercial concerns. The recent successful flotation of the all nuclear company British Energy shows that under some conditions of risk management and government guarantees, nuclear can be a fully functioning commercial asset. It is quite uncertain, however, if these conditions can be replicated in other countries, particularly the US.[9]

Case 7 involves price suppression in the presence of efforts to privatize. The example chosen to illustrate this case is Hungary (IEA, 1995), although there are probably similar cases elsewhere. The Hungarian government is pursuing a broad range of economic policies to hasten the transition from a more centrally planned framework to one involving more market forces and increased private ownership. As part of this process, the government has organized the assets of the electricity sector into 6 distributors and 8 generating companies. All of these companies are candidates for privatization except for the nuclear power company. Four of the generating companies have been sold to private investors as of the end of 1996. One of the sale conditions was assurance that the government would raise consumer prices for electricity to levels that would allow investors to earn competitive returns. The actual price increases implemented at the end of 1996 appear to have fallen short of this goal. As a result at least one foreign investor is threatening to cancel its acquisition.

Here is a case where privatization has preceded industry restructuring in a way that will make subsequent change more difficult. The government has lost some credibility with investors, because it was unable to fulfill promises to put the electricity sector on a more solid commercial basis. If prices had been rationalized prior to privatization, this loss of credibility could have been avoided and the prices obtained for electricity assets might have been higher.[10] This case is an illustration of the general theme that governments need to commit to private institutions and the associated property rights in a number of ways to support investment (Bergara, Henisz and Spiller, 1997).

Ownership issues may pose bigger constraints on electricity restructuring than the purely technical properties of these markets.

Implications

The point of this discussion is to argue that ownership issues may pose bigger constraints on electricity restructuring than the purely technical properties of these markets. The latter issues are amenable to commercial innovations, the former are much more resistant. For this reason, it is widely recognized that restructuring the electricity industry is easier when the starting point is public ownership.[11] Once public assets are transferred to private owners, the property rights become a barrier to further structural change.

There is some commonality to the ownership issues discussed above. A number of them involve sharing problems where the surplus created by cooperation needs to be allocated among participants. The transmission rate pancaking problem described in Case 2 could be solved if a way could be found to allocate the benefits of increased regional electricity trade among participants. In this particular case, there have been previous efforts at benefit sharing involving transmission that have failed to achieve public consensus.[12] There are also cases where stranded cost recovery in a market regulated by a single authority with multiple firms also has the quality of a sharing problem.[13] The economic literature on sharing mechanisms, or equitable allocation, provides some insights into problems of this kind.[14]

Nonetheless, since ownership conditions have a peculiarly local flavor, it is not obvious that solutions to ownership constraints in one market will translate easily into other settings. It is the lack of transferability that makes for limitations on learning. Electricity deregulation, therefore, cannot be expected to be completed quickly or easily.

Acknowledgements

This work was partially supported by the Electric Power Research Institute. I appreciate comments from Sally Hunt, Peter Griffes, Jean-Michel Glachant, Robert Marritz, Luis Rodriguez Romero, Ignacio Perez Arriaga.

Notes

1. Studies such as Kahn et al (1997), LCG (1996) and Borenstein and Bushnell (1996) each develops different estimates of the nature and extent of potential transmission congestion in the new California market.
2. Johnson *et al* (1996) is an interesting critique of the use of unit commitment software in competitive electric markets.
3. The proposed auction rules have included a provision at the last iteration for bidders to offer "revenue deficiency" bids that would resemble the UK process to a certain degree, in that the market maker would have to choose the least cost bids of this type and collect the excess revenue somehow.
4. Pereira and Compodonico (1997) describe this and outline an approach to addressing it.
5. This issue is discussed briefly in a 1995 review of competitive options in British Columbia (BCUC, 1995, pp. 62-64).
6. See Kahn (1997b) for a discussion of this case.
7. Recent developments in California show an increasing tendency toward a supply entitlement equilibrium in the political economy. Municipal utilities, obliged to participate in the competitive market by legislative direction, have opted for an entitlement position by announcing their intention to declare all of their production "regulatory must-take" thereby removing it from the competitive arena. Substantial quantities of generation are also subject to entitlement protect for reliability. These are called "reliability must-run" units. They are discussed by Jurewitz and Walther (1997).
8. See NGMC (1996), in particular, Clause 3.9.6 "Pricing Under Excess Generation Periods," and Clause 3.8.15 "Excess Generation."
9. Kahn (1997a) discusses these questions in more detail.

10. The prices obtained by governments privatizing assets depend on numerous conditions including the structure of the industry to which the assets belong and the prices prevailing in the product markets. One of the better discussions of these trade-offs in the case of the electricity sector is the chapters on Chile in Galal *et al* (1994).
11. This point is made in the context of the UK by Newbery and Green (1996) and in the context of developing countries by Rosenzweig and Voll (1996).
12. Maliszewski (1995) describes this case.
13. The market in Spain, described in Kahn (1997b), has this feature.
14. Moulin (1995) is a comprehensive treatment of this literature.

References

Advisory Committee on Competition in Ontario's Electricity System to the Ontario Minister of Environment and Energy, *A Framework for Competition*, 1996.

Bergara, M., W. Henisz, and P. Spiller, "Political Institutions and Electric Utility Investment: A Cross-Nation Analysis," University of California Energy Institute working paper, 1997.

Borenstein, S. and J. Bushnell, "An Empirical Analysis of the Potential for Market Power in California's Electricity Industry," University of California Energy Institute working paper, 1997.

British Columbia Utilities Commission (BCUC), The British Columbia Electricity Market Review: Report and Recommendations to the Lieutenant Governor in Council, 1995

Falcone, C., "Efficient Transmission Pricing for the Midwest ISO," Fourth DOE-NARUC National Energy Forum, 1996.

Galal, A., L. Jones, P. Tandon and I. Vogelsang. *The Welfare Benefits of Selling Public Enterprises*. Oxford University Press, 1994.

Gilbert, R., E. Kahn and D. Newbery, "Introduction," *International Comparisons of Electricity Regulation*, R. Gilbert and E. Kahn ed., Cambridge University Press, New York, 1996.

Hunt, S. and G. Shuttleworth, *Competition and Choice in Electricity*, John Wiley, 1996.

International Energy Agency (IEA), *Energy Policies of Hungary 1995 Survey*. Paris: OECD, 1995.

Johnson, R., Oren, S., and A. Swoboda, " Equity and Efficiency of Unit Commitment in Competitive Electricity Markets," *Utilities Policy*, v. 6, no. 1 (1997) 9-20.

Joskow, P., "Restructuring, Competition and Regulatory Reform in the U.S. Electricity Sector," *Journal of Economic Perspectives*, v. 11, no. 3 (1997) 119-138.

Jurewitz, J. and R. Walther, "Must-Run Generation: Can We Mix Regulation and Competition Successfully?" *The Electricity Journal.* v. 10, no. 10 (1997) 44-55.

Kahn, E., "Can Nuclear Power Become an Ordinary Commercial Asset?" *The Electricity Journal.* v. 10, no. 7 (1997a) 16-21.

Kahn, E., "Introducing Competition to the Electricity Industry in Spain: The Role of Initial Conditions," *Proceedings of the International Workshop on the Deregulation of Electric Utilities*, Montreal, 1997b.

Kahn, E., S. Bailey and L. Pando, "Simulating Electricity Restructuring in California: Interactions with the Regional Market," *Energy and Resource Economics* (1997).

London Economics (LE), "PX Auction Testing," PX Appendix 3, Attachment B, Pacific Gas and Electric Company, San Diego Gas and Electric Company and Southern California Edison Company, Phase II Filing of the California Power Exchange Corporation, Federal Energy Regulatory Commission Docket Nos. EC96-19-001 and ER96-1663-001, 1997.

Lotus Consulting Group (LCG), "Modeling Competitive Energy Markets in California: Analysis of Restructuring," California Energy Commission, October 3, 1996.

Maliszewski, R., "American Electric Power Company Case Study," *Regulating Regional Power Systems*, ed. C. Andrews, IEEE Press, 1995.

Moulin, H. *Cooperative Microeconomics: A Game Theoretic Introduction.* Princeton University Press, 1995.

National Grid Management Council (NGMC), National Electricity Market Code, 1996.

Newbery, D. and R. Green, "Regulation, Public Ownership and Privatisation of the English Electricity Industry," *International Comparisons of Electricity Regulation*, R. Gilbert and E. Kahn ed., Cambridge University Press, New York, 1996.

Pereira, M. and N. Campod∴nico, "Stochastic hydrothermal scheduling in a competitive environment," PICA Conference, 1997.

Perl, L., "Regulatory restructuring in the United States," *Utilities Policy*, v. 6, no. 1 (1997) 21-34.

Rosenzweig, M. and S. Voll, "Sequencing Power Sector Privatization: Is Reform its Pre-Condition or Result?" NERA, 1997

Ruff, L., "An Efficient, Competitive Electricity Industry: Can the Vision Become Reality," *The Electricity Journal*, v. 10, no. 1 (1997) 8-16.

Wilson, R., "Bidding Activity Rules for the Power Exchange," PX Appendix 3, Attachment A, Pacific Gas and Electric Company, San Diego Gas and Electric Company and Southern California Edison Company, Phase II Filing of the California Power Exchange Corporation, Federal Energy Regulatory Commission Docket Nos. EC96-19-001 and ER96-1663-001, 1997.

Wolak, F., "Market Design and Price Behavior in Restructured Electricity Markets: An International Comparison," University of California Energy Institute working paper, 1997.

9 INVESTING IN TRANSMISSION FACILITIES- WHY, BY WHOM, FOR WHOM[1]

Martin L. Baughman

Introduction

The business of providing electricity transmission services is undergoing sweeping changes nationwide. Historically, transmission services were provided principally by vertically integrated companies in which regulated monopoly providers produced, transmitted, and delivered electricity to the final consumer. The transmission facilities of these vertically integrated providers were paid for almost exclusively by the native load customers served by the owner of the facilities.

With the growing recognition that competition in the supply generation services is workable, indeed desirable, in 1996 the Federal Energy Regulatory Commission (FERC) issued Orders 888 and 889[2] mandating that transmission providers unbundle their transmission services from their generation and distribution activities and open their transmission facilities to use by third-party wholesale electricity providers and users. Order 888 put forward a comparability criterion, requiring that an owner of transmission facilities provide transmission services in a non-discriminatory manner to third-party users under the same terms and conditions that it takes the service itself. Order 889 required that systems be created to provide timely information about the availability and prices of services to all users of the transmission systems in a non-discriminatory manner. The overall objective was, and is, to make it possible for competitive providers of generation services to have open access to their potential markets with equal information about service availabilities and costs.

Proposals to restructure the way transmission services are provided have been or are being developed across the country. A great deal of attention has been devoted to developing institutional and market structures that will allow competition in the supply of generation to work while coordinating the operation and use of the transmission facilities so as not to degrade system reliability. Less attention has been devoted to developing institutional structures and incentives to assure appropriate transmission investments are made in the future.

When should additional new transmission facilities be invested in, where should they be installed, for what purpose, and who will provide the funds to finance the additions? These questions do not necessarily need the same answer for every market restructuring proposal, but they must have answers if expansion and reliability of transmission service is to be assured in the long run. The purpose of this paper is to examine alternative reasons why additional investments in the transmission system might be justified and to question whether institutions are being designed with incentives to make the necessary transmission investments to safeguard economical and reliable service in the future.

The remainder of the paper is organized as follows. Section 2 discusses the traditional transmission planning and investment process. The traditional goal has been to build an integrated system of generators, transmission facilities, and distribution networks that provided reliable service at lowest cost. Section 3 then discusses the growth in the role of the system operator in the new open-access world. The independent system operator is an important new institution in the restructured electricity market, but its purpose is primarily to coordinate short-term operations, not to plan nor undertake long-term investment. Section 4 puts forth some new transmission planning and investment considerations that restructuring has precipitated. It also questions whether the institutions being put into place can manage the multiplicity of conflicting economic interests while providing for orderly system expansion and continued transmission system reliability.

The Traditional Transmission Planning Process

Traditionally, the overall goal of transmission system designers was to plan an integrated system of generators, transmission system components, and distribution equipment that provided electrical service to the native load customers at adequate levels of reliability while minimizing the combined costs of generation, transmission, and distribution. The key words here are 1) integrated-- the transmission plan was integrated with the expansion plans for the generation and distribution systems, 2) native load-- the goal was to minimize costs to one's own franchise customers, not third party users, and 3) reliability-- discussed further below.

The three principal reasons for adding new transmission facilities were:
1. to allow larger generators to serve larger load (economical because of economies of scale in generation)
2. to network (add redundancy) existing transmission paths to increase reliability
3. to interconnect to other control areas or regions to facilitate economical interchange, to share reserves, and to provide emergency backup

These are still good reasons for adding new transmission facilities, but as will be pointed out in the next section, there are now also new reasons why new facilities might be desirable. But since reliability has been and continues to be such an important driver of new transmission facilities, the principle threats to reliability are summarized below.

The primary threats to reliability in the transmission system are a) voltage collapse; b) system instability; or c) cascading line, transformer, and/or generator outages, particularly in response to some electrical system disturbance or outage contingency.

The condition of voltage collapse can occur when a load and the transmission system delivering power to it require such a large amount of reactive power (compared to the real power component of the load) that it exceeds the capability of the reactive power sources to supply the needs. When this occurs, a precipitous voltage drop accompanies any increase in load, and the voltage "collapses." The process of voltage instability is usually triggered by some form of disturbance, such as a line or generator outage, or other change in operating conditions which creates increased demand for reactive power. In most cases, the situation can be mitigated by reducing load/power transfer, and/or by switching on local shunt capacitors, if available, to serve as sources of reactive power.

The concept of system stability revolves around whether generator electro-mechanical oscillations that may follow a disturbance and affect system voltages, currents, power flows, and so forth, will automatically dampen and restore to a stable, steady, and secure operating condition. If not, the system is considered unstable. The types of disturbances that can trigger dynamic stability problems include sudden transmission line outages, transformer outages, generator failures, load changes, transmission line faults (shorts across lines or from line to ground), lightning striking equipment, and a host of other contingencies. As a first line of defense, a protective relaying system and its associated switchgear provide the means for isolating the problem and protecting expensive equipment from serious damage. The operation of this protection equipment, however, can lead to other problems, because the loss of service from one piece of equipment can lead to overloads on other equipment. Dynamic stability problems resulted in the outages in the WSCC in the summer of 1996, leading to system segmentation, overloads, and blackouts elsewhere in the region.

If the equipment loadings are such that when one item of equipment fails, the physical laws governing operation of the system lead to a new set of equipment loadings that overload more items of equipment, in turn causing them to trip out of service which then leads to more overloads, and so forth, then system security is threatened. As an example, the condition might be precipitated by a transmission line failure caused by a falling tree branch. In response to the outage, all remaining transmission line flows adjust according to Kirchoff's law, leading to another line overload that, in turn, trips, and so forth, until the whole system cascades into failure. These cascading overloads are an obvious threat to secure system operation, and were the main reason for the spread of the Great Northeast Blackout in the 1960's.

Any of the three conditions cited—voltage collapse, system instability, or cascading overloads—can lead to system segmentation and/or failure, and interruption of service to the customer.

Each of the regional reliability councils that make up the North American Electric Reliability Council (NERC) have evolved technical operating and planning criteria that serve as standards for transmission system design and operation to protect against the occurrence of the kind of system failures described above. Some of the regional planning and reliability assessment activities to which member utilities have voluntarily contributed include the following:

- long-range (10-year) capacity and reserve forecasts
- long-range (10-year) transmission plans
- seasonal operating studies
- voltage studies
- security evaluations
- maintenance of loadflow and stability databases
- transfer capability studies
- evaluation of disturbances

Much of the planning evaluation centers on analyzing current or future system operations under various contingency conditions. Various engineering and technical committees within the regional councils have responsibilities for delineating a range of contingencies to be analyzed and for coordinating the analyses.

In contingency analysis, one or more generators and/or transmission system components is assumed to be out of service. Such contingency analysis often include all single contingencies (the set of system configurations in which each generator or transmission line is out of service, one at a time), perhaps also double contingencies (two generators, two lines, or one generator and line out of service, in various combinations), and a selection of the more common fault conditions the system might experience. If any of the transmission line flows, system voltage profiles, or system stability indices fall outside the range of acceptability for any of these contingencies, then system expansion and upgrade opportunities to alleviate the potential problems are created and compared.

In the past, after the relative merits of the design alternatives had been evaluated, the utility certified to provide service in area of the proposed addition would initiate the certification process with the appropriate regulatory authorities, then proceed with the project financing and construction if certification were granted. Depending upon the environmental sensitivities and the magnitude of the project, the entire process could take as long as 5 to 10 years from the start of certification until the planned addition would enter service.

In the future, who will be responsible for overall transmission planning and evaluation and the party or parties who will do the investing may be different from the franchised transmission provider. The institutions are changing and there is a multitude of new market players. The next section discusses the possible role of the system operator, an important new institution that is emerging.

Open-Access And The Advent Of The System Operator

FERC Orders 888 and 889 initiated a transformation in the business of providing transmission services that is still underway. In all regions of the country the owners of transmission facilities and prospective users of those facilities have been coming together to create new institutions empowered to coordinate and manage the joint use of transmission facilities that were generally constructed by the monopoly providers for their own exclusive purposes. In addition, new pricing rules are being, or have been, created and put into place to compensate owners of transmission facilities for their use by third-party users.

Most regions of country are creating and formalizing new entities variously called a Network Coordinator (NC), Transmission System Operator (TSO), Power System Operator (PSO), Independent System Operator (ISO), or just System Operator (SO), to coordinate and manage transmission system operations under the new open-access rules. Since, historically, the owners of transmission facilities have voluntarily coordinated their transmission operations and planning activities at the regional level under the direction of NERC, it has been natural that many of the system operators that are being proposed will coordinate and manage the use of facilities within a geographical extent that matches the regional reliability councils of NERC. However, there are exceptions. For example, the California utilities, in response to state PUC initiatives adopted there, have proposed a state-wide California ISO even though the state is heavily interconnected with other states in the west and is a member of the Western Systems Coordinating Council, the regional council that coordinates operations and planning in the entire western portion of the North American continent. In the midwest, an ISO is proposed to coordinate the operations of most the utilities that now make up two neighboring reliability councils that border on the Great Lakes.

At the time of this writing only one ISO is formally in operation. This is in Texas, or more specifically the Electric Reliability Council of Texas (ERCOT).[3] In California, it is proposed that the ISO begin operations on January 1, 1998. The ISO proposed for New England just received conditional approval from FERC, but will not go into full operation until 1998. The Mid-America Power Pool expects to file its ISO organizational plan with FERC late in 1998. In the Midwest the proposed ISO will not go into full operation until around the year 2000. Other regions have proposed for their system operators to begin operations on various dates in 1998 or later.

The details of how the market for generation services is supposed to work within these market areas where operations will be coordinated by an ISO vary a great deal from one restructuring proposal to the next. Additionally, the specifics of the menu of transmission services and how those services will be priced also varies from one market area to the next Consequently, the scope of operational and management responsibilities of the system operator varies too. Generally, however, every system operator has responsibility for coordinating and managing system operations in a way that will assure safe and reliable operation within its area of jurisdiction and to coordinate with neighboring system operators.

Specific system operator responsibilities include, but are not limited to, processing and coordinating requests for transmission service so as to prevent violation of system operating constraints, managing the system redispatch and/or orderly curtailments of service whenever unforeseen contingencies or emergency conditions require it, and overseeing the calculation, updating, and posting of available transmission capabilities (ATC).[4] In some cases the system operator also performs various accounting functions and does the billing for transmission services usage. In other market areas the system operator may determine when congestion charges need to be added to flows over congested transmission interfaces, quantify the amounts of the charges, bill for their collection, and distribute them to their rightful recipients. The specifics vary a great deal depending upon the market structure proposed.

In all cases, the system operator's responsibilities are primarily, if not exclusively, directed toward issues of system operation for the next hour, week, month, or perhaps as long as a year. The longer-run issues of when, where, and why invest in additional transmission facilities are generally not within the purview of the system operator, though most proposals do acknowledge an important advisory and coordination function that the system operator can play in investment planning.   Important questions delineating the full extent of the ISO's responsibilities and authority are, nonetheless, still being debated:

  • Should the ISO be authorized to do planning, or simply facilitate and
  coordinate plans of transmission owners in the system?
  • Should the ISO be allowed to override the capital budgets of the
  transmission owners?
  • Should the ISO be allowed to construct and own facilities itself?
  • Should the ISO be allowed to arrange alternative financing for new
  facilities?
  • Should the ISO be allowed to arrange for alternate transmission owners?

Moreover, new considerations in transmission planning and investment must be accommodated. Some of these are discussed in the next section.

New Transmission Planning And Investment Considerations

With transmission now functionally unbundled from generation, distribution, and customer service, the historical transmission planning and investment paradigm must be re-examined. The transmission provider is still part of the production chain from generator to consumer, but no longer operated and planned as part of a vertically integrated production unit. And even though economies of scale have disappeared in the generation segment of the industry and competition is considered workable there, there are still tremendous economies of scale in transmission that make competition in this segment of the industry unworkable. Consequently, transmission providers will likely continue providing services as franchised monopolies subject to cost-of-service regulation at the local, state and/or federal level.

This does not mean that certain aspects of transmission cannot be deregulated. For example, in some markets it is proposed to have energy prices reflect the difference in costs of producing energy at opposite sides of congested transmission interfaces. A secondary market in transmission rights, i.e., the rights to the "congestion rentals" that accrue to a line across the interface because of the different costs of energy that such flow limitations might create, could evolve.[5] It has been proposed that trading of such rights could take place in an unregulated marketplace. Secondary trading of reserved transmission capacity might also take place in an unregulated market. In neither of these examples, however, is the return to the owner of the "wires" to be deregulated and left to the market, only the return to the owner of the rights or the reservation holder(s).

NERC and regional planning and operating criteria will continue to serve as technical touchstones for system planners and operators. But the new economics of electricity supply dictates that new non-technical non-reliability related criteria for planning transmission investments might have to be accommodated.

This derives, in part, from the fact that the price of energy and many ancillary services will be market-determined, not based upon costs and administratively-determined. Consequently, the notion that one uses the transmission system only to move energy from a given set of generators to serve only native load customers at lowest cost and at adequate levels of reliability is no longer valid. In the future, transmission providers will serve basically as transporters of an energy commodity. As such, their role might be characterized as facilitating and enabling orderly and efficient trading in the energy market while maintaining quality of the delivered product. This is a very new role for transmission, and traditional transmission planning and investment practices may need to be adapted in response.

In the new deregulated energy marketplace, what might be some of the new reasons for investing in new transmission facilities? Consider some the following.

In markets in which locational or zonal energy price differentials will be a fixture of the energy marketplace, transmission investment might be market-driven. This would come about because one purpose of adding new facilities could be to capitalize upon congestion rentals. To illustrate, consider the case of California. Within California it is now conceptualized that two zones of relatively homogenous energy prices will be established. These two zones are separated by a transmission bottleneck that constrains flows a relatively large proportion of the time. Whenever the transmission constraints are binding, a difference in energy prices is created across the interface that reflects the difference between the respective incremental supply costs/bids on each side of the interface.   The purpose of adding the new transmission capability in such a situation would be to allow those paying congestion charges to reduce or forgo entirely future congestion payments.   One could expect the principal proponents of the new capability would be those who will pay reduced congestion charges as a result of the line addition.

In such a case, the new line might be added and owned by the existing transmission franchise in the area, with the rights to the congestion rentals belonging to customers/financiers of the facility, or a new franchise might be created.   In either case, the owner of the "wires business" would be regulated and presumably receive no more than the administratively determined "cost-of-service" for owning and operating the line.   The owner(s) of the transmission rights would receive compensation either in the form of speculative congestion rentals over the life of the investment, or in form of contractual payments from the beneficiaries of the line in lieu of their foregone congestion rentals.   Either/both of these potential income streams would provide the incentive for the prospective owner(s) of the transmission rights to promote the project.   It is hoped that such market-driven investments will help to relieve much of the congestion in markets where such incentives are proposed.

Not all new transmission investment will be market-driven, however.   Many regions of the country are proposing or adopting transmission pricing structures that have no explicit congestion charges.   When limitations in transmission capability are encountered in these market areas, the ISO will administer curtailment protocols to allocate the available transmission resources.   The notion of congestion rentals in this market structure is meaningless; there are no explicit congestion charges. Consequently, investments in these market areas can not be market-driven, but rather will have to be administratively-determined.[6]   In addition to the traditional reasons to expand the system to maintain system security, some new "administrative" reasons for investing in transmission facilities might be those below.

One administrative reason to add new transmission facilities in a market area with no transmission price signals to drive investment might be to provide buyers/sellers access to expanded markets.   Since most electric utilities historically pursued supply strategies of self-sufficiency, in which they attempted to build, own, or have under contract sufficient generation to serve their loads, the only inter-area transmission capabilities constructed were sized to provide for emergency needs, not to enable significant or large-scale wholesale trading.   Such transfer capability limitations exist not only between many of the region-wide electric reliability councils, but also between many of the sub-regional control areas.   Since, in the future, the industry is being restructured to facilitate trading of electrical energy as a commodity, new transmission infrastructure may be necessary to provide customers in these transmission-limited areas and sub-areas broader access to supply alternatives.

A variation of the expanded market objective is to add facilities to mitigate market power in the supply of generation services.[7]   For historical reasons, there can be a great deal of market power concentrated in the business organization that was the traditional franchise provider for a service area. And although there are many potential new entrants to the business of providing generation services, a large concentration of the operating generation resources may still be under the control of one generation supplier. It could be advisable to "connect" other generation providers to the area simply to mitigate that market power of the existing generation provider.

Other non-reliability related reasons for adding new transmission facilities in the future might include:

- to reduce risks in generating costs to some customer groups
- to reduce loop-flow impacts of trades between certain remote market players
- to isolate some market players from perceived threats to reliability
- to reduce environmental and/or human health impacts of existing transmission facilities

Creating a complete list of new reasons why someone might want, or want someone else, to add new facilities is probably not possible today. This is because there will be many non-traditional market players promoting new planning and operating objectives for the transmission system in the new electricity marketplace. Moreover, every proposal for new facilities will create both winners and losers.

To preserve reliability of operation in the future, it will be necessary that coordinated transmission planning and assessment continue under whatever institutional arrangements are made to facilitate open-access in transmission. New stakeholders with new interests and goals will be clamoring for new transmission facilities. Establishing institutions that can balance the multiplicity of stakeholder interests while preventing gridlock in the planning and investment process will be a tremendous challenge.

Concluding Remarks

Are the institutions that are being created to plan the transmission systems in this new open-access environment being designed to balance the competing stakeholder interests with both the traditional engineering and the new economic objectives in mind? Are the appropriate incentives, procedural safeguards, and governance structures being adopted? Since investment, by its nature, is only manifested in the long-term, only time will tell.

Notes

[1]Steve Stoft and Ross Baldick are gratefully acknowledged for offering valuable comments on an earlier version of this paper.
[2]Federal Energy Regulatory Commission, Promoting Wholesale Competition Through Open Access Non-discriminatory Transmission Services by Public Utilities & Recovery of Stranded Costs by Public Utilities and Transmitting Utilities, Docket No. RM-95-8-000 and Docket No. RM94-7-001, Order 888,

Washington, D. C., April 24, 1996 and Federal Energy Regulatory Commission,Open Access Same-Time Information (formerly Real-time Information Networks) and Standards of Conduct, Order 889, Washington, D. C., April 24, 1996.

[3]Martin L. Baughman, "Pricing of Open-Access Transmission Services in Texas," *Utilities Policy,* September 1997.

[4]North American Electric Reliability Council, Available Transfer Capability Definitions and Determination, Princeton, NJ, June 1996.

[5]William W. Hogan, Contracts Networks for Electric Power Transmission, Journal of Regulatory Economics, Vol. 4, pp. 221-242, September 1992.

[6]Steve Stoft made the following excellent point in a review of this paper, "As we know, non-price rationing is inefficient, and although the private market might well build lines to avoid it, this type of rationing would almost certainly produce significant inefficiencies in any market outcome. But isn't this just an argument for better transmission pricing and not an argument for regulated transmission investment? So the question remains do we really need regulated reliability investments or does it just appear that we need them because the transmission access market has been misdesigned?"

[7]R. Baldick and E. Kahn, "Transmission Planning in the Era of Integrated Resource Planning: A Survey of Recent Cases", Lawrence Berkeley Laboratory LBL-32231, September 1992.

References

R. Baldick and E. Kahn. 1992. "Transmission Planning in the Era of Integrated Resource Planning: A Survey of Recent Cases", Lawrence Berkeley Laboratory LBL-32231, September.

Martin L. Baughman. 1997. "Pricing of Open-Access Transmission Services in Texas," *Utilities Policy,* September.

Federal Energy Regulatory Commission. 1996. *Promoting Wholesale Competition Through Open Access Non-discriminatory Transmission Services by Public Utilities & Recovery of Stranded Costs by Public Utilities and Transmitting Utilities,* Docket No. RM-95-8-000 and Docket No. RM94-7-001, Order 888, Washington, D. C., April 24.

Federal Energy Regulatory Commission. 1996. *Open Access Same-Time Information (formerly Real-time Information Networks) and Standards of Conduct,* Order 889, Washington, D. C., April 24.

William W. Hogan. 1992. Contracts Networks for Electric Power Transmission, *Journal of Regulatory Economics,* Vol. 4, pp. 221-242, September.

North American Electric Reliability Council. 1996. *Available Transfer Capability Definitions and Determination,* Princeton, NJ, June.

10 THE ROLE OF RESEARCH AND NEW TECHNOLOGY IN A RESTRUCTURED NETWORKED ENERGY SYSTEM

M. Granger Morgan

Introduction

While the revolution in telecommunications has been driven by rapid technical change, this paper argues that technology has thus far played a more modest role in the revolution now sweeping the electric power industry. However, it argues that there are a number of new technologies now on the horizon that could have profound impacts on the future structure and operation of the electric power industry. How these technologies will evolve is unclear. Some could push the system toward greater centralization, some could lead to dramatic decentralization, and some could result in much greater coupling between the gas and the electric networks. The evolution of the networked energy system is likely to be highly path dependent. Because of shrinking research budgets, and the relatively short time constant of markets, there is a risk that the full social benefits of these new technologies will not be realized. The paper closes with a proposal for a new mechanism to produce the investments in basic technology research that will be needed to develop these promising technologies in a timely fashion to allow informed social choices.

Background

Some years ago the wholesale market for the production and transport of natural gas was deregulated and competition was introduced. Natural gas prices fell, and estimates of supply have gone up. Today, privatization and competition are being introduced into electric generation and substantial changes are being made in the organization, administration and operation of electric power transmission systems. The changes are sufficiently fundamental that, if they proceed across the US as now anticipated, it is appropriate to refer to them as a "revolution" in the electric power industry.

In contrast to the revolution that swept the telecommunications industry, which was driven by dramatic changes in technology, to-date new technology has played a more modest role in the deregulation and restructuring of the electric power industries. Cheap plentiful gas, efficient new gas turbines (including remarkably efficient combined cycle systems), and computers that can rapidly handle many transactions, have all played a supporting role. However, at its root, the current changes in the structure of the electric power industry, like those that previously occurred in the gas industry, are being driven by a faith in the benefits of privatization and competition in free markets, albeit one informed by economic theory.

Barring major blackouts, or other events which could induce dramatic changes in political attitudes toward electric power over the next few years, it appears likely that significant competition will be introduced in the generation and marketing of electric power across much of the country. This will probably lower average costs. Because states play a major role in the regulation of electric power, at least the interim solutions are likely to differ significantly in different regions. And, because there are powerful economic and institutional forces at play, we should anticipate that some of the outcomes will fall rather short of the full competition among all comers on a level economic playing field that is being advanced as the goal of restructuring. Probably the lower costs these new arrangements should yield will outweigh the increased costs from the complexity of negotiating more transactions. Probably they will be passed on to many, perhaps even most, customers.

In considering this restructuring, it is important to remember that electric power systems are considerably more complex than gas systems. Making the transition to competition poses enormous organizational, technical and regulatory challenges. Today, most of the attention of industry managers, legislators, regulators and academics is focused on fairly short-term issues related to how to make the needed changes happen. While this focus is understandable, it is also important to step back from the current debates to ask how the technology may evolve.

Because it is a networked system, that requires large capital investments and long-term social commitments (such as land for transmission lines), the future evolution of the electric power system is likely to be highly path dependent. Institutional and technical choices made over the next few years could impose major constraints on the evolution of the system for decades. In order to assure that the future energy system meets the broad needs of society, it is important to look ahead, to try to anticipate future capabilities and make choices today that will encourage the most socially desirable future outcomes.

The Future Role of Technology

While technology has played a limited role in the first wave of the electric power revolution, it is likely that there will be a second wave, driven by dramatic technological change. What sorts of technical developments could lead to this second wave? Examples include:

* Low cost solid-state power electronics which make it possible to isolate and control the flow of power on individual lines and subsystems within the power transmission system.

* Low cost sensors, communication and computation which in combination allow better control of both individual loads and the overall power system.

* Low cost superconducting technology which makes possible very high capacity underground transmission.

* Low cost technology for converting gas to electricity, and electricity to gas.

* Low cost storage technology.

* Low cost solar voltaic technology.

In the next several pages, I briefly discuss some of the ways in which these technologies might evolve. The key point to remember as we go through this discussion is that nobody can predict which technologies will win the race to become cheap and practical: which will be adopted, and which will be passed over, or relegated to special niche markets. While some technologies push toward decentralization, others encourage continued centralization. Some of them push toward the integration of the electric and gas networks into a single networked energy system. Others push toward continued separate operation.

> *While technology has played a limited role in the first wave of the electric power revolution, it is likely that there will be a second wave, driven by dramatic technological change.*

Whether the future will see more or less decentralization, and whether it will see closer integration of the gas and electricity systems, depends critically upon policy choices made today, the rate at which different technologies emerge, the relative price of different fuels, and the nature of the broader institutional and market environment. What does seem clear is that big changes are possible. With them may come further dramatic changes in the structure of the industry and in the control strategies and institutions which would be best for operating the system.

Solid State Power Electronics

Solid state power electronics has been developed for a variety of applications (Bose, 1992; Harashima, 1994) including industrial motion control, induction heating, electric locomotive and rapid transit drives (allowing the use of induction motors), uninterruptable power system control and power conditioning, power supplies in lighting and consumer products, DC power transmission, and a number of military applications. As power levels and device speeds have increased, and costs have fallen, EPRI has encouraged the application of these same technologies to the flexible control of AC power systems (Hingorani, 1996; Stahlkopf, 1996).

If a DC power source is connected to a set of electrical loads such as lights and motors, it is appropriate to think of the wires that carry the direct current to the loads as analogous to stiff mechanical drive shafts (the friction in the bearings is like the resistance in the wires). However, when loads are supplied by alternating current the stiff-drive-shaft analogy is no longer valid. To maintain a rough mechanical analogy, we can replace the shafts with horizontal springs, some very stiff, some quite compliant, depending on the length and electrical capacity of the various interconnections. This is illustrated in Figure 1. It is still possible to transmit mechanical power through this system by rotating one end of a spring around its long axis and extracting power from the other end. However, the dynamical properties of such a system are very different from those of a system comprised of rigid drive shafts. Under some circumstances, torsional or twisting oscillations can build up along the springs. In addition, if one tries to transmit too much power through a spring, it will ultimately twist out of shape into a tangled mess, and useful power transmission will cease. In an AC power system, such loss of electrical synchrony can result in the loss of a line, and if problems propagate to other lines, ultimately to a system-wide black out.

In traditional AC power systems, the dynamical properties of the system are controlled by changing the output of the generators, by switching connections to transformers (loosely analogous to shifting to different diameter gears in Figure 1), and by connecting and disconnecting various electrical devices (large capacitors and inductors), which, at least loosely, in the mechanical analogy, can help to determine the stiffness of the springs.

When abrupt changes occur in a large AC power system, the resulting dynamic response can be very rapid. Because traditional computers have not been fast enough to model most such changes in real time, and because electrical and mechanical control systems have been fairly slow, power systems are operated so as to keep them far away from situations in which serious oscillations or loss of electrical synchrony might occur. Solid state power electronic devices can be combined, under the control of a microprocessor, to produce "flexible AC transmission system," or FACTS, technology which can respond to and control the electrical properties of a transmission line *much* more rapidly. In some circumstances these systems can also reduce the need for large expensive capacitors and inductors. One result should be that a line can be operated at much higher

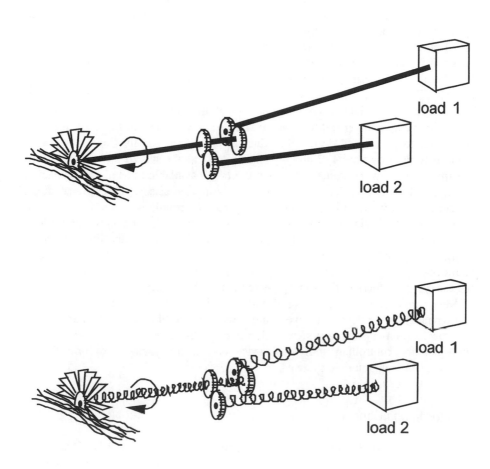

Figure 1: Mechanical analogs of a DC power system (above) and an AC power system (below). In the analog of the AC system, the stiff drive shafts of the DC system are replaced by springs with varying degrees of stiffness.   Under some circumstances, twisting oscillations can build up along the springs. In addition, if one tries to transmit too much power down a spring it will ultimately twist out of shape into a tangled mess, and useful power transmission will cease.

power loading (closer to its I^2R thermal limit) because, with rapid control of its electrical properties, it is no longer necessary to operate it in such a conservative manner. In the analogy of Figure 1, adding FACTS to a line is like replacing a spring with something that comes very close to being a stiff drive shaft.

The amount of power that a long transmission line can carry is not only limited by the thermal rating of the line. It is also controlled by the relationship between the electrical phase of the AC wave form at the two ends of the line (the larger the phase difference, up to some stability limit, the greater the power flow). FACTS technology can be used to manipulate this phase relation and thus increase a line's capacity. Because of the dynamic electrical properties of traditional AC systems, there are decided limits to a system operator's ability to control where power flows. Thus, for example, if generator A, in the simple system shown in Figure 2, wants to sell power to consumer M, not all of the power will necessarily flow over line 3. Some may flow via lines 1, 2 and 4. This means that the sale of power by A to M can impose a "network eternality" on generator B's available transmission capacity. By controlling the electrical properties of lines more precisely, FACTS can direct the flow of power, minimizing or eliminating such externalities.

Finally, transmission system operators must be constantly concerned about how the system will behave under emergency conditions when key lines or other components suddenly become unavailable and power surges down new and unexpected paths. Imaginative use of FACTS can limit where power can flow and reduce system vulnerabilities to unexpected equipment outages.

Such applications of advanced power electronics are still in their infancy. Much work remains to be done: on developing lower cost and higher performance solid state devices, on improving system design and reliability, and on devising effective strategies for controlling individual systems and the joint operation of, and interaction among, multiple systems.

Monitoring and Control

Computer-based supervisory control and dispatch has been a standard feature of electric power systems for several decades. Rapid progress is being made on improving the operation and capability of such systems. As transmission systems become more heavily used, and as FACTS technology is introduced in significant quantity, the continued development of monitoring and control technology will become even more important.

Monitoring and control are also becoming important at lower levels in the power system. Distribution automation has been introduced into many systems and is likely to grow in importance as distributed generation and other innovations occur. "Smart" control, which combines sensors, microprocessor-based controllers and power electronics, is also becoming a common feature of many industrial and consumer devices and systems.

A great deal of electric power is consumed by electric motors. It has long been understood that variable speed motor drives could yield both improved

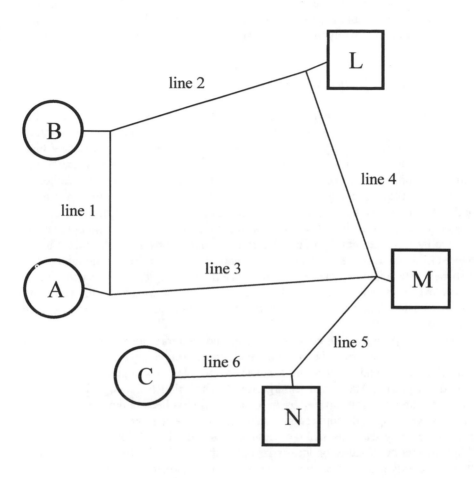

Figure 2: It is not possible to precisely control the path over which power flows in an AC power system. If, in this simple illustration, generator A wants to sell power to consumer M, not all of the power will flow over line 3. Some may flow via lines 1, 2 and 4. This means that the sale of power by A to M imposes a "network externality" on generator B's available transmission capacity. By controlling the electrical properties of lines more precisely, FACTS technology can direct the flow of power, minimizing or eliminating such network externalities.

performance and increased energy efficiency (Slemon, 1994). However, until the advent of modern power electronics and microprocessors, such control was too expensive to be feasible in most applications. As costs fall and capability grows, such applications are likely to become common.

Superconducting Technology

In recent years, due to environmental and esthetic concerns about the possible health risks posed by AC electric and magnetic fields, and the increasingly litigious nature of American society, it has become extremely difficult to build new high voltage transmission lines. Fortunately, because of substantial existing capacity and improved end-use efficiency, these obstacles to building new lines have resulted in only selected local and regional difficulties. But the problem will grow over time, and may ultimately become very serious. Several new technologies could help postpone to alleviate the difficulty. As noted above, FACTS technology can be used to increase the capacity of existing lines, sometimes by as much as a doubling. More efficient use of electrical energy, particularly in motor drives and lighting can also help. In addition, some of the distributed technologies that we will discuss below may reduce the need for additional long distance transmission. However, sooner or later, it seems likely that significant numbers of large new lines will be required.

The basic problem with conventional high voltage transmission is that it is big and visually compelling. If it could be made more compact, particularly if it were placed under ground, most of the obstacles to building new transmission capacity would disappear. Traditional underground transmission technology is extremely expensive on a per unit capacity basis. Thus its use has been limited to urban cores and to very special applications such as underwater crossings. Practical superconducting cable technology could change all that. Because even the new "high temperature" superconductors require substantial infrastructure for cooling, this technology is unlikely to ever become cheap in absolute terms. But because the carrying capacity of a superconducting transmission line could be very large, the cost per unit of power transmitted could become reasonable. If unit costs can be gotten down, and if high reliability can be achieved, superconducting technology could transform electric power transmission. Demonstrations of transmission technology are now beginning (Sweet, 1997). Problems involve issues such as how to fabricate flexible wires from ceramic materials, how to maintain the superconducting properties of the cable under high loadings, and how to economically provide the required cooling to liquid nitrogen temperatures.

Before superconducting transmission cable comes into widespread use, superconducting materials are likely to find important uses in other power system applications such as compact, higher capacity transformers, motors and generators and short-term energy storage devices. None of this will happen on its own. There is still a large gap between trial demonstrations and practical devices. A considerable amount of basic technology research is needed before reliable cost effective applications will become possible.

Technology for Converting Gas to Electricity, or Electricity to Gas

We have grown accustomed to thinking about electricity and gas as two separate systems. In the future they are likely to be seen as two coupled elements of the network energy supply system. On the user side there is already stiff competition between electricity and gas in consumer applications such as space conditioning, water heating and cooking and in a variety of manufacturing and industrial process applications. Gas is also becoming the fuel of choice for much new electric generation. This trend is likely to continue given the low capital costs, low emissions, and rapid siting associated with gas turbines and combine cycle plants. The turbines used in these systems have been derived from jet aircraft engines. Combined cycle systems use the hot exhaust gas from the gas turbine to make steam which is used to drive a steam turbine ("bottoming cycle"), thus increasing the overall efficiency with which heat energy can be converted to electrical energy. The conversion efficiency of combined cycle gas turbines is now about 55%.[1]

The new turbine technology has already prompted a move toward decentralization of generation. This trend could be considerably accelerated by much smaller units, in the range of 25kw to 50kw, which have recently begun to appear on an experimental basis (Sutherland, 1997). These micro turbines are easy to site, and can add considerable reliability if they are distributed throughout a system. Exhaust heat might be used for space and water heating in apartment buildings or similar applications.

Although they are small, they do require significant specialized maintenance. However, it should be possible to quickly swap individual units in and out in much the same way as is done in aircraft maintenance operations. A utility that had a significant number of such devices could maintain a few extras and swap them in and out for both scheduled and unscheduled maintenance as needed, perhaps keeping costs low by relying upon a specialized aircraft engine maintenance contractor to actually service the units.

Fuel cells are another technology that could push both toward decentralization and integration of the gas and electric systems. While they have been around since the early part of the last century, fuel cells have only recently begun to become technically and economically interesting for power system applications (Blomen and Mugerwa, 1993; Hirschenhofer and McClelland, 1995). Several hundred are now in use to provide back-up power in settings such as hospitals and data centers. A number of utilities in the US, Japan and Europe have installations which range in size from a few kW to over 10 MW.

Fuel cells face virtually the same theoretical limits as those of combustion engines on their ability to convert the chemical energy in fuel into electrical energy. However, they can achieve significantly higher practical efficiencies, because the efficiency of real combustion engines is not limited by thermodynamic theory so much as by the high temperature properties of materials. A high temperature fuel cell combined with a steam turbine bottoming cycle, can get very close to the limits of a "perfect" thermodynamic engine (Appleby, 1993). In the near term, practical fuel cells will have to convert natural gas or some other fuel into hydrogen. This, together with compressor and other losses reduces the efficiency of practical units. Nevertheless, while the heat rate of a good coal/steam plant is about 10,000 BTU/kWh, the operating efficiency of a high temperature fuel cell system should be about 6,000 BTU/kWh (Appleby, 1993).

Fuel cells have recently become a leading candidate for low emissions motor vehicles. Particularly if they are powered by pure hydrogen, they have the great advantage of producing only water as their effluent. Several major auto manufacturers have recently announced new research and demonstration initiatives. The power plant for an automobile is larger than the electrical load of most homes. If fuel cell automobiles become common, and their operating life is long, then it is entirely possible that when cars are at home they could be plugged into a gas supply and used to provide power to the home and surplus power to the electric system -- a dramatic move toward decentralized generation that would effectively turn the distribution system inside out!

Low Cost Storage Technology

One big advantage of gas over electricity is that gas can be easily stored, both in large storage tanks and underground caverns connected to the system, and in portable tanks. Since demand is not uniform over the course of a day or a week, or from season to season, storage has enormous benefits in the operation of a networked energy system. Power companies have long managed to obtain some storage capability by regulating the flow of water through hydroelectric dams. In addition, in a number of cases, special pumped storage hydro facilities have been constructed, which use low cost off peak power to pump water up hill, and then use this same water to generate electricity during periods of peak demand. On a more limited basis, compressed gas, stored in natural underground reservoirs, has also been used for storage.

To date, most interest in fuel cells has been in going from gas to electricity. However, there are applications, most notably in association with solar or wind energy, in which it is attractive to consider running a fuel cell "backwards" so as to make easily stored hydrogen gas.

Battery technology has long provided an expensive strategy for storing limited amounts of electric energy. Before the advent of nuclear propulsion, batteries were used to propel submerged submarines. They have been used as back-up power for critical applications such as emergency lighting and communications systems, as power for limited-range special need vehicles such as fork lifts (in enclosed spaces where emissions are a concern) or golf carts (where quiet operation is desirable). There have even been a few installations in power systems (Anderson and Carr,

1993), although cost has limited, and is likely to continue to limit, such applications.

In recent years there has been a burst of interest in batteries for motor vehicles, motivated by the desire to reduce urban air pollution (Moore, 1996). Electric vehicles have made significant improvements (e.g., efficiencies up by a factor of four) over the past two decades, but the biggest improvements have come from the use of power electronics in power trains. Storage batteries still have a long way to go before they will compete effectively with conventional fuel. Current energy densities are between 50 and 100 watt-hours/kg and projected to reach 150 early next century. For comparison, the energy content of a kg of gasoline is just under 13,000 watt-hours (which for a proper comparison should be derated to a few thousand in order to include the conversion efficiency of a heat engine).

Because most batteries contain heavy metals, used in large quantities they may present significant environmental problems resulting from leakage during materials recycle (Lave et al., 1995). Future recycle technology may resolve these difficulties. New internal combustion engines have become extremely clean. In addition, as noted above, a number of major auto companies have announced efforts based on fuel cells. Which, if any, of these strategies will capture the market in the long run is very much an open question.

Fly wheels which store kinetic energy, may also play a role in future energy systems. Modern fly wheel designs, sometimes called "electromechanical batteries," use a fiber-composite rotor spinning on magnetic bearings in a vacuum chamber. Storage capacities of 1 kW-h in units appropriate for mobile applications and 25 kW-h for stationary installations should be technically feasible (Post et al., 1993). The ability of electromechanical storage devices to respond to large short-term loads (such as the rapid acceleration of a vehicle) is likely to be much better than that of electrochemical batteries for the foreseeable future.

Finally, as noted above, superconducting technology may prove valuable for short-term storage (a few cycles) applied to applications in power quality and reliability.

Low Cost Solar Voltaic Technology

A photovoltaic cell is a very simple solid states device (a junction diode) into which photons from sun light enter and are absorbed creating charge separation (hole-electron pairs). The result is that a voltage develops across the cell. If a number of cells are used together, significant power can be obtained.

There are two basic obstacles to the widespread use of photovoltaic cells: cost and efficiency. The two are related since of course the higher the efficiency, the lower the collecting area that is needed to obtain a given amount of energy. Yearly average solar flux ranges from above 240 w/m^2 in the South West to under 150 w/m^2 in the Pacific Northwest and upstate New York (Bennett in Penner and Icerman, 1975).

Like fuel cells, photocells have already seen wide application in settings, such as power for space craft, in which costs are not a serious limitation. Coupled with trickle charge batteries, they are now finding substantial nitch markets for applications such as lighting for remotely located highway signs, emergency telephone call boxes, and vacation cabins.

The cost of energy from photovoltaics continues to fall, but is still at least a factor of ten too high to be competitive with conventional technologies. The US Department of Energy now estimates costs to be about 20 cents/kWh (Hoffman, 1997). The best conversion efficiencies reached are now about 20%. In a recent review, Schwartz (1993) has argued that "it seems entirely reasonable that one can expect flat plate panels manufactured using low-cost techniques with conversion efficiencies in excess of 20%. Single junction high-concentration cells," that use lenses or mirrors to concentrate the sun light, "should be capable of conversion efficiencies in the range of 30% and tandem cells in high concentration systems should approach and possibly exceed 40%." One step that could help reduce costs, beyond progress on the materials and manufacturing process use in the production of the solid state materials, is the integration of cells into structural building materials such as roof and wall panels (Davis, 1997).

While costs should continue to fall, and performance improve, the Energy Information Administration predicts that penetration will remain slow for the next two decades. They forecast less than 2% of on-grid capacity in 2015 (EIA, 1996). In addition to technical change, there are a number of social and environmental circumstances that could induce more rapid introduction.

Because the sun only shines in the day time it makes sense to think of using them in conjunction with advanced storage technology, or with fuel cells which can use the electrical energy to make hydrogen gas. Depending upon how they evolve, such developments could further promote the tighter integration of the networked energy system and also contribute to greater decentralization.

System Philosophy and Control Strategy

Closely linked to the emergence of new technologies is the question of how best to operate and control the electrical part of the future networked energy system. Today power companies and regulators are busily setting up new Independent System Operators (ISOs) to operate and coordinate the transmission system in a centralized manner. Centralized operation has been the norm for power systems in the past, and may continue to offer the best strategy in the future. However, some new technology could make other strategies more attractive. For example, widespread adoption of FACTS together with substantial distributed generation might create an environment in which control was better done in a decentralized manner, perhaps by a number of independent but cooperating autonomous software agents.

As we create new organizations to manage power systems today, we should bear in mind the uncertainties about what architecture and control strategies will be optimal several decades in the future. We should try to design organizations that are likely to remain flexible so that institutional inertia and established standard operating procedures, will not become a major obstacle to adopting promising future technologies and control strategies.

Dealing with Externalities

In the long run, a new more integrated networked energy system holds the potential to significantly reduce the environmental burdens of energy production and use. Factors that could contribute include:

- A move away from coal to cleaner, more efficient, natural gas.

- A growth in the use of photovoltaics and other renewable fuels

- The development of "zero" or low emissions motor vehicles.

In the short run, the impacts are less easily anticipated. To the extent that restructuring drives less efficient coal plants into early retirement, to be replaced by combined-cycle gas plants, it could yield substantial, and fairly rapid, environmental benefits on both a local and a global scale. To the extent that it promotes the early retirement of expensive nuclear plants, to be replaced by greater use of existing coal plants, the environmental impacts at a global scale could be negative, due to increased emissions of CO_2. Because of increased emissions of SO_2 and NO_x, the local and regional environmental impacts could also be negative.

While there may be controversy, local, state and federal environmental regulatory agencies certainly should be able to deal with any adverse short-term impacts. The larger concern is figuring out how to support adequate medium and long-term power systems related to environmental research. In the past, the electric power industry has made substantial investments in such research through EPRI. As the industry has become more competitive, support for EPRI has decreased, and much of the research has adopted a shorter-term, more applied, focus. Despite reductions, EPRI has managed to continue to maintain a significant program of environmental research. Whether this will remain possible in the future, as competitive pressures continue to mount, is unclear.

A second area in which restructuring could have adverse externalities involves energy conservation programs. Over the past decades, a number of utilities have mounted efforts to promote conservation. Because of the inherent difficulty in measuring conservation impacts, and because utilities have had clear economic incentives to over-state these impacts, the conservation impacts reported by utilities have been viewed with skepticism.

In a Ph.D. at Carnegie Mellon, Parfomak (1996) recently examined the aggregate commercial and industrial conservation impact reported *ex post* by 39 utilities in the Northeast and California through 1993. He found that 99.4% of the reported impacts can be statistically observed in system level sales after economic and weather effects are accounted for. However, he also found that unless environmental externality costs are included, decreasing costs of generation are likely to make most such conservation activity less attractive in the future. Without externality costs, he projected that only 12% to 37% of conservation potential is likely to be cost effective between 1995 and 2000. Applying median estimates of externality costs to energy prices raises this estimate to between 35% and 73%. If, as a consequence of increased competition, the price of electric power falls, and if nothing is done to internalize the environmental externalities associated with electric power generation, it may become much harder to promote conservation activities in the future.

The Need for Research

Without some external intervention, it seems unlikely that a new freer market will make socially optimal research investments to:
Develop the technologies needed to fuel the next wave in the power revolution;

- Perform the system studies and policy studies that will be necessary to determine whether present system architectures, and regulatory and management systems will be compatible with future needs; and.

- Perform the environmental research that is needed to deal with current and future power system technologies.

Competition in the free market may be able to produce dramatically lower electric rates, especially for large commercial customers. And it may be able to support short- and medium-term applied research to get some new technologies into the field. However, as in many other sectors, it is unlikely to seriously under invest in basic technology research for which the practical pay-offs may be several decades in the future, or in public interest research on general policy matters or on broad environmental concerns.

At the same time, for different reasons, the research budgets of the two main sources of long-term and public interest support for power system research in the United States, the Electric Power Research Institute, and the US Department of Energy, are both declining.

Over the past few years, as the industry has tried to cut costs and get ready for the introduction of competition, EPRI's budget has fallen from about $600-million to about $450-million. EPRI management is working hard to respond to the changing environment. They have focused more on short-term issues, moved to a "menu" approach which allows companies to pick and choose what they want to support, are actively widening their base of support, and in selected cases are spinning-off commercially promising activities into for-profit entities. They have also instituted a program of strategic R&D which is supported by a surcharge on the more applied work.

Recently, utility support for long-term and public interest research at EPRI has stabilized. Whether this situation can be maintained or improved will depend in part on just how competitive the industry becomes. Without a requirement to participate in EPRI or other research, firms will always face pressures in highly competitive markets to cut costs by reducing expenditures on long-term and public interest research. On the other hand, for at least the next decade, only the two ends of the industry, generation and marketing, are likely to be deregulated. Transmission and distribution will probably remain regulated, at least until FACTS becomes inexpensive and widespread. After the current disruption has passed, regulated transmission and distribution entities could reemerge as an important core for EPRI support.

On the Federal side, NSF supports about $3.5 million in power-system engineering.   The DoE program on electric transmission and distribution technologies, was zeroed out last year. DoE still has substantial research programs on various large central station generation technologies. However, their support for smaller scale distributed technologies is much more modest, for example it runs about $50-million per year for utility-oriented fuel cells and about $60-million per year on photovoltaics, of which most is going to shorter-term issues such as improved manufacturing processes. DoE support for the superconducting cable effort is running about $20-million per year. DARPA has recently become an important player in FACTS technology, committing about $15-million to a new effort that promises to have dual-use applications.

If the US makes insufficient investments in basic technology research, new technologies which could make power systems more efficient, reliable, effective and environmentally sound, could be seriously delayed. In addition, because there are likely to be strong path-dependent features to the evolution of the networked energy system, without careful long-term assessment and informed public policy, the US could easily find itself stuck with sub-optimal technical and organizational arrangements that could not easily be changed.

State and Federal regulators are scrambling to deal with the pressing short-term issues of industry restructuring. Most have not given much thought to the issue of how to support longer- term basic technology and public interest research in a restructured industry. Some haven't even figured out that there is a problem. When I have discussed this issue with regulators who are aware of the problem, they have usually talked in terms of a State administered "wire charge" that would create a fund to deal with various public interest matters such as research.

But, particularly if they are administered at the State level, wire charges are unlikely to produce a satisfactory solution. Things may work reasonably well in California, which has a major State energy program, several leading research universities, and happens also to be the home of EPRI. The outlook is less promising in many other States. When a State collects research money, it is unlikely that it will be willing to allocate much of it to out-of-state organizations. Despite the best of intentions, political pressures to spend the funds in the State will just be too large. Local political pressure would probably also push toward a focus on short-term fast pay-out projects, as it

When a state collects research money,...local political pressure would probably also push toward a focus on short-term fast pay-out projects. ...The US could find much of its research effort balkanized.

already appears to be doing in California. If we continue down the path of separate wire charges in each State, the US could find much of its research effort balkanized. The absolute amounts might be substantial, but they would be spread around in too many small pots. Too much of the money might get spent at places not able to perform state-of-the-art basic technology and public interest research. And, too much of the focus could end up on short-term work better left to the market.

Needed: A new and better way to support research

A better system to support basic technology research and public interest research for the electric power industry should have three attributes:
- Minimal free riders.

- Diversity in both who commissions and in who performs research.

- Incentives to use the best research groups available and to maximize the cost efficiency and the quality of the research.

This could be achieved through a federal requirement that every *electric generator* and *gas supplier* who is connected to the regulated public electric or gas pipeline grids, must make a research investment in basic technology and public interest research which is proportional to some combination of the total energy they produce for the network and the capacity of their connection to the network. The requirement should apply to *all* network based energy systems since there is a good chance that over time they will become more integrated. The charge should include the size of the connection, not just the amount of energy moved through the connection, so as to include a consideration of reliability services. Otherwise, large customers who install co-generation or other energy facilities of their own, would be able to enjoy the reliability benefit of remaining connected to the grid, without bearing any of the costs of research.

Long experience suggests that diversity is the best way to assure a robust research system in which at least *somebody* asks the right questions and adopts the right strategy. The regulated transmission companies should collect the fees and then, working collectively, should allocate them through a system that requires systematic consultation with representatives of suppliers, users, and the public interest. Some flexibility in the institutional arrangements for doing this should be allowed so as to benefit from experimentation. The allocation process should not get down to the level of administering individual research grants. That should be done by existing organizations that have experience in running such programs. Investments could go to a somewhat redesigned EPRI and GRI or to a merged version of the two, to Universities and other non-profit research labs who operate collaborative centers, and to research consortia. If some transmission companies didn't want to participate in this system, the US Department of Energy could receive their fee and manage that research.

If the regulated gas and electric network companies are to play a central role in allocating research funds, how could one assure that there is not a bias toward technologies that depend on the continued existence of networks? The different and competing interests of gas and electricity should help. Thus, while electric network companies might pay less attention to materials for fuel cell membranes than to other promising areas, gas network companies would certainly view such research as important. Customer and public interest participation in decision making would be important to insure adequate investment in areas such as materials for building-integrated photovoltaics.

My proposal focuses on the *producers* of electricity and gas, not on end customers, for two reasons. The number of players is much smaller, and the political difficulties involved in implementing such a research investment, which opponents will surely try to characterize as a tax, is likely to be much greater if it applied to consumers. If for some reason it were judged better to apply the research fee to consumption, rather than to production, Leonard Hyman of Smith Barney has suggested that the fees paid could result in consumers acquiring shares in any intellectual property that might ultimately result from the research. As many a University and non-profit research lab can attest, getting rich on royalties from basic technology research is at best a chancy proposition. For this strategy to succeed some way would have to be found to avoid the inevitable pressure to increase yields by switching to short-term higher pay-out work, better done by the market, since such a switch would undermine the objective of supporting basic technology research for the energy system.

Some of my politically savvy friends tell me that any proposal to support basic technology and public interest research "can't possibly fly in today's political climate." Maybe they are right. But, if we can't figure out some way to fund the basic technology and public interest research we need to assure a smooth transition through the second stage of the electric power revolution, the future of the networked energy industries in the US, and probably in many other parts of the world, may not be as bright as it could be.

Notes

1. This efficiency is stated in terms of HHV (high heat value) so as to be comparable to similar numbers stated for steam plants. Combustion turbine efficiencies are often reported in terms of LHV (low heat value), which yields higher numbers, in this case about 60%.

2. I thank Sarosh Talukdar, Eduardo Componogara, Marjorie Widmeyer, and Cristian Dragnea for helpful discussions. The work was supported in part by NSF grant ECS-9165599 and by Academic Funds at Carnegie Mellon University.

References

Anderson, Max and Dodd S. Carr, "Battery Energy Storage Technologies," *Proceedings of the IEEE*, March 1993, *81*, 475-479.

Appleby, A. J., "Characteristics of Fuel Cell Systems," pp. 157-198 *in Fuel Cell Systems*, Leo J. M. J. Blomen and Michael N. Mugerwa (eds.), Plenum Press, 1993, 614pp.

Blomen, Leo J.M.J. and Michael N. Mugerwa (eds.), *Fuel Cell Systems*, Plenum Press, 1993, 614pp.

Bose, Bimal K., "Power Electronics - A technology review," *Proceedings of the IEEE*, August 1992, *80*, 1303-1334.

Davis, Bert N., "Building Integrated Photovoltaics: Technology and Policy Issues," Department of Engineering and Public Policy, Carnegie Mellon University, January 1997.

Energy Information Administration, Annual Energy Outlook 1996, EIA/DoE, 1996, US Government Printing Office, 275pp.

Harashima, Fumio, "Power Electronics and Motion Control - a future perspective," *Proceedings of the IEEE*, August 1994, *82*, 1107-1111.

Hingorani, Narain G., "Flexible AC Transmission System (FACTS)," pp. 240-257, in Michael Einhorn and Raiz Siddiqi (eds.), *Electric Transmission Pricing and Technology*, EPRI/Kluwer, 1996, 282pp.

Hirschenhofer, John H. and Richard H. McClelland, "The Coming of Age of Fuel Cells," *Mechanical Engineering*, October 1995, 84-88.

Hoffman, Allan R., "Looking Forward: The Status of Renewable Technologies," *Physics and Society*, April 1997, *26*, 10-12.

Lave, Lester, Chris Hendrickson, and Francis McMichael, "Environmental Implications of Electric Cars," *Science*, 1995, *258*, 993-995.

Moore, Taylor, "The Road Ahead for EV Batteries," *EPRI Journal*, March/April 1996, 6-15.

Parfomak, Paul W., "Electric Utility Conservation Programs: Empirical Studies of Impacts and Cost-Effectiveness," Ph.D. thesis, Department of Engineering and Public Policy, Carnegie Mellon, Pittsburgh, 1996, 255pp.

Penner, S.S. and L. Icerman, *Energy* (three volumes), Addison-Wesley, 1975.

Post, Richard F., T. Kenneth Fowler, and Stephen F. Post, "A High-Efficiency Electrochemical Battery," *Proceedings of the IEEE*, March 1993, *81*, 462-473.

Schwartz, Richard J., "Photovoltaic Power Generation," *Proceedings of the IEEE*, March 1993, *81*, 355-364.

Slemon, Gordon R., "Electrical Machines for Variable-Frequency Drives," *Proceedings of the IEEE*, August 1994, *82*, 1123-1139.

Stahlkopf, Karl, "The Second Silicon Revolution," pp. 259-275, " in Michael Einhorn and Raiz Siddiqi (eds.), *Electric Transmission Pricing and Technology*, EPRI/Kluwer, 1996, 282pp.

Sutherland, J. Paul, "Little Micro Turbines: Big Power Generators," Technology Report, Southern California Edison, March 1997.

Sweet, William, "Power and Energy," *IEEE Spectrum*, January 1997, 38-42.

11 DESIGN PRINCIPLES

Robert Wilson[1]

Introduction

This chapter outlines some broad principles useful in the design of the various submarkets required to implement competitive wholesale markets for electricity. I focus on the markets for energy, transmission, and ancillary services, and emphasize the major structural features. I begin with some background and issues that motivate the subsequent discussion. The following sections consider the general architecture of wholesale markets for electricity. The first examines the choice among forms of organization, such as bilateral contracting or multilateral trading, and in the latter, the choice between a market-clearing exchange or a tight pool with centrally optimized scheduling. The second examines the transmission market in some detail, and the third examines the energy market similarly. The final two sections examine linkages among multiple markets in decentralized designs, focusing on the role of contractual commitments and the requirements for inter-market efficiency.

To establish a point of departure: the current restructuring of electricity markets is consistent with the analysis by Joskow and Schmalensee in *Markets for Power*, 1983. They foresaw competitive markets for generation, transmission facilities operated on an open-access common-carrier basis, and retail competition among power marketers that rely on regulated utility distribution companies for delivery. Regulation of the wholesale and retail energy markets would be reduced to structural requirements and operational guidelines and monitoring, while retaining substantial regulation of the "wires" markets for transmission and distribution. These changes entail unbundling energy from T&D, thereby reversing the vertical integration of utilities.

The current issues that I address here concern mainly the organization of the wholesale markets for energy and transmission, interpreted as including ancillary services and other requirements for system reliability and security. The examination of these issues can benefit from the history of restructuring in other countries such as Britain, Canada, Australia, New Zealand, and Norway, newly implemented designs in countries such as Spain, and current developments in several states in the U.S. I emphasize the implications of the general principles of market design based on ideas from economics and game theory, but on some pragmatic aspects my views are parochial because my practical experience has been mostly in California.

The peculiar features of the electricity industry that must be considered include temporal and stochastic variability of demands and supplies, accentuated by the non-storability of power, multiple technologies with varying sensitivities to capital and fuel costs and environmental and siting restrictions, and dependence on a reliable and secure transmission system. The economic problems include substantial non-convexities (immobility of generation and transmission facilities, scale economies in generation, non-linearities in transmission), and externalities (mainly in transmission). As regards generation these problems have eased sufficiently in recent decades to enable competitive energy markets, but they remain important considerations in designing these markets.

The criteria for selecting among market designs include efficiency over the long term, including incentives for investment in facilities for generation and transmission. However, my exposition focuses on short-term efficiency, since this is the immediate concrete problem, and it is required for long-term efficiency.

To motivate the subsequent sections, I describe three parts of the overall problem of market design. The basic design choice is the architecture of the market. There are many contending options. The market can be centralized or decentralized; it can be based on bilateral contracting, a centralized exchange, or a tightly controlled pool; trades can be physical or financial obligations, and they can be forward or spot contracts; the market can include financial hedges or not; the "official" market can be mandatory or optional, and encourage or discourage secondary markets. As will be evident, my opinion is that on most dimensions, the purported advantage of one extreme or the other is illusory. I favor designs that mix the two extremes to capture some of the advantages of each from parallel operations. For instance, for the three time frames of long-term, day-ahead, and real-time, there are corresponding advantages from bilateral contracting, a central exchange, and tightly controlled dispatch.

After the market architecture is established, a host of details must be specified. I do not address operational aspects here, and I refer the reader to my work for

California that elaborates the key role of procedural rules. Procedural rules must be constructed carefully to suppress gaming and promote efficiency. It is not only a matter of closing all loopholes; rather, the procedural rules must solve some basic economic problems, such as effective price discovery that enables more efficient decisions by suppliers. All this pre-supposes that the market will be sufficiently competitive to produce an efficient outcome, so if not, then further measures are required to diminish the market power of dominant incumbents and to promote entry by newcomers. The fact that I focus on the market architecture as the basic structural decision does not mean that it should be decided first; rather, parallel consideration of several designs and their implementation is useful in the early stages so that their merits can be compared in light of stakeholders' interests.

My perspective is conditioned by my emphasis on strategic behavior. This seems paradoxical, since my aim is to construct a design that suppresses gaming or renders it ineffective in favor of greater efficiency. The principle, however, is to treat the market design as establishing a mode of competition among the traders. The key is to select a mode of competition that is most effective in realizing the potential gains from trade.

To illustrate, I describe a common fallacy. It is deceptively easy to conclude that a mandatory pool based on a centralized optimization of all generation, transmission, ancillary services, etc. – as in the UK – can realize the full productive potential of the system. This view does not recognize that the schedules derived from an optimization program, such as an optimal power flow (OPF) program, are no better than its inputs. In fact, suppliers can and do treat the program as a device whose outputs can be manipulated by the inputs they provide in the form of purported cost functions, availabilities, etc.[2] Thus, the mode of competition consists of contending efforts to influence the "bottom-line" results from the program, such as dispatched quantities and prices for energy, transmission, and ancillary services. In terms of economic theory: reliance on an OPF affects the form and strength of traders' incentives at various points in the process, but it does not obviate the role of incentives. A central design problem is to identify the best locus of incentives and competitive forces.

In addition to my strategic perspective, I appreciate that traders have practical motivations that are not included in standard economic theory. For instance, suppliers are typically skeptical of designs that make their financial viability dependent on prices derived as shadow prices (Lagrange multipliers) on system constraints included in the formulation of an optimization program, and centrally planned operating schedules that are several steps removed from the cost data they submit. They prefer market-clearing prices derived directly from the terms they offer, and they prefer to devise their own operating schedules to fulfill offers accepted in the market. Similarly, they are leery of intrusions by the transmission system operator (SO) into the energy markets, fearing that the SO's extraordinary powers could bias the competitive process. I see two sources of these preferences. One is informational: submitted cost data is never sufficient to describe the full range of considerations relevant to a supplier. The other pertains to governance: the SO is usually described as the ISO, emphasizing its independence and adherence to operating standards derived from principles of power engineering, but few designs address the basic problem of incentives for the SO. For example, the SO is not liable for the financial consequences to traders of strict security standards that are motivated more by avoidance of any chance of mishap than an economic tradeoff between reliability and energy costs. Current designs rely on standards of transmission management inherited from the era when it was internalized within utilities who owned and operated transmission facilities for their native loads, but as this inheritance decays it will be useful to re-examine the issues of governance and incentives for the SO. An important challenge is to ensure that the SO provides enough transmission capacity to make local markets contestable, even if this runs counter to the interests of major stakeholders.

Radical Designs

Because the subsequent sections concentrate on designs that are close to current norms, I first mention radical designs that are excluded. One version stems from the view that the historical importance of system reliability may be less critical with the advent of computer controlled operations. For example, the airline industry has many similarities to the electricity industry but it is organized quite differently, and the reason may be that failures or errors in a transmission grid have enormous external effects throughout the system.[3] It might be that a decade from now the best designs are more decentralized, like the airline industry, because the reliability of the transmission system can be assured without the centralized operations inherited from vertically integrated utilities. In particular, the vulnerability of the transmission system stems presently from weak monitoring and controls on injections and withdrawals, and primitive metering devices, all of which could be eliminated by technological advances. An extreme variant imagines that the functions of the system operator could as well be managed as a franchise, provided the firm managing operations has appropriate incentives, such as liability for costs imposed on energy traders who rely on the transmission system.

Another view is that the current system designs are residues from the era of regulation in which there were inadequate incentives for product differentiation; e.g., power service differentiated by priorities or incentives for voluntary or automatic curtailment in peak periods could reduce the reliance on supply-side controls and enable more efficient investment in base-load generation facilities.

A third view is that the only unique feature of the power industry is that an optimal pricing scheme is based on congestion charges for over-demanded transmission lines, which is complicated by the implications of Kirchhoff's Laws. Organizing the entire system around this consideration seems a high cost to pay, and some argue that it would suffice to use "postage-stamp" charges for transmission, presumably differentiated by service priority, or to rely on secondary markets for trading of firm transmission rights, or even to build a transmission system sufficient to reduce congestion to a trivial minimum. This view depends on a judgment that the gains from a thoroughly optimized system for transmission and ancillary services are small compared to the gains from vigorous competition in energy markets, and in particular, avoidance of the inefficient investments (with hindsight) in generation capacity that have plagued the electricity industry over the past quarter-century.

I assume that these radical departures from current designs are not immediately relevant, if only because they imply electricity markets that are more decentralized and privately managed than is likely soon. So I focus on those design aspects that are closer to established practice.

Pools, Exchanges, and Bilateral Markets

The structural feature of broadest significance is the organization of the market. Among the myriad of possible forms, the ones most common in commodities markets are bilateral exchanges. Those organized as "rings" or "pits" depend on oral outcry of bids and asks (usually by traders or brokers acting for customers), whereas others use computerized bulletin boards to post offers. Those that depend on market makers to establish prices are conducted by specialists who clear orders from a book or dealers who post bid and ask prices. Market makers are usual where it is important to sustain inter-temporal continuity of prices and reduce volatility, and typically they trade for their own accounts and maintain inventories. Market makers in the energy industries often play an important role reconciling differences among short and long term contracts, and more generally, providing a variety of contract forms and auxiliary services.

Compared to the other organizational forms discussed below, the most salient distinction of bilateral markets is the continual process of trading, with prices unique to each transaction. The experimental and empirical evidence indicates that in general bilateral markets are not less competitive or efficient than exchanges or pools. Among those with market makers, further distinctions are the "product differentiation" represented by the variety of contracts and terms tailored to individual customers, and the maintenance of some degree of price continuity.

On the other hand, bilateral markets encounter a fundamental problem maintaining efficiency in related markets for transportation or transmission. The demand for transportation is a "derived" demand; in particular, for each bilateral transaction the associated demand value for transportation to fulfill the contract is the sum of the two parties' gains from trade in that transaction. When parties are matched somewhat randomly into pairs for bilateral transactions, their gains from trade are also random, and thus in the aggregate express inaccurately the actual demand value of transportation. When transportation is scarce or expensive, as in the case of power transmission, market makers face a substantial task in utilizing transmission facilities efficiently. They might accomplish this by aggregating transmission demands, or by brokering transmission services, but I know of no viable theory that assures the outcome is likely to be fully efficient, taking account of the inherent externalities. Thus, on matters of efficiency in transmission, faith in purely bilateral markets requires confidence in the ingenuity of market makers. This is not necessarily an argument against bilateral markets, however, since bilateral markets can operate alongside exchanges that carry more of the responsibility at the margin for insuring efficient utilization of transmission facilities. The California design includes this feature, and in Scandinavia NordPool accounts for less than 20% of the market.

Exchanges and pools offer several advantages and also bring some disadvantages compared to bilateral markets. One advantage is a central market that establishes a uniform clearing price and more accurately expresses the derived demand for transmission. The uniform clearing price has some minor potential to realize the last iota of the gains from trade, but often the motives are more practical.[4] For a critical commodity like electricity there is also a perceived advantage in establishing an "official" exchange with minimal transactions costs, unhindered access for all traders, transparency to enable regulatory and public scrutiny, and countervailing power against the emergence of private market makers with sufficient market power to extract some portion of the potential rents. The disadvantages lie in the reliance on restrictive contract forms and inflexible procedural rules, and if the governance structure is inadequate, some potential to dictate restrictive procedures that are more convenient for administrators than traders. In addition, most pools and exchanges rely on private bilateral markets for auxiliary services such as financial contracts to hedge prices. Attempts to maintain pools and exchanges for contracts with longer terms than a day ahead have mostly failed due to lack of interest, so typically they are confined to short-forward and spot transactions.

Here I use the term exchange for a simple market clearing system. Typical examples are the exchanges in Alberta and California whose functions are confined almost entirely to establishing prices for each hour that clear the forward markets for day-ahead and hour-ahead trading. Closely related are their real-time markets conducted by the system operator, who selects among those bids offered for increments and decrements in supply and demand to manage the transmission system. Exchanges can minimize transaction costs (as evident in Alberta where transaction charges are quite small) and largely preserve traders' prerogatives to determine their own scheduling. A disadvantage of an exchange confined solely to sales and purchases of energy is its separation from the transmission market. For example, in California the day-ahead energy market in the Power Exchange (PX) clears before the transmission market opens, so traders must rely on predictions about the transmission charges they will encounter later, and transmission management relies on traders' offers of incremental and decremental adjustment bids to alleviate congestion on inter-zonal lines. In some cases the exchange might be only a "pretend" market as in Alberta, where the generation and distribution subsidiaries of the major firms are so heavily hedged via contracts that the exchange price is little more than a transfer price.

I use the term pool to describe a system in which participation is mandatory and the "market" includes substantial intervention into scheduling. Pools are carried over from the operational procedures of vertically integrated utilities who entirely managed their own generation and transmission systems to serve their native loads, for which they had regulated monopolies, and in some cases, regional "tight" power pools with full control of scheduling. Typical examples today are in the U.K. and in the northeastern U.S. (New England, New York, and Pennsylvania-New Jersey-Maryland). Pools are distinguished from exchanges by the thorough integration of the energy, transmission, and ancillary services markets, and most significantly, by a centralized optimization of unit schedules that takes account of operational considerations – not just energy generation but also capacity availability, minimum generation requirements, ramping rates, etc. At the heart of such a system is a massive computer program that decides nearly all aspects of unit scheduling, usually on both a day-ahead basis and then again in real-time operations. This program is not just an OPF for energy flows but rather includes (mixed-integer nonlinear) optimization of schedules subject to system and security constraints.[5] A price in such a system is not a market clearing price in the usual sense that it equates demand and supply; rather, it is obtained as the shadow price on a system constraint in an optimization program whose inputs include detailed operating specifications and purported cost data. Although these prices are used for settlements *ex post* as in an exchange, they do not represent prices offered by traders.

The advantage of a pool is the tight integration of all aspects of system operations, which might enable more productive efficiency, and it is invulnerable to imperfect links among the prices in a sequence of energy and transmission markets. Its disadvantages lie in the consequences of complete centralization, since it requires mandated participation and compliance with specified operating schedules. Suppliers are often reluctant to assign the prerogatives of scheduling and some are leery of prices obtained from a computer program rather than submitted bids; indeed, they may see the program as a black box whose outputs can be affected by the cost data they submit. The prices themselves are problematic since typically they include, besides energy prices, subsidy payments for capacity or availability that are more easily manipulated (as purportedly has been the case in the UK) and in any case depend on arbitrary parameters such as the assigned value of lost load and an assessed probability of lost load. Mandatory participation is a fundamental problem because it precludes development of competing markets, either exchanges or bilateral, that might prove superior or bring innovations.[6]

A point to be emphasized is that the choices among these basic organizational forms are not mutually exclusive. A system that mixes forms is feasible, such as an exchange that complements a bilateral market for forward trades, followed by real-time operations managed like a pool. One justification for a mixed system recognizes the role of timing. A pool is inherently a market for physical transactions, which is appropriate and even necessary on a short time frame such as real-time operations. Exchanges and bilateral markets are essentially forward markets for financial transactions, since physical deficiencies are inconsequential and ordinarily they are settled at the subsequent spot price.

A pool is inherently a market for physical transactions .... Exchanges and bilateral markets are essentially forward markets for financial transactions.

Hence, the longer time frame of forward markets increases the appeal of these organizational forms.

It is important to recognize that local preferences are important too: the New England pool is a direct extension of the familiar tight power pool that has had operating authority there for years, whereas in California the initial design based on a pool was ultimately discarded in favor of a more decentralized organization.[7] And of course those parties eager to profit as market makers are advocates of bilateral markets and reluctant to compete with an exchange whose transaction costs are likely to be low.

Transmission Management

Except in tight power pools, there is usually some separation between the markets for energy and transmission. This is partly a functional separation that isolates the complexity of transmission management from the simplicity of energy trading. It also reflects the fact that, unlike the private-good character of energy, transmission has substantial public-good aspects, pervasive externalities, and highly nonlinear behavior described by Kirchhoff's Laws. These features of transmission make the market design highly dependent on how property rights are defined.

If there were no scarcity of transmission capacity then energy markets could be conducted like other commodity markets. The fundamental problem in transmission is that real-time balancing and security requires control by a single authority that can draw on resources offered on a spot basis, or failing that, ancillary services held in reserve. Thus, real-time operations are invariably managed by a system operator (SO).[8] The design problem is therefore focused on how far to extend the authority of the SO, and in doing so, how much to rely on market processes.

One dimension is the extent of forward balancing. NordPool and California are representative of designs in which the SO clears a forward market for transmission on a day-ahead basis (and in California, also hour-ahead). Both clear on an inter-zonal basis and rely on adjustment bids (incs and decs) to alleviate congestion, imitating the procedures used by vertically integrated utilities. For the adjustment bids NordPool uses bids carried over from the energy market, whereas in California adjustment bids are voluntary and need not bear much relation to bids in the energy market.[9] Just as there is a sequence of energy prices at which transactions in the day-ahead, hour-ahead, and real-time markets are settled, so too there is a sequence of binding usage charges for transmission that apply to these transactions. Alternative schemes defer full resolution of congestion management closer to dispatch, as in recent proposals in Alberta that would defer declarations to two hours before dispatch.

Even though it is the SO who conducts the day-ahead transmission market, one motive for this market is to minimize the interventions of the SO.[10] That is, the aim is to enable a market for adjustment bids, seen as an extension of the day-ahead energy markets, to handle most transmission management by achieving inter-zonal balance before moving into same-day operations where the SO has tighter control on all aspects. This leaves the SO with what in California is called intra-zonal balancing, although in fact on short time frames it is managing the entire transmission system, as well as generation to follow loads. If the link between the day-ahead and real-time markets is sufficiently tight then the forward prices in the day-ahead markets can be expected to approximate the real-time prices, while providing a sufficient planning horizon for suppliers to schedule their units optimally.

The California system is also motivated substantially by the desire to enable competing forward markets for energy, so they must also compete equally in a forward market for transmission. This is carried to an extreme in the provision that the SO must retain the energy balance of each scheduling coordinator (SC) conducting an energy market; e.g., each inc/dec pair selected to alleviate congestion must come from the same SC. This runs some risk of short-run economic inefficiency because it does not assure equalization of the SCs' energy prices. This risk is viewed by some stakeholders as necessary to realize the longer-term benefits of vigorous competition among the SCs' energy markets, but it has been widely criticized because it lacks a clear economic justification. The partial remedy provided in California is allowance for inter-SC trades of adjustment bids, although due to its limited role as a pure market-clearing exchange the PX cannot easily participate in these trades.

At the other extreme from the NordPool and California forward markets are the designs that provide one form or another of transmission "rights" in the form of reservations, priorities, or insurance. These designs minimize the SO's role by auctioning reservations for most transmission capacity far in advance, such as six months or a year, and rely on trading in secondary markets to achieve an efficient reallocation for each hour. Those that provide physical rights encounter two fundamental problems. One is how to define and allocate rights in advance of the actual circumstances, such as loop flow that restricts capacity, or residual transfer capability enabled by the actual pattern of injections and withdrawals that occurs. The second is how long before dispatch to require release of a reservation if it is not scheduled, and setting penalties for noncompliance: if release is too close to dispatch then hoarding by a holder of an unused reservation could impair efficiency or enable one with market power to corner the market. For instance, if release can be deferred until after the day-ahead market then forward trades in that market can be impaired by hoarding of transmission capacity. If releases are frequent and substantial then the SO winds up managing transmission on a real-time basis, which can be precarious. And there is the practical difficulty that physical rights require the SO to monitor the allocation of rights to verify that submitted schedules conform to the entitlements owned. These considerations indicate that financial rights are preferable unless stringent controls on physical rights can ensure non-discriminatory open access to transmission.

Those systems that provide insurance or hedges issue transmission congestion contracts (TCCs) that reimburse the holder for the SO's transmission usage charge, or contracts for differences (CFDs) that achieve the same effect. In principle, private markets could provide such financial instruments, and so far the California design assumes they will, but other systems such as NY and PJM rely on TCCs to allocate financially-firm transmission rights. A contentious issue is whether holders of TCCs should be accorded priority in scheduling when there are insufficient adjustment bids to clear the forward market for transmission. Insufficiency is seen as a possible problem because traders who are fully insured by TCCs or CFDs might have reduced incentives to provide voluntary adjustment bids, so the SO might not be able to clear the day-ahead inter-zonal market with the adjustment bids it receives, implying that inter-zonal spillovers must be alleviated in real-time by attracting sufficient resources into the (supposedly intra-zonal) imbalance market. A further problem with TCCs is that they might be abused, say by overscheduling.

A TCC supplemented by scheduling priority is the same as a firm transmission right for most practical purposes. In the extreme case that the entire transmission capacity is allocated via TCCs with scheduling priority, the SO's adjustment market collapses, since whenever there is congestion, usage charges assessed against their necessarily zero net flows across interfaces have no financial consequences for customers unprotected by TCCs. In this case, inter-zonal congestion management is accomplished entirely by the secondary markets for TCCs.

All systems that rely on voluntary forward markets for adjustments to resolve congestion are vulnerable to insufficient participation by traders, with resulting spillovers into the real-time market that might be of much larger magnitudes than this market is intended to handle. Among the measures that can mitigate this problem is a high default usage charge when the adjustment market fails to clear – a price high enough to ensure that ample resources are submitted to the real-time market. An alternative is to require adjustment bids, but this can be fruitless unless there is some assurance that they reflect accurately the traders' opportunity costs; e.g., the practice in NordPool of re-using the bids in the energy market as the adjustment bids provides stronger assurance than California's design in which the submission of adjustment bids is entirely voluntary (although a high default price when the market fails provides a strong incentive to submit bids sufficient to enable the market to clear). On the other hand, the California design enables suppliers to account for their inter-temporal operating constraints via their adjustment bids. At the heart of the California design is a free-rider problem, in the sense that each trader or market-maker can take the view that it is others' responsibility to provide sufficient adjustments to clear the market for transmission.

A major design feature of transmission markets is the price determination process, which is closely linked to the definition of property rights. As mentioned, those systems that allocate firm transmission rights or priorities (FTRs) in advance use an auction to establish initial prices that are then updated continually in secondary markets. Such systems require the auxiliary services of a SO to establish real-time prices that exhaust the residual transfer capacity of the transmission system, but the intent nevertheless is to enable secondary markets for FTRs to allocate most of the capacity. Similarly, those that provide TCCs or CFDs to hedge transmission charges still rely on a SO for real-time operations that include setting usage charges.

In its purest form, real-time congestion pricing of scarce transmission capacity sets a usage charge for each directional link in the system, or equivalently (using Kirchhoff's Laws) an injection charge at each node. The choice between these is often based on practical considerations: there may be many more links than nodes, thereby favoring nodal pricing, but perhaps only a few links are congested recurrently, in which case link pricing is simpler.[11] More frequently, only a few major links or nodes are priced explicitly, and for forward markets it is sufficient to establish injection charges only for nodal hubs or for large zones, or usage charges for major inter-zonal interfaces as in NordPool and California.[12] These practices have important implications for the specification of rights and hedges; e.g., secondary markets are illiquid or inactive if the FTRs or TCCs are specified in point-to-point terms rather than zone-to-zone. In principle TCCs are required for every nodal or zonal pair but in practice it suffices to consider only those nominated by traders, and then issue a subset consistent with the system capacity and security constraints. Due to loop flow, a TCC can have a negative value and require the holder to pay rather than receive a usage charge; if this is impractical then the SO must absorb the cost, whereas link prices are always nonnegative.

In a competitive market, injection or usage charges are derived from the costs of alleviating congestion, not a tariff or "postage stamp" based on embedded cost. In an optimized pool the charge represents the shadow price on capacity, but in decentralized markets it represents the difference at the margin between the cost to the SO of accepting an inc (say, of supply in an import zone) and the revenue from a dec (of supply in an export zone), or the reverse in the case of a demand inc/dec pair. For example, in a two-zone situation the usage charge for the inter-zonal interface is typically the difference in terms of $/MWh between the most expensive inc in the import zone and the least profitable dec in the export zone, among those accepted by the SO. When the configuration is more complicated the SO uses an OPF program to select the bids that are accepted, taking account of loop flow and security constraints. Congestion pricing in this fashion is based on the principle that the transmission system is an open-access public facility in which (non-discriminatory) charges are imposed *only* to alleviate congestion on over-demanded interfaces. In particular, the owners of transmission assets cannot withhold capacity nor affect prices.[13]

Judging from systems in the U.S., where most transmission assets are privately owned, the typical flow of funds can be traced as follows. The SO sends the invoice for usage charges to the traders directly in the case of a pool, or to the management of an exchange (such as a scheduling coordinator (SC) in California) which then bills the traders, perhaps on a *pro rata* basis as in the PX. The payments to the SO are then conveyed to the holders of TCCs, if any, or to the owners of transmission assets to offset their revenue requirement for capital recovery. Revenue from auctions of FTRs or TCCs are similarly passed to the asset owners. In either case, the allocation among owners depends on an approximation of their revenue shares.

These schemes provide no incentives for owners to strengthen their transmission lines, which would reduce congestion rents, so the longer-term problem of congestion remains unsolved. Further, if the governance structure of the SO allows incumbent suppliers to veto expansion proposals, then they can foreclose opportunities to improve the competitiveness, or more accurately the contestability, of the market; indeed, it can be that all suppliers within a control area are reluctant to strengthen inter-ties that could increase imports. I know of no design presently that addresses fully the longer-term (and, due to the complex externalities and nonlinear features of transmission networks, theoretically unsolved) problem of creating incentives for efficient strengthening or expansion of the transmission system, or that collects surcharges reserved to pay for future expansion. One partial measure is that traders who build a new link to ease congestion are entitled to receive usage charges, perhaps in the form of TCCs.

Lastly, I mention a problem with transmission markets based on congestion prices. When usage charges are derived solely from the costs of alleviating congestion, traders can opt to "self-manage" congestion by curtailing their proposed power transfers sufficiently to eliminate usage charges. This is unlikely at the level of a small individual trader unless charges are imposed at the level of injection nodes or particular links. But even with large zones, market makers conducting exchanges or bilateral contracting that account for large fractions of transmission demand can self-manage in an explicit attempt to capture the congestion rents.[14] The California design encourages self-management, and indeed there is no concern about who captures the rents provided congestion is alleviated one way or another. In contrast, it is fundamental to the justification for optimized pools that all congestion rents are captured via usage charges. This depends on a naïve view of incentives and strategic behavior unless market power is so dispersed that price-taking prevails. More likely, the opportunity to capture congestion rents encourages concerted efforts to capture them.[15]

The Process of Market Clearing and the Mode of Competition

The mode of competition is strongly affected by structural features of the market design. In this section I provide some examples in energy markets, and briefly, in markets for ancillary services and transmission.

Underlying these specific examples is the general view that incentive effects are not eliminated by one market design or another; rather, the form in which they are expressed depends on the specific features of the market structure. The advantage of a superior design derives from the extent to which it enables traders to express accurately the economic considerations important to them. Gaming strategies are inherent in any design that requires traders to manipulate their bids in order to take account of factors that the bid format does not allow them to express directly.

The bid format is a key factor. For example, if the market is organized to provide hourly schedules and prices, then this tends to serve the interests of demanders for whom the time of power delivery is important, and suppliers with flexibility (e.g., storage hydro), whereas it tends to ignore the considerations of suppliers from thermal sources, who are mainly concerned with obtaining operating schedules over consecutive hours sufficient to recover the fixed costs of startup and who are unconcerned about timing *per se*. Schemes have been devised that allow demanders to bid on a time-of-day basis while suppliers bid for operating runs of various durations; prices can then be stated equivalently in terms of hourly prices for demanders and duration prices for suppliers. Similarly, for ancillary services it is usually important to distinguish between availability payments for reserving capacity and payments for delivered energy when called by the system operator. Schemes have also been devised to allow bids in terms of priorities or adjustments, such as demands that are curtailable above a specified real-time price. I bypass these more elaborate schemes here in order to focus on the basic problem of clearing an hourly market for firm energy, either forward or spot.

In energy markets there is a basic distinction between static and iterative market processes. In a static design for a pooled market each trader provides a single bid, usually in the form of a demand or supply function, with or without a separate capacity bid or a minimum revenue requirement, and perhaps in the form of a portfolio bid for multiple generation sources that is only later converted into unit schedules. The static character lies in the fact that the initial market clearing is also the final one. The theory underlying a static design is the Walrasian theory of markets, in which the market finds a price that equates stated demands and supplies. The mode of competition lies in each trader's selection of the bid function it submits – which requires substantial guesswork since others' bids are unknown when the submission is made.

If the bids are purely for hourly energy then a static design can cause problems for suppliers with fixed costs and ramping constraints because the revenue may be insufficient to cover total costs. Designs of this sort therefore provide approximate remedies: the UK provides capacity payments and Spain allows suppliers to specify a minimum revenue requirement. Without elaborating details here, my view is that these auxiliary provisions engender as many gaming problems as they solve, and in the case of capacity payments based on an assumed value of lost load, are inherently arbitrary.

An iterative market process works quite differently, and reflects the Marshallian theory of markets. As in an auction with repeated bidding, it is those traders whose bids are at the margin who contend to get their bids accepted, and in each round they can base their bids on the tentative results from previous rounds. For example, suppose that as usual a supplier's bid is submitted as a series of steps at successively higher prices. In this case a an "extra-marginal" supplier, one with a step above the market clearing price, realizes that by reducing its price for that step it can be more competitive in the next round – thereby ejecting an infra-marginal bidder who in the next round becomes extra-marginal and therefore must itself improve its offered price. Thus, Marshallian competition works by inducing competition among those bidders whose steps are actually near the margin, in contrast with Walrasian competition in which the price offered for each step must be based on a conjecture about the competitive situation in the event that step is at the margin.

Iterative processes require procedural "activity" rules to ensure serious bidding throughout (and thus reliable price discovery) and to ensure speedy convergence, but they have the advantage of avoiding *ad hoc* measures to assure bidders' fixed costs are covered.[16]   In a day-ahead auction the key feature is that an iterative process enables "self-scheduling" in the sense that each supplier can adapt its offers in successive rounds to the observed pattern of hourly prices. With good information about the prices it can obtain in each hour, a supplier with steam plants can itself decide on which units to schedule, their start times, and their run lengths. Similarly, a supplier with storage hydro sources can better tailor its releases to take advantage of the observed prices in peak periods. In the California PX this enables pure-energy portfolio bidding: only after the energy market clears do the portfolio bidders need to report to the system operator their unit schedules that provide the energy they sold. Instead of the detailed operating data required by the UK's static pool to run its centralized optimization program, California's decentralized design assigns authority to the suppliers to schedule their own units to meet the commitments contracted in the energy market.

These considerations are not unique to the operation of markets organized as exchanges with an hourly market clearing price that applies uniformly to all trades. Most markets for bilateral trades allow a dynamic process in which bid and ask prices are posted continually, and any posted offer can be accepted at its offered price at any time. As in an exchange using an iterative market clearing process, traders can monitor the posted prices and the prices of completed transactions to obtain good information about the prevailing pattern of prices. And because the contracts are bilateral, each party can set its own schedule to fulfill the bargain. There are also designs for bilateral markets in which all contracts are tentative until the market clears, and then the same hourly prices apply to all completed transactions.[17]

The mode of competition for transmission is also affected by structural features of the market. At one extreme are systems that assign scheduling priority to those who hold firm transmission rights or reservations (FTRs). In these systems traders compete to acquire FTRs in the initial auction or in the secondary market, leaving the system operator with only residual responsibility for real-time balancing and security of the system. At the other extreme is the California system in which the system operator accomplishes day-ahead inter-zonal balancing by exercising options offered as adjustment bids by demanders and suppliers. Congestion on inter-zonal lines is alleviated by accepting sufficient bids for incremental generation and decremental demand in import zones, and decremental generation in export zones. Thus, in this system the transmission market is an extension of the energy market to remedy congestion by altering the location of generation.[18] Intermediate designs are those in which the system operator manages transmission by setting nodal (or zonal) injection charges based on an OPF program, but traders can obtain financial insurance by acquiring TCCs or CFDs that provide hedges

> **Iterative processes require procedural "activity" rules to ensure serious bidding throughout (and thus reliable price discovery) and to ensure speedy convergence, but they have the advantage of avoiding *ad hoc* measures to assure bidders' fixed costs are covered.**

against the charges imposed by the system operator. In those versions in which holders of TCCs are also accorded priority in scheduling transmission, they obtain the equivalent of firm transmission rights since they are immune to the risk that transmission charges are high. In this case, traders compete for TCCs in the initial auction and in secondary markets, but only for financial insurance rather than physical rights to schedule. Of these three, the first presents some obvious problems of inefficiency and market power if FTRs can be hoarded by dominant firms, and the second might be vulnerable to insufficient adjustment bids to enable the system operator to fully alleviate congestion.[19]

Ancillary services are especially sensitive to the bid format. Using spinning reserve as the example, it is clear that suppliers must be paid for capacity availability as well as energy generation. On this basis one might surmise that suppliers should bid both components, but this causes problems. The initial problem is that the system operator must evaluate such two-part bids by giving some weight (interpreted as the duration that spinning units will be called to produce) to the energy bid. But as in most multi-part bidding schemes, this is fraught with gaming problems; e.g., a bidder who thinks that a call is less probable or shorter than the weight used by the SO prefers to exaggerate the capacity bid and shrink the energy bid, and the opposite if a call is more probable or longer. Thus the merit order of energy bids reveals less about actual costs of generation than expectations about the likelihood that spinning reserves will be activated. These incentive problems are alleviated when different procedures are used for bid evaluation and settlements. In the simplest scheme bids are accepted solely on the basis of the offered capacity price, and then settlements for energy generation are based on the system real-time energy price rather than the offered energy price.[20] That is, the offered energy price is interpreted only as a reserve price below which the supplier prefers not to be called. Thus, it provides a merit order for calling generation without distorting incentives. This scheme separates the competitive process into two parts corresponding to the two parts of the bid, one for capacity availability, and another for priority in being called to generate.

The argument is occasionally made that an energy exchange might as well augment each demand bid by the required proportion of ancillary services, or at least spinning reserve – as is typically done for transmission losses.[21] This argument recognizes that on the demand side spinning reserve is a necessary complement to planned energy deliveries. It is mistaken, however, because on the supply side energy and spin are substitutes, not complements. Moreover, technologies differ considerably in their characteristics for spinning reserve; e.g., storage hydro sources and fast-start turbines are not subject to the ramping constraints and no-load costs of steam plants, but on the other hand, thermal plants can provide spinning reserve by operating below capacity. It is better therefore to establish a separate market for spinning reserves (and curtailable loads) along with other ancillary services so that these differing characteristics can be reflected in bids.

A peculiarity of some optimized pools is payment to suppliers for capacity in addition to energy, based on so-called multi-part bids that include components for both fixed costs and incremental energy costs, with compensating charges to demanders for "uplift". These are not payments for capacity reserved for ancillary services but rather for planned generation. This holdover from the era of regulation is unique to the electricity industry, which is the only one that does not expect suppliers to cover fixed costs, such as capital and maintenance, from the market price of its output. Although a long-run equilibrium in the industry implies prices in peak periods adequate to cover the costs of capacity idle in other periods, the motive for these payments is apparently the short-run concern that market-clearing prices for energy will be determined by incremental generation costs that will be insufficient to recover the costs of capital and O&M. Such an outcome is mainly a consequence of reliance in optimized pools on shadow prices that reflect only purported incremental costs, based on a parallel optimization of unit commitments that takes account of start-up costs, ramping constraints, and minimum generation levels, as well as the uncertainty of demand and the imputed value of lost load.[22] Without elaborating fully here, I am skeptical of any such payment scheme that is not tied to explicit reservation of capacity, such as for ancillary services, because I see it as an open invitation for manipulation. Designs such as those in California, Scandinavia, and Australia dispense with these payments by clearing the market for energy entirely on the basis of prices offered for delivered energy, leaving scheduling decisions to suppliers. It might indeed be that prices in California will reflect only incremental costs that are insufficient to recover the O&M costs of installed units, but if so then that signals excess capacity that in the long run should be mothballed or decommissioned.

Contract Commitments and Settlements

A significant dimension of market design is the character and timing of the commitments made by participants during the market process. The most important aspects of commitment are the prices on which settlements are based. Commitments are often presumed to be physical, but in fact they are usually financial since a breach is remedied by charging the defaulting party the spot price of purchases or sales to make up the difference.

In a pure bid-ask market with bilateral contracts concluded continually this aspect is usually hidden by the prevailing presumption that each contract is an immediate commitment and settlement is based on the price agreed in the transaction. However, there also designs for bilateral markets in which all agreements are tentative until a final market clearing price is established that then applies uniformly to all contracts. Also, many commodities markets operate on the principle that long-term contracts are physical commitments, with settlements pegged to prices in spot markets (which often represent only a small percentage of transactions). One power market, in Finland, operates as a financial market in which prevailing prices for futures contracts provide the "signals" used by traders arranging bilateral contracts.

In markets organized as pools we can distinguish at least three forms. In an optimized tight pool in which traders submit purported costs and availabilities, a trader commits to accepting both the prices and the unit schedules obtained from the optimizing algorithm, possibly with penalties for noncompliance. Exchanges with self-scheduling can operate either as coordinating devices or as genuine price-setting mechanisms for forward contracts. Those that settle day-ahead contracts on the basis of later real-time spot prices (e.g., Alberta, Victoria) serve mainly to allocate supplies to demands on the basis of tentative clearing prices that are not binding for settlements. In an exchange there is a strong presumption in favor of using the final market clearing price even if several iterations are used to reach that conclusion. In the California PX, for instance, tentative clearing prices are established in each round, but only the final round's prices are binding.

On standard economic grounds one might conclude that the only relevant price for allocative efficiency is the real-time spot price, and on that basis surmise that settlements should be based on this price – implying that earlier forward contracts are not binding as regards the nominal transaction price. However, this view ignores the substantial incentive effects. To motivate the subsequent discussion, I contrast the Alberta and California designs.

The design of the California PX may seem awkward at first, and indeed it is awkward in terms of the software required for settlements, since each MWh of energy might be assigned any one of several prices. In the PX's energy market, one clearing price is financially binding for trades completed in the day-ahead forward market, another clearing price is binding in the hour-ahead forward market, and the spot price in the real-time applies to ancillary services and supplemental energy purchased by the SO. On the other hand, the advantage of this design is that traders have an incentive to bid seriously in each of the forward markets, since the trades concluded there arc financially binding at the clearing price in that market.

Alberta uses the opposite design in which all settlements are made at the final spot price, calculated ex post. That this design produces incentive problems can be seen in the rules required to implement it. Traders were originally prohibited from altering their day-ahead commitments, but then pressures from suppliers led to a compromise in which each trader was allowed a single re-declaration, and lately the argument has been over whether the final time for all declarations should be moved to just two hours before dispatch. These developments reflect all suppliers' preference to delay commitments until close to the time at which prices for settlement are established, so that uncertainty is reduced, and each supplier's advantage from committing last so that it can take maximal advantage of the likely pattern of prices thereby revealed. The Alberta design has also invited a kind of gaming. Importers and exporters are allowed to submit multiple "virtual" declarations. They have used this opportunity to declare several alternatives on a day-ahead basis and then to withdraw all but one shortly before dispatch in order to obtain the best terms. Of course the other traders in Alberta now want the same privilege.

My opinion is that the difficulties implementing the Alberta design are intrinsic to any design in which transactions are not financially binding at the clearing price in the market in which they are made. One can argue that a sequence of binding forward prices might sacrifice some efficiency compared to one in which settlements are based on spot prices, but my view is that this sacrifice is necessary to ensure that bids are serious in the forward markets. If viable forward markets are unnecessary, as perhaps in a purely hydro system, then spot-price settlements are sufficient, but it seems to me that justifications for forward markets also justify binding transactions at the clearing prices in these markets. One must, of course, ensure that the sequence of forward markets is sufficiently contestable to enable arbitrage that keeps forward prices in line (in expectation) with subsequent spot prices.

One should also keep in mind the range of alternatives for the form of the commitment. An important distinction is between physical and financial commitment. Bilateral markets are more dependent on physical commitments if there is not a viable spot market in which to remedy deficiencies – or at least a dealer or broker who provides the remedy. Optimized pools depend to some extent on a presumed physical commitment to the dispatch schedule, since otherwise the optimization would be a useless exercise. In other pools, however, I have yet to see a cogent argument for physical commitments, as compared to financial commitments, in forward markets. Provided those who default on prior commitments are liable for making up the difference with purchases at the spot price, the incentives for compliance are sufficient. Further, due to the considerable stochastic variation in supply and demand conditions in power markets, the flexibility allowed by purely financial commitments is superior.[23]

The second distinction concerns the counter-party to a contract. Bilateral trades are contracts between the transacting parties, or perhaps with a dealer, whereas in an exchange or pool the counter-party to every transaction is the exchange; that is, suppliers sell to the exchange and demanders buy from it. Typically, the exchange defines standard contractual terms, and it administers the apparatus of settlements. There is no harm in this *per se*, but it encourages the growth of alternative market-makers who offer a greater variety of contractual terms and auxiliary services more closely tailored to the needs of select customers. A mandatory pool is naturally beset by pressures to remedy one or another perceived deficiency or favoritism in the rules and contracts, since invariably the pool's standard terms are inadequate to serve equally the diverse interests of a heterogeneous group of traders.

Multiple Markets and Inter-Market Efficiency

In its ideal form, an "optimized" pool manages everything, providing a single market for energy, transmission, ancillary services, etc. Using submitted data on availabilities, costs, and demands, and with complete data about transmission capacity, it establishes initial schedules and then supplements these based on developments in real-time. That is, it provides the services previously managed by vertically integrated utilities, or in some cases, established regional tight power pools. Here I address some of the issues that arise when this unified market is replaced by multiple markets of one form or another. I assume that transmission scheduling and real-time system control is conducted by a system operator (SO) who can drawn on ancillary services and supplemental energy offers to maintain system security, balancing, and load following. I divide the discussion between parallel markets and sequential markets.

Parallel Markets

Parallel markets exist elsewhere. One is NordPool in Scandinavia, which is a "marginal" market in the sense that less than 20% of energy is traded through the exchange. This structure, consisting of a large bilateral market for long-term contracts operating in parallel with a central market for spot trades, is common in various commodity industries – prominent examples are the metals markets, where as little as 5% of trades pass through the metal exchanges even though nearly all contract prices are pegged to the spot prices.

The California design has made parallel markets a prominent issue. The debate between proponents of private bilateral markets and a pool was resolved there by allowing both. That is, in California the pool, called the Power Exchange (PX), is mandatory only for the incumbent utilities and only for a few years. Other private market makers called scheduling coordinators (SCs) can, like the PX and some large traders with direct access, submit balanced schedules for implementation by the SO (the California ISO). These private energy markets can operate in any format, as pools or bilateral contract markets or whatever they devise. The argument for the California design is that competition among alternative market designs is ultimately the best way to establish their relative merits. There are some practical reasons for establishing the PX as an official pool initially, and because the utilities are required to participate, it has a fair chance of establishing itself as the preferred market design.[24]

Efficiency could be jeopardized by different energy prices in the various markets. If the PX remains viable, this is unlikely in the long run, since non-utility traders can trade in any market with better prices, and in any case the non-PX market makers can themselves trade in the PX to erase persistent price differentials. Admittedly this argument is asymmetric, because as a pure market-clearing mechanism the PX cannot trade in other SCs' markets. The problem could be more substantial in the short run, since on any particular day the energy prices in the various markets might differ. The solution adopted in California is to allow inter-SC trades of adjustment bids, and in the real-time market, incs and decs that need not be paired within the same SC, and indeed for load following need not be paired at all.

The long term problem is the viability of the PX. Its role as an official market that assures open access, uniform pricing, and transparent operations would presumably not be filled by private markets. Its survival in competition with other SCs is jeopardized by its charter restriction to market clearing. For example, it cannot trade for its own account with other SCs (nor in their markets, although they can trade in the PX) to arbitrage the markets for energy and transmission. Another consideration stems from regulatory concerns. An official exchange or pool is easier to monitor and regulate. And if the market-making function for a critical commodity like electricity were dominated by private interests then new regulatory authority might be required to intervene in these markets to assure service in the public interest. This scenario has not occurred in the other basic commodity and service industries that have been deregulated, so it must rely on some aspect peculiar to the electricity industry. The presumed candidate is a market maker so successful that it can capture monopoly rents, but my impression is that the authority of electricity industry regulators is so pervasive as to make these concerns moot at present.

Inter-Market Efficiency

A pool tries to eliminate inefficiencies by a centralized explicit optimization based on submitted cost and engineering data, some of which is monitored for accuracy. The program allocates quantities subject to system constraints, but it also obtains shadow prices used for settlements. In principle, a dual formulation could be implemented as a single market with explicit prices determined by simultaneous clearing of the markets for each of the main ingredients, such as energy, transmission, and ancillary services. Several designs have been proposed for conducting these markets simultaneously, and at least one has received some experimental testing. For example, in one version the system operator (SO) continually monitors transactions in a bilateral market based on posted bid and ask prices for energy, and then using the energy flows implied by these transactions, the SO solves a simplified dual problem that imputes shadow prices for injections at each node.

In practice, however, these markets are usually conducted in a sequence reflecting the fact that transmission demand is derived from energy transactions, and the supply is fixed. Similarly, the demand for ancillary services is nearly proportional to the demand for energy, since most system operators maintain reserves on that basis, and the supply consists mostly of residual generation capacity after accounting for the main energy transactions. Thus, the typical structure is a cascade in which the initial market is for energy, followed by a transmission market in which energy flows are adjusted to keep within the transfer capacity, then a market for ancillary services such as spinning and non-spinning reserves (for which some transfer capacity was previously set aside). These forward markets on a day-ahead (and perhaps hour-ahead) basis are followed by a real-time market in which the SO draws on supplementary offers to maintain system balancing on a short time scale, and when these are insufficient or expensive, calls on the ancillary services held in reserve.

The sequential market structure is convenient administratively and potentially as efficient as a simultaneous market. Realization of this potential depends, however, on several factors. The most obvious requirement is that the clearing prices must be tightly linked:

• The forward price for energy should be an unbiased estimator of the subsequent spot price.

- Traders transacting in the energy market should have accurate expectations about the usage charge that will be imposed later for transmission.
- Sales in the energy market should be based on accurate expectations about the opportunity cost of committing capacity there as opposed to offering it as an incremental bid in the transmission market or as reserve capacity in the ancillary services market.

The key to all three of these requirements is the accuracy, or at least the unbiasedness, of expectations about subsequent prices. Power markets are generally considered good candidates in this respect because they are repeated daily, basic energy and transmission capacity is largely fixed in the short term, and aggregate hourly demand can usually be estimated a day ahead within a few percent points – although unplanned outages and extreme weather conditions can produce larger discrepancies occasionally. In addition, that part of stochastic price variation that is insurable can be hedged via financial contracts, such as TCCs and CFDs.

Nevertheless, these favorable characteristics must be complemented with design features that provide structural support for the formation of accurate expectations. The most important is that all markets in the sequence must be easily contestable so that any significant price differences can be erased by arbitrage. Thus, systematically high prices for ancillary services should induce higher supply bids in the energy market from suppliers who recognize that they could leave some capacity uncommitted there in order to offer it as spinning reserve. And, systematically high usage charges for transmission should attract ample incremental and decremental bids that enable the SO to reduce congestion cheaply. The most important requisite for contestability is that participation in each market is voluntary, so that traders can move from one market to another to exploit apparent price advantages.

The problem lies in the term "systematically" above, since on any particular day it could be that higher or lower prices in subsequent markets were not anticipated in earlier markets, especially the energy market. Some of these unanticipated discrepancies can be reduced by provision of informative data and predictions by the SO and by market makers; e.g., the manager of the energy market can provide reports on inter-zonal imbalances after each iteration or bilateral transaction in the energy market so that traders can better estimate the magnitude of the inter-zonal balancing that must be solved in the subsequent transmission market.

A useful structural mechanism provides corrective markets that take account of the discrepancies. The following provide some indication of how this is done in the California design.

- One example is the provision for both day-ahead markets and a repetition (typically on a smaller scale) in hour-ahead markets (actually, two hours). Thus disparities detected after the close of the day-ahead markets encourage trading in the hour-ahead markets to exploit the price differences.
- Another is that after the initial calculation of day-ahead usage charges by the SO the non-PX scheduling coordinators are allowed to trade adjustment bids before submission of their final schedules. Also, the non-PX scheduling coordinators can trade in the PX in order to arbitrage price differences between their markets.

- A third is that portfolio bids are allowed in the day-ahead energy market, so that commitments of individual generation units need not be specified until after the hourly clearing prices for energy and the interzonal power flows are established.
- A fourth is that the day-ahead energy market is conducted iteratively, which allows traders to develop some consensus about the likely pattern of energy prices across the hours of the next day, which in turn reflect expectations about transmission, ancillary services, and real-time prices.
- Lastly, the ancillary services markets are also conducted in a cascade, so that bids rejected for one service, say spinning reserve, can be carried over to compete for another service, such as non-spinning reserve.

Despite these provisions, the link between the energy and transmission markets remains the most vulnerable. An extreme occurs when the adjustment bids, if they are voluntary, are insufficient to clear the market for transmission, but more routinely it could be that usage charges are too volatile to enable reliable predictions by traders in the energy markets. Transmission pricing based solely on congestion is inherently volatile because the usage charge across an interface can be zero if capacity slightly exceeds demand, and significantly positive if the unadjusted demand slightly exceeds capacity. And other minor procedural aspects can impair predictability; e.g., if multi-zone portfolio bids are allowed then the power exchange cannot provide reliable estimates about the magnitude of the interzonal flows implied by the tentative trades during the iterative process; and prohibition against trading adjustment bids among scheduling coordinators (adopted in California as a "simplification" for the first few months to facilitate startup) can yield exaggerated usage charges because an increment from one SC cannot be matched with a decrement from another.[25] For these reasons it is clear that a design priority is to strengthen the link between the day-ahead energy and transmission markets, and perhaps to adopt a design that integrates these two key markets.

Concluding Remarks

My examination of the architecture of wholesale electricity markets presumes that the ingredients for effective competition are present. It is important to emphasize further that market architecture is distinctly secondary in importance to market structure, in the sense of competitiveness or contestability. Monopoly power in generation, or local monopolies due to transmission constraints, can impair efficiency regardless of the market design implemented. Oligopolies are inherently more damaging to the public interest in power markets because their daily interaction offers ample opportunities for punishment strategies to police collusive arrangements, whether explicit or implicit. Thus, structural solutions to the market power of dominant incumbents are necessary.

In the same way, procedural rules are less important than architecture: no amount of fiddling with procedural rules can overcome major deficiencies in the links among the energy, transmission, and ancillary services markets. There is therefore a natural priority in the design process that starts with ensuring a competitive market structure, proceeds to the selection of the main market forums, and then concludes with the detailed issues of governance and procedures. Some procedural rules, of course, must be designed to mitigate market power and prevent collusion; e.g., it is usual to maintain the secrecy of submitted bids to thwart efforts by a collusive coalition to punish deviants.

An aspect omitted here is the role of transaction costs. This consideration affects all three stages of the design process. Procedural rules must obviously be designed to avoid unnecessary transaction costs, but it is well to realize too that a complex array of decentralized markets imposes burdens on traders, who may well prefer a simpler structure that avoids managing a complex portfolio of contracts, bids, and schedules. A simple design can also promote competition by bringing all traders together in a few markets with standardized contracts, bid formats, and trading procedures. The virtues of simplicity can be especially important in jurisdictions with few participants and small volumes of trade.

Notes

1. An earlier version of this chapter was prepared as a report to the Competition Bureau of Industry Canada and included as an appendix to the Bureau's public comments to the Ontario Market Design Committee, May 1998.
2. Expositions that address these issues include Mark Armstrong, Simon Cowan, and John Vickers, *Regulatory Reform: Economic Analysis and British Experience* (MIT Press, 1994, Chapter 9); Michael Einhorn (ed.), *From Regulation to Competition: New Frontiers in Electricity Markets* (Kluwer, 1994, Chapters 2-7); and Nils-Henrik von der Fehr and David Harbord, "Competition in Electricity Spot Markets: Economic Theory and International Experience" (ISBN 82-570-9166-9, Economics Dept., University of Oslo, Norway, January 1998).
3. The similarities include economic importance and external effects, stochastic demand, capital and fuel intensity, wastage of unused capacity (because inventories are impossible), importance for efficiency of optimal scheduling, injection (i.e., takeoff and landing) charges for use of the system, the necessity of a traffic control system for safety and reliability, the high costs of failures or errors, dependence on advanced technology, etc. This analogy is due to Severin Borenstein.
4. For instance, in California the Power Exchange's price is used to settle grandfathered contracts, and affects payments for recovery of stranded costs. Requiring the incumbent utilities to trade through the PX also makes it easier to monitor market power. In the UK initially, hedging contracts used to mitigate the incentives of incumbents with substantial market power were based on the exchange price.
5. Due to the inherent complexity of this centralized optimization, such programs rely on many ad hoc techniques, so the optimization is best interpreted as an approximation.
6. Sources of superiority could be lower transaction costs, longer-term contracts or contracts better tailored to traders' needs, provision of auxiliary services, or differentiated products such as curtailable service or price hedges or firm transmission rights.
7. Rebellious stakeholders in California occasionally referred to the pool design as Gosplan, alluding to the central plan in the former Soviet Union, whereas those in New England apparently view their tight pool as an obvious convenience.

8. There is a distinction between the SO as the manager of a control area and the manager of the transmission system. When some assets or entitlements are owned by parties, such as municipal utilities, for whom the SO's transmission management is optional, the SO accepts the schedules they provide and they are immune to measures to alleviate congestion and immune to usage charges.

9. To avoid problems at startup, the PX initially mandates adjustment bids, but this is a temporary measure.

10. Another evidence of this motive is the provision that traders in the energy markets need not rely on the ancillary services acquired by the system operator, but instead can provide these themselves.

11. When only a few links have positive prices it is still true that nearly all nodes have nonzero injection charges.

12. In these systems the SO operator absorbs the cost of real-time intra-zonal balancing via the imbalance market.

13. An exception in the U.S. is that some owners of transmission assets or grandfathered entitlements, such as municipal utilities, can opt whether to assign their capacity to the SO for transmission management. If they choose not to do so, then the SO accepts their schedules without any pricing of congestion.

14. This is not necessarily easy to do, since there is a significant free-rider problem engendered by each exchange's preference that others bear the greater share of the burden in curtailing their aggregate transmission demands. The game is repeated daily, however, so implicit collusion is potentially feasible.

15. Theoretical models as well as experimental results indicate that energy traders capture some portion of congestion rents, and empirical studies of the UK market confirm this prediction.

16. The activity rules for the California PX are adapted from the FCC's auctions of spectrum licenses, which have been notably successful and are now used worldwide. The PX rules were tested in laboratory experiments at Caltech with good results, but they will not be implemented in the PX until late 1998, so there is presently no factual evidence on their performance in practice.

17. This design has been studied experimentally in the University of Arizona laboratory, but I have not seen a practical implementation.

18. The separation between the day-ahead energy and transmission markets in California is due to the allowance for multiple competing markets for energy, which are then reconciled in the transmission market if congestion is revealed by the schedules they submit.

19. This is not necessarily serious on a day-ahead basis, since the main effect is spillover into real-time balancing. When the California system begins operation in the Spring of 1998 it will be clearer whether ample adjustment bids are offered.

20. One qualification to this statement is that bids that would not be least cost for any duration of generation are screened out before ordering the capacity bids in merit order.

21. Most systems assign to suppliers an approximate cost of losses, without attempting an exact calculation. In California, for instance, a "generation meter multiplier" is assigned to each node and updated continually to account partially for losses, and the residual is absorbed by the SO.

22. It is also a consequence of relying entirely on supply-side management, taking demand as fixed and inelastic. At the very least comparable payments should be provided to demanders who accept curtailable or lower-priority service. Demand-side measures can reduce the probability and imputed value of lost load, and thereby the reliance on peaking capacity that is idle much of the year.

23. The California PX allows portfolio bids for energy, which do not require specific unit commitments. This provision provides more flexibility to suppliers with many plants, so it might be construed as favoring larger firms, but it is also true that smaller single-plant suppliers can band together to submit portfolio bids.

24. The practical reasons include monitoring of the market power of incumbent utilities, and using the PX price to settle grandfathered long-term contracts.

25. The California design has inherent structural biases. The day-ahead transmission market relies on inc/dec pairs to balance interzonal flows, whereas the real-time market is not confined to matched pairs, and further, SCs pay the cost of interzonal balancing whereas the SO absorbs the cost of intrazonal balancing.

References

Mark Armstrong, Simon Cowan, and John Vickers, *Regulatory Reform: Economic Analysis and British Experience*, MIT Press, 1994, Chapter 9.

Michael Einhorn (ed.), *From Regulation to Competition: New Frontiers in Electricity Markets*, Kluwer, 1994, Chapters 2-7.

Nils-Henrik von der Fehr and David Harbord, "Competition in Electricity Spot Markets: Economic Theory and International Experience" (ISBN 82-570-9166-9), Economics Dept., University of Oslo, Norway, January 1998.

Paul Joskow and Richard Schmalensee, *Markets for Power,* MIT Press, 1983.

Robert Wilson, "Activity Rules for an Iterated Double Auction," in K. Chatterjee and W. Samuelson (eds.), *Applications of Game Theory*, Kluwer Academic Press, to appear 1999.

12 AN INSTITUTIONAL DESIGN FOR AN ELECTRICITY CONTRACT MARKET WITH CENTRAL DISPATCH

Hung-po Chao and Stephen Peck[1]

Introduction

In the 1990's, we are witnessing a period in which competitive forces are sweeping across the electric power industry around the world. A central issue as more of the market becomes subject to competition is the design of an efficient and robust market organization, a task which is complicated by some unique technological characteristics associated with electric power transmission. An electric power grid differs from other types of networks in that power flows must observe physical laws. This gives rise to the loop flow phenomenon, creating widespread externalities in the markets for electric power, whose complexity only grows with the size of the system. It is widely recognized that these externalities, if not mitigated, will cause inefficient resource allocation.

The transmission network plays a strategically important role in a modern electric power system. By providing the critical connection between local markets, it broadens the geographical scope of the electricity market. It offers substantial potential benefits by fostering economies of scale in generation plants, system reliability and security, economies from pooling diverse demands and supplies, and economies from maintenance coordination. However, in the presence of externalities, it is unlikely that the users of the transmission network will take into consideration the effects of power flows that diverge from the contract path.[2] In other words, they do not confront the true costs of congestion and resistive losses that are imposed on others. As a consequence, market failure ensues. The social cost of market failure will be reflected in higher transaction costs for electricity exchange between local markets. The negotiation of power exchange contracts is commonly beset not only by these complex technical details of an electric power network but by motivational problems characterized by incomplete information and informational asymmetry with geographically dispersed traders. The resulting economic losses are potentially significant in terms of lost trading opportunities and local market power created by transmission congestion. To mitigate some of these problems, generation and transmission resources are traditionally dispatched by a central power pool to achieve economic efficiency.[3]

Chao and Peck (1996) introduce a new approach to the design of an efficient market that explicitly incorporates these externalities so that market efficiency can be restored. The main idea is the introduction of tradable transmission capacity rights that closely match physical power flows and a trading rule that codifies the effects of power transfers on power flows and transmission losses throughout the network in a way that is consistent with the physical laws. The trading rule specifies the transmission capacity rights and transmission loss compensation required for electricity transactions. It is demonstrated that the market mechanism will produce an efficient allocation in equilibrium, and a dynamic trading process that involves electricity trading and transmission bidding will converge to a market equilibrium in a stable manner.[4]

From a long term perspective, the new approach provides a conceptual vision for the use of decentralized mechanisms to organize competitive markets for electric transmission services and electricity. Obviously, a decentralized market mechanism, whenever feasible, is generally preferable to a centralized mechanism, for it fosters dynamic efficiency--innovation and discovery of new ways of using electricity. In the near term, however, due to technological constraints, central coordination may still be required to ensure system security and reliability. Therefore, the institutional structure for electric power will need to accommodate a hybrid of decentralized market mechanism and central control. To match the organizational structure with functional characteristics, financial transactions and the physical control need to be separated. While financial transactions of electricity contracts can be efficiently organized through decentralized markets, the physical control is best conducted by a central agency. Given such a hybrid structure, an important institutional design issue that we address in this paper is concerned with the construction of an incentive scheme to motivate the system operator so that the electric power system can function efficiently and reliably.[5] The main idea can be summarized as follows.

We envisage that markets will be developed to facilitate the trading of the basic electric contracts during the pre-dispatch period. In addition, the system operator will provide all traders a menu of priority insurance against interruptions due to deviations from the pre-dispatch contracts. Each trader can choose from the menu an insurance option commensurate with the financial losses incurred if the contract is interrupted. The concluding contracts resulting from market trading in the pre-dispatch period will form the basis of the dispatch schedule in the subsequent

We envisage that markets will be developed to facilitate the trading of the basic electric contracts during the pre-dispatch period. The system operator will provide all traders a menu of priority insurance against interruptions due to deviations from the pre-dispatch contracts. Each trader can choose from the menu an insurance option commensurate with the financial losses incurred if the contract is curtailed in actual dispatch.

dispatch period. During the dispatch period, the system operator will centrally coordinate the physical operation of power generators with dual objectives: 1) to ensure system security and reliability and 2) to honor the contracts in the pre-dispatch market. When these two objectives are in conflict, the system operator will adjust the dispatch schedule, deviating from the pre-dispatch contracts. In the post-dispatch period, the differences will be settled through insurance disbursement payments according to priority insurance provisions. We show that this settlement procedure will motivate the system operator to conduct the real-time dispatch efficiently and even to exploit any inefficiency that might exist in the electric contract market.

The remainder of the paper is organized as follows: In Section 2, we describe an institutional structure to provide a consistent context for discussion. In Section 3, we provide a non-technical description of how the market mechanism works in the pre-dispatch period. In Section 4, we describe a settlement procedure that integrates the two different institutions into a unified structure. In Section 5, we conclude with a summary of the key points. In the Appendix, we demonstrate that the settlement procedure is efficient and illustrate results for the more general case with transmission losses and reactive power.

Institutional Structure: A Scenario

In recognition of the still evolving structure for the electric power industry, we describe next an internally consistent scenario to provide an institutional context for our discussion. A key feature of this scenario is the separation of economic transactions from physical controls.

It is evident that the traditional structure of vertically integrated utilities is in the process of being unbundled into at least three separate segments: generation, transmission, and distribution. It is widely believed that the generation assets will be organized by competitive firms with diversified ownership, and that the distribution assets will be managed by locally regulated utilities or self-regulated cooperatives. However, the future structure of transmission remains somewhat uncertain.

An electric transmission system is operated through system dispatch. It is generally held that system dispatch is a natural monopoly, and thus central control is necessary. Generally speaking, system dispatch has two objectives: 1) to achieve economic efficiency, and 2) to maintain system security and reliability. We submit that the first objective can now be achieved by using a market mechanism, such as one that is demonstrated in Chao and Peck (1996). However, for reasons explained below, the second objective still has to rely on central control under the current technology.

What distinguish the electric power system from other network systems are two fundamental technological characteristics: 1) the electricity output is practically nonstorable, and 2) electricity demand is not deferrable or curtailable at the end-use level. Therefore, on one hand, electricity, once produced, has to be consumed immediately, and on the other hand, it has to be generated in real time once demanded. This implies that electricity supply and demand have to be synchronized strictly in real-time. Operationally, this is accomplished by monitoring power frequency and voltage levels to ensure that they are kept within a narrow range. Otherwise, any imbalance in generation and load, even over a short period of time, will cause frequency shifts or voltage drops and may jeopardize system security and reliability with dire consequences.

There is a basic asymmetry between electricity supply and demand in their controllability. While the output from individual generators can be regulated in real-time by using modern control devices such as Automatic Generation Control (AGC), electricity demand remained virtually uncontrollable until recently. Unlike telephone calls in a telecommunication network, electricity demand can not be selectively curtailed or deferred at the end-use level when the network is congested, because most electric meters and switches do not have two-way communication and control capabilities. The rigidity in electricity demand creates severe constraints on electricity transactions. In fact, this creates a different kind of externality problem with profound implications for efficient market organization. That is, each incremental demand would increase the risk to system security and reliability faced by all customers. Unless a spot market that runs over a very short time period (say, on the order of a second with the use of distributed control devices) can be implemented to internalize the social cost of marginal demand, the maintenance of reserve capacity is essential, and centralized physical operation provides an effective way to ensure system security and reliability.

The rigidity of electricity demand is rapidly diminishing, however, as technical advances in telecommunications and microelectronics have made two-way communication/control systems increasingly affordable and versatile. Some large industrial and commercial consumers have already begun to modernize their electric meters in order to take advantage of alternative rate options. Introduction of competition is likely to accelerate the penetration of these technologies in electricity markets, a trend which is likely to foster greater innovation on the demand side. It is conceivable that in the future, the central system dispatch may evolve toward a decentralized market mechanism that relies on publicly available information (*e.g.*, weather, spot prices, system condition, etc.) and distributed controls. In light of these developments, it is important to consider an institutional structure that will accommodate the diverse needs of central system dispatch and decentralized contract markets in the short run but, more importantly, will also facilitate a continuous evolution toward a fully decentralized structure in the long run.

In this scenario, we assume that transactions of electricity contracts will be conducted in an organized market, and a central system operator will coordinate the physical dispatch. We further assume that the transmission segment is functionally organized around two entities: a power exchange and a system operator. The relationship between the power exchange and the system operator for an electric market is analogous to that between a futures exchange and its affiliated clearinghouse for a financial market. The power exchange provides an organized marketplace with uniform trading rules and standardized contracts. It may operate markets for spot electricity, options, and futures of electricity and will provide price information as well as other services to the public. Through the power exchange, buyers and sellers of electricity may engage in bilateral or multilateral trading of electricity. Information on those trades will be posted continuously on a publicly available bulletin board. Market transactions in the power exchange could proceed on a daily cycle. Since the trading activities must precede the actual dispatch, we may distinguish three stages of daily activities: 1) pre-dispatch, 2) actual dispatch, and 3) post-dispatch. The time between the end of the pre-dispatch period and the beginning of the dispatch is determined by the lead time needed technically and administratively to prepare and perform the dispatch. As telecommunications and information technologies improve, the market trading could be conducted closer and closer to the actual dispatch approaching the ultimate form of spot market.

We assume that in the pre-dispatch period, the basic electric contracts will be traded in an open market, which is administered by the power exchange.[6] By the close of the market activities each day, these contracts will be submitted to the system operator serving as the dispatch schedule to be executed during the dispatch period. Following the schedule based on the contracts traded in the pre-dispatch period, the system operator coordinates the dispatch of generators and transmission facilities but has full authority to make adjustments as needed to ensure system reliability and security. The system operator may change this schedule during the actual dispatch, or re-dispatch, in anticipation of possible contingencies that threaten system security (*e.g.* loss of transmission facilities). Differences between contracts and actual flows are reconciled according to a settlement procedure in the post-dispatch period.

In the settlement procedure, financial payments are determined between contract holders and the system operator for differences between the actual dispatch and pre-dispatch contracts. The settlement rule is based on a priority insurance scheme which will be described below. Except for the unlikely event that pre-dispatch markets completely cover all the contingencies, the settlement rule will entail nonzero payments. This settlement rule will ensure the financial integrity of pre-dispatch contracts and, at the same time, provide the system operator incentives to re-dispatch efficiently.

A Market Mechanism

In this section, we describe in a non-technical language the basic principles of a market mechanism based on Chao and Peck (1996) for the pre-dispatch period. For expository purposes, we first consider a transmission network without losses. Then we show how these principles can be modified for the case with transmission losses.

Basically, the externalities arise from the reality that actual power flows in an electric power network must observe a set of physical laws, known as Kirchoff's laws. One of the consequences is that the power flow paths generally diverge from the contract paths, making the apparent cost of running generator sets different from the real costs. This leads to divergence between the private cost and the social cost in electricity transactions and thus causes a potentially costly dislocation of resources in the power pool.

The problem is somewhat analogous to that of the environmental externality associated with emission of air pollutants. Since the atmosphere is a public good, the private cost of air pollution is virtually zero but the social cost, if not mitigated, could be significant. The divergence between the private cost and the social cost leads to excessive emission of air pollutants. In recognition of this problem, the 1990 Clean Air Act Amendment established a market for tradable emission allowances for sulfur dioxide. Actually, the approach that we shall describe below builds on the basic ideas underlying emission trading. Specifically, a set of tradable transmission capacity rights are issued, and the numbers of these rights required for each transaction are determined by a trading rule which essentially represents a set

Figure 1. A Simple Three Node Network

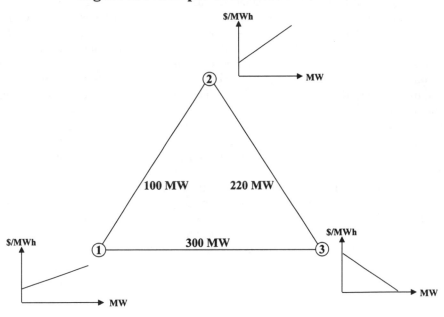

of power flow loading factors. A market is created for these rights so that the external effects associated with a transaction could enter into private decisions explicitly.

To illustrate how the basic principles work, we consider a simple example of an electric power network with three interconnected nodes as shown in Figure 1. In this network, we assume that nodes 1 and 2 are supply nodes, and node 3 is a demand node. Table 1 shows the specific assumption about the marginal cost and inverse demand functions during a peak and an off-peak period. The transmission

Node	Function Type	Off-Peak Period	Peak Period
1	Marginal Cost	$10 + 0.05q$	$10 + 0.05q$
2	Marginal Cost	$20 + 0.1q$	$35 + 0.1q$
3	Inverse Demand	$80 - 0.2q$	$140 - 0.2q$

Table 1: Assumption on demand and supply functions

capacities for lines (1,2), (1,3) and (2,3) are 100 MW, 300 MW and 220 MW, respectively.[7]

For expository purposes, we assume that these transmission lines have identical electrical characteristics (i.e. line impedance) and initially, that transmission losses are negligible. The power flows always follow Kirchoffis laws, which imply for the present case that for any amount of power transferred from node 1 to node 3, two thirds of it flows directly through link $1 \rightarrow 3$ and the remaining one third flows through links $1 \rightarrow 2$ and $2 \rightarrow 3$.[8] Similarly for power transferred from node 2 to node 3, two thirds flows on link $2 \rightarrow 3$ and one third on links $2 \rightarrow 1$ and $1 \rightarrow 3$. A contract path $1 \rightarrow 3$ may be defined for purchase of power at node 1 and sale at node 3, and likewise for a contract path $2 \rightarrow 3$. The movement of power along multiple lines different from the contract path is a phenomenon known among electric engineers as 'loop flow'.

Given the above setup, we can define a set of transmission capacity rights. From the perspective of economic activity analysis, the three-node network in Figure 1 can be viewed as consisting of six directed links, $1 \rightarrow 2, 2 \rightarrow 1, 1 \rightarrow 3, 3 \rightarrow 1, 2 \rightarrow 3$ and $3 \rightarrow 2$, each of which has fixed capacity to carry power along a power line in a specified direction. In this case, we may define the transmission capacity rights for each of the six links as the right to send a unit of power on a specific link.[9] For example, we may issue 100 MW of transmission capacity right for link $1 \rightarrow 2$ and 100 MW for link $2 \rightarrow 1$. Next we define a trading rule which specifies the quantities of transmission capacity rights needed or credited for any power transfer. For example, to transfer 1 MW of power from node 1 to node 3, needs 2/3 MW of link $1 \rightarrow 3$, 1/3 MW of link $1 \rightarrow 2$ and 1/3 MW of link $2 \rightarrow 3$, and earns as credit 2/3 MW of link $3 \rightarrow 1$, 1/3 MW of link $2 \rightarrow 1$ and 1/3 MW of link $3 \rightarrow 2$. Intuitively, the trading rule plays a role that is functionally analogous to direct measurement of the marginal impacts of an electric power transaction on the physical flows throughout the network. For practical purposes, this measurement does not have to be exact in order to capture most of the potential efficiency gains from market competition.

As a starting point, we consider the case with an off-peak period in which the network is not congested. For this case, the externality problem does not arise, and the transmission charges could be set at zero. The generating resources at the two supply nodes can be pooled into a single aggregate supply curve. As shown in Figure 2, the optimal plan, determined by the intersection of the marginal cost function and the inverse demand function, is to generate 257 MW at node 1 and 29 MW at node 2 for a total consumption of 286 MW at node 3. This means that the power flows along the contract paths $1 \rightarrow 3$ and $2 \rightarrow 3$ are 257 MW and 29 MW, respectively. However, the physical power flows are different from the contract flows. For instance, Kirchoff's laws dictate that two thirds of the power supplied at node 1 and one third of the power supplied at node 2 will flow through link 1 → 3. Therefore, the physical power flow on link 1 → 3 is 181 MW (=257×2/3+29×1/3). With unconstrained transmission capacity and zero transmission charges, the equilibrium price of electricity at node 3 is $22.86 per MWh, and the marginal cost at nodes 1 and 2 is also $22.86/MWh.

Figure 2. Market equilibrium in an uncongested network

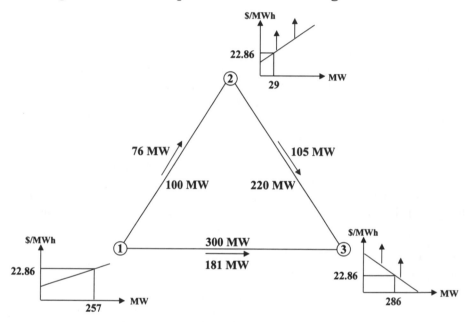

Next, we consider the case with a peak period in which the demand and supply functions are shifted so that link 1 → 2 now becomes congested. Suppose provisionally that transmission capacity rights did not exist; the immediate effect of such a shift is shown in Figure 3. At a temporary equilibrium, the market price could rise to $44/MWh with a market demand of 480 MW.[10] The output at nodes 1 and 2 would be 390 MW and 90 MW, respectively. A set of interim transactions can be envisaged between producers at node 1 and customers at node 3 for 390 MW and between producers at node 2 and customers at node 3 for 90 MW. The prices and quantities as well as the flows on the transmission links from these transactions would be posted on a publicly available bulletin board. While the marginal cost at node 2 equals the market price, the marginal cost at node 1 is $29.5/MWh, which is $14.5/MWh below the market price. The producers at node 1 cannot increase their output due to the transmission capacity constraint of link 1 → 2 but, instead, would collect a total congestion rent of $5655/h (=14.5×390), which implies implicit collusion among suppliers. Clearly, this is an inefficient allocation. How can an efficient allocation be attained through a properly designed market mechanism?

Figure 3. Network congestion in the absence of transmission capacity rights

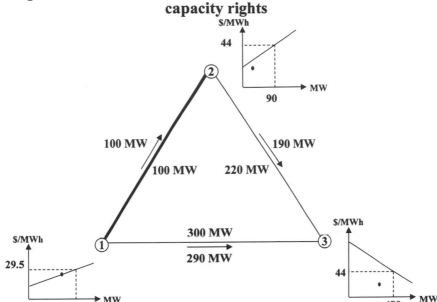

We now introduce the trading of transmission capacity rights and show how this helps the market evolve from the temporary equilibrium in Figure 3 toward a competitive equilibrium. Suppose that the prices of transmission capacity rights are established through bidding among competing traders. For illustrative purposes, let us assume that initially, the bidding of transmission capacity right raises the price for link 1 → 2 to \$15/MWh and the price for link 1 → 3 to \$3/MWh. The situation is clearly one of disequilibrium which will last only temporarily, because a positive price for link 1 → 3 is not sustainable as long as the link remains uncongested. As shown in Figure 4, this implies a positive injection charge at node 1 but a negative one at node 2. More specifically, the right to inject power at node 1 requires a price of \$7/MWh but one for power injection at node 2 earns a credit of \$4/MWh, because according to the trading rule, an injection of 1 MW at node 1 (for sale at node 3) requires 1/3 MW of link 1 → 2 and 2/3 MW of link 1 → 3, and an injection of 1 MW at node 2 requires 1/3 MW of link 1 → 3 but earns a credit of 1/3 MW of link 1 → 2. The updated information would be provided on the publicly available bulletin board. One of the immediate effects of transmission bidding is that the price at node 1 must be lowered to \$37/MWh to remain competitive.

Let us define the merchandising surplus as the difference between the revenue of electricity sold and the cost of electricity bought in the network. In this case it equals \$2730/hr (=480×\$44 - 390×\$37 - 90×\$44). We also define the transmission rental as the total income of the transmission line owners. In this case, it equals \$2370/hr (=100×\$15 + 290×\$3). Chao and Peck (1996) demonstrate that the difference between the merchandising surplus and the transmission rental is indicative of 1) the potential for the transmission right owners to increase the

Figure 4. Transmission bidding sets nodal injection charges/credits

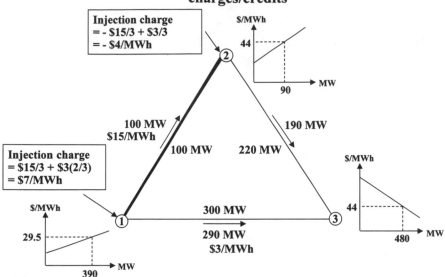

transmission rental or 2) profitable arbitrage opportunities through multilateral electricity trading. Furthermore, as a result of a series of trading activities that exploit these opportunities, the social welfare will increase, and the dynamic trading process will converge to an efficient market equilibrium.

One such profitable arbitrage opportunity is to buy an equal amount of electricity from node 1 and node 2 simultaneously and sell it to node 3. The cost of the transaction equals $42/MWh (= (37 + 44)/2 + 3×(2/3 + 1/3)/2), which implies a profit of $2/MWh. Such a trade poses no net demand for the transmission capacity right on link 1 → 2 and can thus be completed without violating the transmission constraint, however, it involves multilateral trades which generally span the entire network and could become quite complicated for a large power network. Transmission bidding facilitates electricity trading by providing useful price information that enables the profitable arbitrage opportunities to be exploited more simply at a local level. For example, the above multilateral trade can be accomplished through two separate local trades: First, with an injection credit of $4/MWh, a broker can transfer power from node 2 to node 3 for a profit of $4/MWh (=44 + 4 - 44). This transaction will increase the supply of transmission capacity rights for link 1 → 2. Then, the producers at node 1 will be able to increase power sales from node 1 to node 3 retaining a positive profit of $7.5/MWh (=44 - 7 - 29.5).

Such trading activities can continue until transmission link 1 → 3 becomes congested as shown in Figure 5. To maximize the transmission rental, the price for the transmission capacity right could be bid up to $20/MWh on link 1 → 2 and $5/MWh for link 1 → 3, implying an injection charge of $10/MWh at node 1 and an injection credit of $5/MWh at node 2. The prices at node 1 and node 2 would converge to the marginal costs at \$30/MWh and \$45/MWh, respectively, and the outputs at these two nodes are 400 MW and 100 MW correspondingly. The price of electricity at node 3 is \$40/MWh, and the power demand is 500 MW. At this point, the merchandising surplus equals \$3500/hr (=500×\$40 - 400×\$30 - 100×\$45), and the transmission rental equals \$3500/hr (=100×\$20 + 300×\$5).[11]   As the merchandising surplus equals the transmission rental that is maximized through competitive bidding, a competitive equilibrium is attained.   The bulletin board's provision of information about nodal prices, quantities and transmission link prices and flows may be used by market participants all through this process to identify profitable electricity production, use or trading opportunities.

Figure 5. Market equilibrium is reached when there are no further arbitrage opportunities

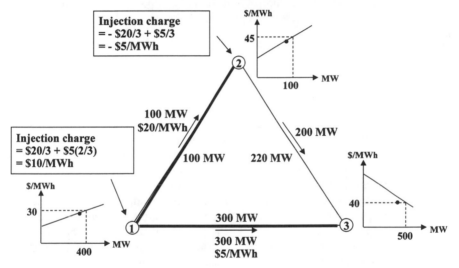

Transmission rental = \$20 x 100 + \$5 x 300 = \$3500/h

Needless to say, there are numerous paths along which the trading process may evolve. The above example illustrates the basic principle that through a dynamic interaction between electricity trading and transmission bidding, they will always converge to a competitive equilibrium.   Therefore, with appropriate design, a market mechanism could incorporate the congestion externalities in an electric power network to achieve the social optimum.

For the case with transmission losses, things are more complicated. We modify the prior trading rule so that market trading will incorporate both transmission congestion cost and transmission losses. (Chao and Peck 1996) Transmission losses in a line depend on the square of the power transmitted and thus the marginal loss increases with the power flow on the line. In this case, each new electricity transfer could affect the distribution of transmission losses throughout the entire network and thus the losses sustained by other users of the transmission system. To achieve economic efficiency and thus the appropriate dispatch of generation and the

> **The institutional structure that we consider is a hybrid of a market (the power exchange) and an internal organization (the system operator). The settlement procedure serves as a critical link in a governance mechanism that holds the two different institutions together in a unified framework.**

appropriate use of electricity, it is desirable for the traders to pay for the marginal transmission losses as well as for the congestion. Since the marginal transmission losses are generally approximately twice the average transmission losses, a new type of economic rent is created, and an allocation rule is needed. In this case, a transmission capacity right entitles its owner to the right to send a unit of power through a specific transmission line in a specific direction and to collect economic rents associated with the transmission losses. The trading rule is also augmented by specifying the compensation for average power losses. An extension of the above numerical example to the case with transmission losses is illustrated in the Appendix.

Discussion

The main insight of the above analysis is that in our model, a system of tradable property rights (i.e. transmission capacity rights) is sufficient for the purpose of setting competitive transmission charges (via transmission bidding). Further, once this system of property rights is established, the control of the transmission system is shifted from physical ownership to contractual ownership, a form which is amenable to decentralization. Therefore, a market mechanism could be designed to overcome market failures due to loop flow externalities and support a competitive market. However, for a detailed prescription of how the market activities should be organized in practice, there are many practical issues that remain to be addressed. With the enormous complexity of electric power systems and the large stakes involved, a systematic evaluation of the cost-benefit tradeoffs of economic and engineering considerations involved in establishing a market is needed.

What might be the drawbacks of such a mechanism in practice? A potential disadvantage with the above market mechanism is its apparent complexity, because there could be a large number of transmission capacity rights in a real network, and thus the information processing cost might be too high rendering the approach impractical. In such a case, we envision that in the initial implementation, the contract market can be supported by a simplified model network, for instance, using a DC-flow model or aggregated pricing zones. The differences between contracts based on the model network and the dispatch for the real network can be reconciled in a subsequent settlement process.[12]

As for other potential difficulties, we recall a well-known folk theorem in economics suggesting that in the absence of market failures (i.e., externalities in the present case), whatever a central agency can do, a market can do better. Thus a corollary is that once the main cause of market failure is fixed, market forces could be relied upon for efficient self-organization. For instance, it is conceivable that transmission brokers will emerge to simplify the trading of transmission capacity rights by aggregating them into transmission capacity contracts in ways that resemble the more pragmatic concept of transmission capacity reservation contracts stipulated by the FERC (1996) or transmission congestion contracts defined in Harvey et. al. (1996). It is also anticipated that aggregators will arise to bundle electricity and transmission capacity contracts over different time periods and contingencies into simple contracts that can be traded among common consumers and suppliers. For instance, as Vickrey (1971) suggested for the case with air flight tickets, forward markets could be established for reservations of transmission capacity rights at various points in time before the actual dispatch. Obviously, such undertakings involve varying degrees of risk, and various risk management contracts will emerge. Nevertheless, we believe that as a minimum, a simple contract will be created that enables an electricity supplier to agree to deliver to a consumer a known quantity of power at a fixed price over a long period of time. After all, a competitive market is known to be surprisingly innovative in self-organizing for informational efficiency.

The Settlement Procedure

The institutional structure that we consider is a hybrid of a market (the power exchange) and an internal organization (the system operator). The settlement procedure serves as a critical link in a governance mechanism that holds the two different institutions together in a unified framework. (Williamson 1985)

The actual dispatch may deviate from the contracts traded in the pre-dispatch period for at least two reasons. First, the trading rule may be based on an approximate representation of the physical system. Therefore, in actual dispatch, adjustments to the contracts may be needed to reflect the difference. Second, unexpected events (e.g., loss of generation units or transmission lines, higher demand than anticipated) may occur after the contract market is closed. Re-dispatch is desirable to attain ex-post efficiency, since the market for contingent contracts in the pre-dispatch period is likely to be incomplete. The settlement procedure serves two main objectives: 1) to reconcile the differences between the pre-dispatch contracts and the actual system dispatch so that the financial integrity of these contracts is ensured, and 2) to provide an appropriate financial incentive that fosters dispatch efficiency.

To meet these objectives, it is important that in some way, the system operator is responsible for the financial gains or losses resulting from re-dispatch. One approach is to require the system operator to provide insurance of service priority, or simply priority insurance, that compensates all contract holders, including generators, demanders and transmission capacity rights holders, for deviations between pre-dispatch contracts and the actual dispatch. Subject to this requirement, the system operator has the full authority to dispatch the physical system and to deal with possible contingencies that could impact the physical power flows in the network.

Under priority insurance, each contract holder can expect to be compensated for an interruption due to re-dispatch by an amount that depends on the insurance premium paid in advance. Theoretically, priority insurance can be shown to be a special form of priority service. (Chao and Wilson 1987; Wilson 1989) With asymmetric information expected to exist between the system operator and market traders, the insurance premium schedule can be designed to be incentive compatible in the sense that it will induce traders to self-select options commensurate with their private costs of interruption. The interruption cost for a consumer is the difference between the marginal value and the market price; for a producer, it is the difference between the market price and the marginal cost; and for a transmission capacity right owner, it is the entire transmission rental for the contracted-but-unused line capacity. Contract holders with higher interruption costs are expected to select greater insurance coverage. Then during the dispatch period the system operator will act in self interest to first interrupt those contracts with the lowest coverage, if it becomes necessary. As a result, the social welfare loss due to re-dispatch is minimized.

A simple example would help clarify the basic ideas. Suppose that there are two types of consumers, called A and B, who value electricity at \$200/MWh and \$300/MWh, respectively, and that the price of electricity established in the pre-dispatch market is \$50/MWh. The consumers do not have to pay, if the contract is interrupted due to re-dispatch. Therefore, the interruption costs for consumers A and B are \$150 and \$250 per MWh, respectively. Suppose that the system operator offers two priority insurance options, referred to as 1 and 2, with the following provisions. Under option 1, each subscriber will be disbursed \$150/MWh in case the electricity contract is canceled in re-dispatch, and the insurance premium is \$1.50/MWh. Under option 2, the insurance disbursement is \$250/MWh, and the insurance premium is \$3.00/MWh. If it becomes necessary to interrupt some of the electricity contracts, the system operator will naturally do so in an increasing order of insurance premium (or disbursement) to minimize the insurance disbursement. Therefore, option 1 is expected to have a higher probability of being interrupted than option 2.   Given this predicable behavior of the system operator, the probability of interruption associated with each option can be estimated.   For convenience, we assume that the probabilities of interruption for insurance options 1 and 2 are 0.02 and 0.01, respectively, and further, the probability of interruption without insurance is 0.03.

Then we can compute the net benefit for each consumer under alternative insurance choices. For consumer A, the net benefit calculations are shown as follows:

(i) Without insurance:

$$(1 - 0.03) \times (200 - 50) = 145.50$$

(ii) With insurance option 1:

$$(1 - 0.02) \times (200 - 50) + 0.02 \times 150 - 1.5 = 148.50$$

(iii) With insurance option 2:

$$(1 - 0.01) \times (200 - 50) + 0.01 \times 250 - 3 = 148$$

Similarly, the net benefit for consumer B under alternative insurance choices is computed as follows:

(i) With no insurance:

$$(1 - 0.03) \times (300 - 50) = 242.50$$

(ii) With insurance option 1:

$$(1 - 0.02) \times (300 - 50) + 0.02 \times 150 - 1.5 = 246.50$$

(iii) With insurance option 2:

$$(1 - 0.01) \times (300 - 50) + 0.01 \times 250 - 3 = 247$$

From the above calculations, the optimal choice for consumer A is option 1, and the optimal choice for consumer B is option 2. According to the theory of priority service, the insurance premium schedule can be designed so that consumers will be induced to select options that reflect the true interruption losses. However, a complete design of such a schedule is technically complicated and is beyond the scope of this paper. See Wilson (1996) for a more detailed discussion of how priority service theory can be applied to such a design.

Priority insurance could be implemented through alternative organizational forms. Obviously, priority insurance could be offered by the system operator as a regulated firm. Alternatively, a non-profit cooperative, which is common for financial exchanges, may be formed by the traders to provide the priority insurance at cost and to oversee the operation of the system operator. Essentially, it is a form of self-insurance that depends on internal management oversight. The governing board could reward the system operator with a performance bonus which is inversely related to the total insurance disbursement. In such a case, regulatory oversight will be needed for the design of an insurance premium schedule, and franchise bidding may be conducted. Finally, priority insurance can also be offered by competitive firms. (Wilson, 1996).

Let us illustrate how the settlement process would work in a network by revisiting the numerical example in Section 3. Suppose that after the market trading reaches an equilibrium in the pre-dispatch period, the rated capacity of transmission line (1,3) unexpectedly falls from 300 MW to 250 MW. Since the original market equilibrium is now infeasible, the system must be re-dispatched. As shown in Table 2, the optimal dispatch under the new condition calls for curtailing demand at node 3 from 500 MW to 411 MW as well as reducing the output at node 1 from 400 MW to 338 MW and that at node 2 from 100 MW to 73 MW.

For illustrative purposes, suppose that consumers have selected insurance coverage that equal their consumers' surplus and similarly for producers. Since the marginal cost drops at node 1 to $26.9/MWh as output is reduced to 338 MW, the producers' surplus loss due to re-dispatch can be computed as the triangle shown in Figure 6. The insurance disbursement to producers at node 1 can be computed accordingly as $96.10/hr (= (400-338) × ($30-$26.9)/2). Similar computation yields the insurance disbursement of $36/hr to producers at node 2 and $788/hr to consumers at node 3, as shown in Table 2.

Since 50 MW of the transmission capacity on link 1 → 3 is lost, the transmission capacity right owners for link 1 → 3 need to be paid $250/hr (= 50×$5) for their financial losses. In addition, the power flow on link 1 → 2 is reduced from 100 MW to 88.3 MW due to re-dispatch. Therefore, the transmission capacity right owners for link 1 → 2 need to be paid $233/hr (=11.7×$20) for the contracted-but-unused rights. The total insurance payment to the transmission capacity right owners is thus $483/hr.[13] Overall, in the above case, the settlement procedure yields a net disbursement of $1403/hr for the system operator. It is demonstrated in the

Figure 6. Priority insurance disbursement reflects social welfare losses

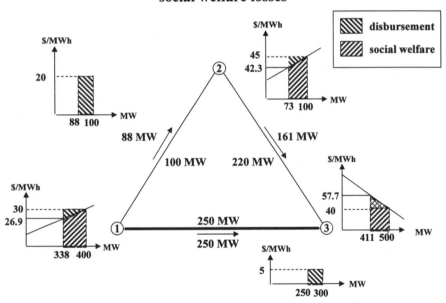

Appendix that this payment equals the social welfare losses due to the loss of line capacity. Therefore, if the system operator is held financially responsible for this payment, it will have an incentive to operate the system efficiently and reliably.

The transmission capacity and priority insurance contracts, which are used here as part of the settlement rule that induces the system operator to pursue market efficiency, need to last only so long as the dispatch period. The transmission congestion contract with a long contract period has been used in the context of the nodal pricing model as a mechanism related to providing security or the correct incentives for generation or even transmission investments. In this paper, we have not dealt with the long period transmission congestion contracts or indeed the contracts for differences (CFD), but we expect that these contracts will be among the risk management tools which arise to assure longer term market efficiency.

In summary, the market contracts will be settled on the basis of ex ante market prices and ex post physical power flows. Differences between the contracted power flows and the physical power flows will be reconciled through priority insurance disbursement. The complexity of priority insurance lies mainly in the computation of the insurance premium/compensation schedule. Otherwise, its implementation is analogous to that of contracts for differences, which have been adopted by the electricity supply market in the United Kingdom rather successfully. In fact, contracts for differences, which compensate for the differences between ex ante contract prices and ex post market prices, essentially provide a form of price insurance. Nevertheless, the priority insurance approach described here is broader in scope, for it engages more fully a greater number of stakeholders in market activities, including generators, consumers and transmission capacity right holders.

Node/ Link	Market equilibrium			Optimal dispatch		Priority insurance disbursement ($/hr)
	Injection charge ($/MWh)	Market price ($/MWh)	Supply/ demand (MW)	Shadow price ($/MWh)	Supply/ demand (MW)	
Node						
1	10	30	400	26.9	338	96
2	-5	45	100	42.3	73	36
3	0	40	500	57.7	411	788
Link						
1 → 2		20	100	0.0	88.3	233
1 → 3		5	300	46.5	250	250
Total						1403

Table 2: A Summary of the Settlement Results

Further, the above settlement procedure can be generalized in a straightforward manner to the case with transmission losses and reactive power.[14] The dispatch of reactive power is a localized operation which can practically be decoupled from that of real power. Therefore, in the pre-dispatch market, the real power flows are organized through market trading, recognizing that in a subsequent step, the dispatch of the reactive power may require some adjustments to the real power contracts. A numerical illustration for such a case is provided in the Appendix.

Conclusion

The externalities due to loop flows in a transmission network represent a critical issue which must be satisfactorily resolved before competition can be successfully introduced into the electric power industry. A market mechanism based on a set of properly defined tradable transmission capacity rights would enable electricity trading and transmission bidding for an efficient electricity market. A significant advantage of this approach is that transmission charges could be determined competitively with active participation of transmission rights owners.

Due to technological constraints, a major challenge for implementation is to find a coherent institutional structure that will support decentralized market transactions (via a power exchange) and, at the same time, motivate efficient central dispatch (via a system operator). In this paper, we describe an incentive compatible institutional design that features priority insurance as the critical bond in the governance mechanism for a unified institutional structure. Essentially, priority insurance enables the deviation of the actual dispatch from market contracts to be reconciled in such a way that provides the system operator the correct incentive to operate the system efficiently and reliably.

Appendix

Suppose that the marginal benefit function of electricity consumption is denoted by $MB_i(q_i^d)$ and the marginal cost function of electricity production is denoted by $MC_i(q_i^s)$ where the subscript i denotes a specific node in the power network. By integrating these functions, we obtain the benefit function $B_i(q_i^d)$ and the cost function $C_i(q_i^s)$. The social welfare associated with node i, a function of the net electricity demand $q_i \equiv q_i^d - q_i^s$, is defined as follows:

$$W_i(q_i) \equiv \{\max_{q_i^d, q_i^s} B_i(q_i^d) - C_i(q_i^s) \mid q_i = q_i^d - q_i^s.\}$$

Kirchoff's laws impose the following constraints on the net electricity demands $(q_1,...,q_n)$:

$$\sum_{i=1}^{n} q_i + L(q_1,...,q_{n-1}) = 0, \tag{1}$$

$$T_{ij}(q_1,...,q_{n-1}) \leq \overline{T}_{ij}, \quad \text{for } 1 \leq i, j \leq n, \tag{2}$$

where $L(q_1,...,q_{n-1})$ is the transmission loss function; $T_{ij}(q_1,...,q_{n-1})$ is the power flow function on line (i,j); and $\overline{T}_{ij}$ is the rated capacity of line (i,j). Equation (1) represents the law of energy conservation, and (2) states that the power flow on each line can not exceed the rated line capacity. The provision of reactive power is embedded in the above formulation.

The social optimum can be obtained by maximizing $\sum_{i=1}^{n} W_i(q_i)$ subject to (1) and (2). We denote a socially optimal allocation by $(q_1^*,...,q_n^*)$.

We assume that the market mechanism implements an approximation of the social optimum, which is the solution to the following problem:

$$\max_{q_1,\ldots,q_n} \sum_{i=1}^{n} W_i(q_i)$$

subject to:

$$\sum_{i=1}^{n} q_i + \hat{L}(q_1,\ldots,q_{n-1}) = 0, \tag{3}$$

$$\hat{T}_{ij}(q_1,\ldots,q_{n-1}) \le \overline{T}_{ij} \text{ for } 1 \le i,j \le n, \tag{4}$$

where $\hat{L}(q_1,\ldots,q_{n-1})$ and $\hat{T}_{ij}(q_1,\ldots,q_{n-1})$ are approximations of the transmission loss and power flow functions, ignoring the reactive power. Let $(\hat{p}_1,\ldots,\hat{p}_n)$ and $(\hat{q}_1,\ldots,\hat{q}_n)$ denote the prices and net demands at a market equilibrium.

In the settlement procedure for the case with transmission losses, the priority insurance disbursement consists of three components:

A. the sum of consumers' and producers' surplus losses,

$$\sum_{i=1}^{n} \int_{q_i^*}^{\hat{q}_i} [W_i'(q) - \hat{p}_i] dq, \tag{5}$$

B. the compensation for contracted-but-unused transmission capacity rights,

$$\sum_{i=1}^{n} (\hat{p}_i - \hat{p}_n)(\hat{q}_i - q_i^*), \tag{6}$$

C. and the compensation for the difference in transmission losses,

$$\sum_{i=1}^{n} \hat{p}_n(\hat{q}_i - q_i^*). \tag{7}$$

Summing up (5) - (7), we obtain the total cost for the system operator, which equals the social welfare losses, as follows,

$$\sum_{i=1}^{n}[W_i(\hat{q}_i) - W_i(q_i^*)].$$ (8)

Therefore, a dispatch plan that minimizes the total cost to the system operator also maximizes the social welfare. In other words, the settlement procedure provides the system operator a financial incentive to dispatch efficiently.

We next extend the above numerical example to the case with transmission losses and reactive power. For illustrative purposes, we assume, in addition, that each of the three transmission lines has an identical inductance of 0.0015 pu and an identical resistance of 0.00015 pu.[15] The market equilibrium assuming unrestricted availability of reactive power for this case is summarized in Table 3. We can compare this case with one without transmission losses as shown in Table 2. With transmission losses, the output at node 2 is increased from 100 MW to 105.5 MW, but the demand at node 3 drops from 500 MW to 484 MW. The injection charge at node 1 rises from $10 to $13.20 per MWh, while the injection credit at node 2 drops from $5 to $2.35 per MWh, as a result of changing power flows.

Node	Market equilibrium			Optimal dispatch		Priority insurance disbursement	
	Injection charge	Market price	Supply/demand	Shadow price	Supply/demand	energy	TCC
	($/MWh)	($/MWh)	(MW)	($/MWh)	(MW)	($/hr)	($/hr)
1	13.20	30.00	400.0	29.64	393.2	1.2	90.3
2	-2.35	45.55	105.5	44.39	94.1	6.6	-26.8
3	0.00	43.20	484.0	46.57	467.1	28.4	0.0
Losses		43.20	21.5		20.1	-59.2	
Total							40.6

Table 3: Settlement Results with Transmission Losses and Reactive Power

In the actual dispatch subsequent to the market trading, the system operator must balance the demand and the supply of reactive power as well. We assume that the power factor of the demand at node 3 is 0.9.[16] This gives rise to a reactive power demand of 224 MVAR (Mega Volt-Amp Reactive) at node 3. The reactive power is supplied from a capacitor bank at node 3, and from the generators at nodes 1 and 2. The dispatch of reactive power is carried out with two objectives: A) to maintain

Node	Marginal cost ($/MVARh)	Demand (MVAR)	Supply (MVAR)	Total cost ($/hr)
1	1.90	0	25.1	23.8
2	1.50	0	3.2	2.4
3	0.00	224	397	0.0
Sum				26.2

Table 4: The Optimal Dispatch of Reactive Power

voltage stability (within ±5% of the target level) and B) to minimize the transmission losses. The results of optimal dispatch are summarized in Tables 3 and 4.

Table 3 contrasts the optimal dispatch of real power with the market equilibrium and displays the settlement results. The priority insurance disbursement is computed in essentially the same way as for the case without transmission losses. The only difference is that we now need to account for transmission losses. For instance, the transmission losses total 20.13 MW under the optimal dispatch and 21.50 MW in the market equilibrium. Settling the difference at the ex ante market price at node 3 (the base node) yields an income of $59/hr(= (21.50 - 20.13) × $43.20) for the insurance provider. To compute the insurance disbursements for the transmission capacity right holders, we assume that the insurance payments will be based on transmission capacity contracts, which can then be easily unbundled into more disaggregated transmission capacity rights. For instance, the disbursement to the transmission capacity contract holders at node 1 is given by $90 (= (400-393.2) × $13.20). Table 4 shows the shadow prices (measured as $/Mega Volt-Amp Reactive Hours) and the optimal dispatch of reactive power as well as the total variable cost of providing that power. Table 5 shows that the total priority insurance disbursement equals the difference between the social welfare with market equilibrium (less the cost of reactive power) and that with optimal dispatch.

Description	Amount ($/hr)
Social welfare with market equilibrium	32,086
The cost of reactive power	26
Social welfare with market equilibrium, less the cost of reactive power	32,060
Social welfare with optimal dispatch	32,019
Net priority insurance disbursement	41

Table 5: Comparison of Social Welfare

Notes

[1] An earlier version of the article appeared in The Energy Journal, 1997, Vol. 18, No. 1, pp. 85-110.

[2] A contract path from node i to node j refers to the transfer of a certain amount of power from node i to node j along a path that is specified administratively without considering the actual flow of power.

[3] The traditional economic dispatch typically emphasizes supply side efficiency. As greater competition is introduced, the immediate challenge is to exploit the opportunities for efficiency gains on the demand side, while retaining and perhaps improving on the advantages conferred by traditional economic dispatch.

[4] In Chao and Peck (1996), the dispatch of real power is decoupled from that of reactive power, and the availability of reactive power is assumed to be unconstrained in the contract market. In a subsequent step, efficient dispatch must take into account reactive power limitations, voltage constraints as well as other sometimes substantial nonlinear effects, and relatively minor adjustments to the real power flows are expected.

[5] How to motivate the system operator to behave properly has been recognized by Joskow (1996) and others as perhaps the most important issue in institutional design.

[6] These contracts, being the closest substitutes for physical delivery of electricity that can be created under the present state of technology, could serve as the basis for various types of derivative contracts, such as futures and options.

[7] In this paper, we shall express the prices in $/MWh, the power flows in MW, and the electricity outputs in MWh.

[8] Roughly speaking, power flow is inversely proportional to the impedance along the path. Since the path along link $1 \rightarrow 3$ is half as long as the path $1 \rightarrow 2$ and $2 \rightarrow 3$, it has half the impedance. Therefore, the ratio of the power flows between them is two to one.

[9] This definition of transmission capacity right is consistent with the Federal Energy Regulatory Commission's emphasis (FERC 1996) on specific performance and matching use to rights.

[10] This could be the result of a Cournot equilibrium, for instance, with price-taking consumers and a large number of producers. (Oren 1996)

[11] It is useful to define the basic transmission capacity contract as a bundle of transmission capacity rights (or obligations, when the bundle includes a negative number of some of these rights) that will enable a trader to inject a unit of power at a specific node. The price of a basic transmission capacity contract is the nodal injection charge. For example, a basic transmission capacity contract for power injection at node 1 calls for a price of $10/MWh but one for power injection at node 2 earns a credit of $5/MWh, because according to the trading rule, an injection of 1 MW at node 1 (for sale at node 3) requires 1/3 MW of link $1 \rightarrow 2$ and 2/3 MW of link $1 \rightarrow 3$, whereas an injection of 1 MW at node 2 requires 1/3 MW of link $1 \rightarrow 3$ but earns a credit of 1/3 MW of link $1 \rightarrow 2$. An alternative way to calculate the transmission rental can be based on injection charges: $400 \times \$10 + 100 \times (-\$5) = \$3500/hr$.

[12] For instance, in the United Kingdom's electricity market, forward prices are determined by ignoring the transmission network initially. The differences between contracts and the actual dispatch are reconciled subsequently using such devices as contracts for differences.

[13] If the settlement procedure is redefined on the basis of transmission capacity contracts, the payments to the holders of these contracts can be calculated as follows: $(400 - 338) \times \$10 + (100 - 73) \times (-\$5) = \$483\$/hr$, which is equivalent to the total disbursement to the original owners of the transmission capacity rights.

[14] Reactive power flows arise when the power factors of certain loads fall significantly below unity. These flows could be prevalent in an electric network, for instance, if consumer appliances such as refrigerators, which tend to create inductive loads, are not compensated electrically with built-in capacitors. While the reactive power does not directly offer consumers any utility, imbalances in reactive power flows could cause voltage drops and threaten the system reliability.

[15] The symbol pu refers to "per unit", which is a relative measure commonly used in power engineering.

[16] The power factor refers to the ratio $P / \sqrt{P^2 + Q^2}$ where P and Q represent the real and reactive power, respectively. With a power factor of 0.9, $Q/P \approx 0.48$.

References

Chao, Hung-po and Stephen C. Peck (1996). "A Market Mechanism for Electric Power Transmission," *Journal of Regulatory Economics*, July, Vol. 10, No. 1.

Chao, Hung-po and Robert Wilson (1987). "Priority Service: Pricing, Investment, and Market Organization," *American Economic Review*, Vol. 77, No. 5, pp. 899-916.

Federal Energy Regulatory Commission (1996). "Capacity Reservation Open Access Transmission Tariffs," Notice of Proposed Rulemaking, RM96-11-000, Washington DC, April 24.

Harvey, Scott M., William W. Hogan and Susan L. Pope (1996). "Transmission Capacity Reservations Implemented Through a Spot Market with Transmission Congestion Contracts," Harvard University.

Joskow, Paul L. (1996). "Restructuring to Promote Competition in Electricity: In General and Regarding the Poolco vs. Bilateral Contracts Debate," presented at the American Economic Association Meetings, San Francisco, January 6.

Oren, Shmuel S. (1996). "Economic Inefficiency of Passive Transmission Rights in Congested Electricity Systems with Competitive Generation," working paper, University of California at Berkeley.

Vickrey, William (1961). "Counterspeculation, Auctions, and Competitive Sealed Tenders," *Journal of Finance*, 16, pp. 8-37.

Vickrey, William (1971). "Responsive Pricing of Public Utilities," *Bell Journal of Economics and Management Science* 2, No. 1, pp. 337-346.

Williamson, Oliver E. (1985). "The Economic Institutions of Capitalism," The Free Press, New York.

Wilson, Robert (1989). "Efficient and Competitive Rationing," *Econometrica*, 57, pp. 1-40.

Wilson, Robert (1997), "Implementation of Priority Insurance in Power Exchange Markets," *Energy Journal*, 18, No. 1, pp. 111-123.

INDEX